The Evolution of Religion

The Evolution of Religion

Studies, Theories, & Critiques

Edited By
Joseph Bulbulia, Richard Sosis, Erica Harris,
Russell Genet, Cheryl Genet, and Karen Wyman

Collins Foundation Press

The Evolution of Religion: Studies, Theories, and Critiques

Published by the Collins Foundation Press
4995 Santa Margarita Lake Road
Santa Margarita, CA 93453

Technical Editors - Joseph Bulbulia and Richard Sosis
Acquisitions and Copy Editor - Erica Harris
Managing Editor - Russell Genet
Production Editor - Cheryl Genet
Promotion Editor - Karen Wyman

Supporting copy edit coutesy of Vera Wallen
Cover design by Cheryl Genet

Includes biographical references

ISBN 0-9788441-1-4

Printed by Sheridan Books in the United States of America

Evolution of Religion website: www.evolutionofreligion.org
Publisher's website: www.collinsfoundationpress.org

Other conferences in the series at: www.evolutionaryepic.org

CONTENTS

Part V Gods in Minds

Part VI Gods in Bodies

Part VII Methodology

Contributors

Alcorta, Candace S. - Department of Anthropology, University of Connecticut
Barrett, Justin L. - Centre for Anthropology and Mind, School of Anthropology and Museum Ethnography, University of Oxford
Bering, Jesse M. - Institute of Cognition and Culture, Queen's University, Belfast
Boehm, Christopher - Jane Goodall Research Center and Departments of Anthropology and Biological Sciences, University of Southern California
Bulbulia, Joseph - Religious Studies, Victoria University of Wellington
Cohen, Adam B. - Department of Psychology, Arizona State University
Cohen, Emma - Centre for Anthropology and Mind, School of Anthropology and Museum Ethnography, University of Oxford
Collins, Dwight - Collins Family Foundation; Presidio School of Management
Coon, Carl - American Humanist Association; United Nations Ambassador (retired)
Dowd, Michael - America's Evolutionary Evangelist
Edis, Taner - Division of Science - Physics, Truman State University
Geertz, Armin W. - Department of the Study of Religion, Faculty of Theology, University of Aarhus
Genet, Cheryl L. - Orion Institute; Cuesta College
Genet, Russell M. - Orion Observatory; California State Polytechnic University; Cuesta College
Gibson, Nicholas J. S. - Psychology and Religion Research Group, Faculty of Divinity, University of Cambridge
Guthrie, Stewart - Department of Anthropology, Fordham University
Harris, Erica - Department of Neurology, Boston University School of Medicine and Boston VA Healthcare System, Jamaica Plain Campus
Hill, Peter C. - Rosemead School of Psychology
Irons, William - Department of Anthropology, Northwestern University
Johnson, Dominic - Department of Politics, University of Edinburgh
Ketola, Kimmo - The Church Research Institute, Tampere, Finland
Kirkpatrick, Lee A. - Department of Psychology, College of William and Mary
Koch, Gretchen - Department of the Study of Religion, University of Aarhus
Kydd, David - Institute of Cognitive and Evolutionary Anthropology, University of Oxford
Lanman, Jonathan A. - Centre for Anthropology and Mind, Institute of Cognitive and Evolutionary Anthropology, University of Oxford
Mahoney, Andrew - Religious Studies, Victoria University of Wellington
Marsh, Barnaby - Department of Zoology, University of Oxford
Martin, Luther H. - Department of Religion, University of Vermont; Institute of Cognition and Culture, Queen's University, Belfast

McCorkle, Brian H. - Center for the Study of Religion and Psychology, The Albert and Jesse Danielsen Institute at Boston University
McCorkle, William W., Jr. - Institute of Cognition and Culture, Queen's University, Belfast
McNamara, Patrick - Department of Neurology, Boston University School of Medicine and Boston VA Healthcare System, Jamaica Plain Campus
Murray, Michael - New College, University of Oxford
Närhi, Jani - Department of Comparative Religion, University of Helsinki
Newson, Lesley - School of Psychology, University of Exeter
Palmer, Craig T. - Department of Anthropology, University of Missouri-Columbia
Pyysiäinen, Ilkka - Department of Comparative Religion, Helsinki Collegium for Advanced Studies, University of Helsinki
Richerson, Peter J. - Department of Environmental Science and Policy, University of California-Davis
Rozin, Paul - Department of Psychology, University of Pennsylvania
Saler, Benson - Anthropology Department, Brandeis University
Sanderson, Stephen K. - Institute for Research on World-Systems, University of California-Riverside
Schjødt, Uffe - Department of the Study of Religion, University of Aarhus
Schloss, Jeffrey P. - Biology Department, Westmont College
Shariff, Azim F. - Department of Psychology, University of British Columbia
Sjöblom, Thomas - Department of Comparative Religion, University of Helsinki
Slone, D. Jason - Religious Studies, Webster University
Soler, Montserrat - Department of Anthropology, Rutgers University
Sosis, Richard - Department of Anthropology, University of Connecticut; Department of Sociology and Anthropology, Hebrew University of Jerusalem
Steadman, Lyle B. - Department of Anthropology, Arizona State University
Taves, Ann - Department of Religious Studies, University of California-Santa Barbara
Teitelbaum, Michael - Religious Studies, Victoria University of Wellington
Wason, Paul K. - Science and Religion Programs, John Templeton Foundation
Wiebe, Donald - Trinity College, University of Toronto
Whitehouse, Harvey - School of Anthropology and Museum Ethnography, University of Oxford
Wilson, David Sloan - Departments of Biology and Anthropology, Binghamton University
Wyman, Karen - North American Science and Religion Foundation; Claremont Graduate University
Xygalatas, Dimitris - Institute of Cognition and Culture, Queen's University, Belfast

Note from the Publisher

This volume is a guidebook of sorts, providing an introduction to the science of the evolution of religion. It documents a scholarly dialog that occurred at a resort nestled into the volcanic foothills of Oahu during a week long conference in early 2007. While its basic form is a compilation of the proceedings from that conference, the general effect is greater than what that form would typically imply. The scope of the subject matter is expansive and the result is a highly inclusive survey, culling from a range of research results and methods, propositions, apologies, rebuttals, and critiques. A broad range of questions necessary to the maturation of this field were posed, together for the first time it seems.

My interest in this subject and this dialog as publisher is at first glance oblique to my organization's expressed goals. The mission of the Collins Family Foundation (www.collinsff.org) and its publishing segment, the Collins Foundation Press (www.collinfoundationpross) is to provide leadership in humanity's efforts to live sustainably. This is executed in a number of ways, including the support of Russ and Cheryl Genet, the co-chairs of this conference. Russ is an accomplished polymath and a dear friend of long standing. His formidable scientific mind is exceeded only by his skill at identifying prescient and underdeveloped lines of inquiry and rallying experts together, making space for progress and innovation. With his background as an accomplished astronomer and student of evolution, he provides me with important perspectives on the topic of sustainability. Cheryl, a scholar of science and spirituality, connects the disparate pieces of conference implementation, thereby melding the fruits of Russ' skills into a viable vessel for the meeting of the experts' minds.

The connection between the contents of this book and the goal of promoting sustainability is direct. Over the last century it has become increasingly apparent that as a species, sustaining the fruits of our global civilization on this resilient but finite planet is challenging our capacity for *cooperation* in ways that humanity has never faced. Specifically the likelihood of impending dramatic changes in climate presents such a challenge. We are entering a bottleneck shaped by the collision of our material success and the planet's finite resources, where the opportunity for reversing current climate trends is steadily diminishing. Over the course of human history, religious institutions have been a major vehicle for managing large scale cooperation. In our predisposition to be religious, I see a potential that needs to be studied and understood in sympathetic ways on a much broader scale. Navigating our way through this bottleneck, to a condition of sustainable human endeavor on our planet, requires a wisdom and understanding that we as a civilization currently lack.

In particular, how could our scientific *understanding* of the role of religion in human behavior help us become sustainable? Consider the example of the tribal social instincts hypothesis proposed by Peter Richerson and Robert Boyd in *Not by Genes Alone, How Culture Transformed Human Evolution*. Pete and Rob point out that these within-tribe instincts that evolved through the dynamic of gene/culture co-evolution predispose us to (1) exhibit guarded altruism to non-relatives, (2) show limited tolerance for leadership, (3) conform to social institutions, (4) sufficiently trust to permit division of labor, and (5) enforce rules of fairness. Simultaneously, other ancient instincts predispose us to make war inter-tribally when the survival of our own tribe is threatened. In what ways can our ancient warring instincts yield to our within-tribe social instincts to help us cooperate more globally? In this context, what would it take for populations of the world to perceive themselves as the one tribe that they truly are relative to the finite natural resources of this unique planet?

It is an honor for me to have been a part of the January 2007 International Conference on the Evolution of Religion, and to sponsor the publication of this book, *The Evolution of Religion: Studies, Theories, & Critiques*. I applaud its more than 50 authors for their initiative in coming together and for their scholarship in producing this comprehensive record.

Dwight Collins,
President,
Collins Family Foundation
November, 2007

Preface

Bringing the *Evolution of Religion* into Being

The *International Conference on the Evolution of Religion* and these proceedings were conceived in February 2006, when Dwight Collins, our close friend of three decades, visited us here in Hawaii. It was only natural, when considering our futures, that our discussion turned to conferences, for we had worked together organizing several in the past.

Some eleven years earlier, in February of 1995, Dwight joined us for a conference held at the Lazy-K-Bar Guest Ranch in Arizona. Russ, on retiring from the directorship of the Fairborn Observatory on Mt. Hopkins, Arizona, was able to pursue his lifelong interest in cosmic evolution—science's integrated "story" of physical, biological, and cultural evolution. What better way to learn than to organize (with Brian Swimme and Loyal Rue) a conference on *The Epic of Evolution?*

In 1996, Dwight flew half way around the world to New Zealand to attend *The Evolution of Humanity*, a conference Russ organized with Michael Corballis (Auckland University), held on the beach at Awaroa in Able Tasman National Park. Subsequently, with Dwight, we organized a *Profitable Sustainability* retreat, held in 2003 at the Hacienda, William Randolph Hearst's picturesque Spanish ranch house inland from his more famous castle on the California coast. In 2004, we organized a conference with world historian David Christian entitled *Cosmic Evolution and Big History*, also held at the Hacienda. Dwight and our good friend Peter Richerson (University of California, Davis) attended. Finally, we were pleased to help Connie Barlow and Michael Dowd organize the "evolutionary salon," *Evolutionary Directionality*, held at The Hacienda in 2005.

As we considered possibilities for future conferences with Dwight, the evolution of religion arose as a natural topic. Russ has a keen interest in cultural evolution, and religion is a key, even central facet, of all human cultures. Cheryl's focus is science and human meaning, and Dwight has an interest in the religious dimensions of sustainability. As the President of the Collins Family Foundation, Dwight kindly agreed, on the spot, to fund the publication of the conference proceedings. His foundation's generosity launched this conferences.

On returning to the mainland, we immediately contacted Peter Richerson. Who were the experts on the scientific study of the evolution of religion? Pete suggested we contact Richard Sosis (University of Connecticut and Hebrew University). Rich sent us his review paper on the topic and put us in touch with Joseph Bulbulia (Victoria University, Wellington) who also furnished his own review paper. We contacted the authors in these review papers, inviting them to the Hawaii conference on the *Evolution of Religion.*

Developing and bringing the conference and proceedings to completion required the work of many individuals. Joseph Bubulia, Richard Sosis, and Armin Geertz (University of Aarhus, Denmark) served as the program organizing committee. It was this team that organized the sessions and set up and directed panels and workshops. In addition, Joseph and Rich lent their expertise to the technical editing and final organization of the conference papers. We were also joined, early-on, by two graduate students, Karen Wyman (Claremont Graduate School) and Erica Harris (Boston University) who handled logistics and implementation. Erica served as the initial copy and format editor for these proceedings. Vera Wallen provided the final copy edit of the entire fifty papers and the front matter. Dan Wyman built and maintained the conference website with exceptional skill and dedication. Michael Dowd supported speakers in the technical and time-limit aspects of their presentations to help the conference run smoothly and on schedule.

The heart of the conference was the speakers themselves. Each brought a unique perspective to the scientific study of religion, to the evolution of religion in the larger evolutionary trajectory, and to the ultimate meaning of religion. They prepared their presentations, traveled (in some cases halfway around the world), shared ideas, and met deadlines for their proceedings papers.

The John Templeton Foundation provided honoraria for graduate students and other financial support, and Paul Wason and Barnaby Marsh, Templeton Foundation scientists, spoke at the conference. The Collins Family Foundation and the Orion Observatory sponsored the daily morning refreshments, and the International Association for the Study of Science and Religion funded the poolside welcome reception that launched the conference. The Orion Institute and the North American Science and Religion Foundation provided logistical support.

As should be evident from this volume, the conference was a dramatic success. Another conference, *The Evolutionary Epic,* will be held at the Makaha Resort on January 3-8, 2008. It will be a reprise, over a decade later, of the earlier *Epic of Evolution.* In that time, science's story has been refined, and is now more widely understood by the public at large. We will, in this upcoming conference, consider both the Epic and how it is faring in its telling and incorporation into education, religion, and humanity's sustainable presence on planet Earth (www.EvolutionaryEpic.org).

Russell M. Genet and Cheryl L. Genet
Conference Co-chairs

Introduction
Religion in Eden

Richard Sosis and Joseph Bulbulia

In early January 2007, scholars from around the world gathered in Makaha Valley, Hawaii to attend the first *International Conference on the Evolution of Religion*. Scientific research on the origin and evolution of religion has made rapid advances in the past two decades.[1] The conference assessed how far the biological and social sciences have come toward explaining religiosity and religious culture, and looked for ways of improving and integrating distinctive naturalistic approaches. The conference also provided venues for those with philosophical and theological interests to raise questions about the relevance of this new research to questions internal to religious faith and practice.

Scholars came from Canada, Israel, Mexico, New Zealand, United States, and throughout Europe. They represented an array of religious backgrounds (Islam, Christianity, Judaism, and Buddhism) and beliefs (secularists, humanists, atheists, agnostics, theists, and even a self-proclaimed "creatheist"). More importantly, the spectrum of disciplines represented was extraordinarily wide, including cognitive psychologists and anthropologists, evolutionary psychologists, behavioral ecologists, anthropologists, evolutionary biologists, religious studies scholars, philosophers of science, historians, physicists, astrophysicists, neuroscientists, ecologists, archaeologists, and theologians.

One of the most successful aspects of the conference was that it brought together three scholarly groups who have otherwise had little sustained contact: religious studies scholars, cognitive scientists of religion, and evolutionary scientists interested in studying religion. While there have been fruitful collaborations between religious scholars and cognitive scientists, and evolutionary and cognitive scientists have also lately begun a productive dialogue, scholars from all three areas rarely find themselves under the same roof. This is unfortunate for many reasons. While evolutionary scientists have garnered considerable media attention from their recent forays into the study of religion, this work has often been pursued independently of, and often uninformed by, current religious scholarship. At this January 2007

---

1 For recent reviews of anthropological research on the evolution of religion, see Dow (2006) and Sosis & Alcorta (2003); and for reviews of evolutionary cognitive studies of religion, see Atran (2006); Barrett (2000); Bering (2006); Boyer (2003); and Bulbulia (2004, 2007).

conference, evolutionary scholars were pleasantly surprised at the depth of empirical research that already exists within the field of religious studies, and encouraged by the openness of some religious scholars to evolutionary ideas, but were somewhat dismayed by the recurrent misunderstandings of how selectionist theories are applied to human behavior. For their part, many religious studies scholars were skeptical about the potential of evolutionary approaches in explaining diverse religious patterns and trends. Most were curious about the possibilities of integrating evolutionary perspectives into their work, but many were cautious, and others were openly antagonistic. As would be expected in an emerging field such as the evolutionary study of religion, calls for more empirical and theory driven research were heard almost daily. Also heard were claims that religious scholarship has already produced an abundance of descriptive materials ready for evolutionary analyses and available to test rival theories. However that debate is decided, all would agree that the number of exciting studies and promising theories presented each day of the conference was impressive.

A fourth group of participants contributed to our understanding of the implications of evolutionary research to practical, political, and spiritual life. These individuals were interested in the future of religion, including its impact on sustainable development, the role that evolutionary science can play in the spiritual transformations of contemporary religions, and the dynamic relationship between humanism and religion. For those of us with our heads buried in research, it was refreshing to see how those outside the academy are interpreting, grappling with, and employing our findings.

As all participants will attest, the conference was physically and intellectually exhausting. There were more than 50 talks over five and half days, and no sessions were run in parallel. Sessions and workshops ran all morning and afternoon, and the daytime activities were capped off every evening with a distinguished plenary address.

Harvey Whitehouse (Oxford University) opened the conference on January 3, with a detailed overview of cognitive and evolutionary studies of religion. He carefully laid out the major issues confronting evolutionary studies of religion, summarizing the leading hypotheses, assessing the current state of understanding, and presenting critical methodological and empirical questions future research must address. The next morning we began the first full day of the conference. By lunchtime we had considered several scenarios for the evolution of religion and initiated discussions about whether religion is adaptive. That evening, noted historian and religious studies scholar, Luther Martin (University of Vermont and ICC, Queens University Belfast), delivered an impassioned and illuminating attack on evolutionary analyses of religion. He thoroughly outlined the concerns that evolutionary scientists must deal with and resolve if evolutionary studies of religion are to successfully impact traditional historical scholarship. His talk stimulated equally impassioned discussion and debate.

The second full day of the conference focused on the adaptive benefits of supernatural beliefs, commitments, and practices. We also considered the application of signaling and sexual selection theories for understanding the evolution of religion. In the evening, Anne Taves (UC Santa Barbara) directed our attention to under-examined questions about cognition and the body, the construction of the self through narratives, and the role of "religious experience" in religious life. Taves urged that the "sui generis" model of this category impairs scientific progress. In its place, Taves motivated an "attributive model of religious experience." Successful re-introduction of "religious experience" to naturalistic approaches appears to provide one of the more promising horizons for scientific exploration.

The third full day of the conference focused on cognitive research in the evolutionary study of religion, including new experimental and observational studies. Renowned philosopher Daniel Dennett (Tufts University) was the evening speaker. Dennett reinforced an important theme of the conference, namely that the intergenerational flow of information is not restricted to lineages of genes. He also presented an account for the taming of wild religion, urging that substantive transformations in the nature of religious information occurred during the major transition from foraging to agrarian and urban lifeways. Dennett's talk generated a spirited discussion on many fronts, about the utility of memetics for understanding the evolution of religion, the relationship between evolutionary research on religion and the lay public, as well the relationship between evolutionary researchers and their (religious) study populations.

On the penultimate day of the conference, we focused on the transmission of religious concepts and the narratives through which religion is understood. We also looked at the function of supernatural concepts and practices through the study of religious brains. That evening, North America's 'evolutionary evangelist', the Rev. Michael Dowd, shared his experience of teaching and preaching a sacred, meaningful view of cosmic, biological, and human evolution. He offered a possible solution to the dead-end debates between theists and atheists, and argued that evolutionary theory may be essential for a deeply inspired life. It was a rare meeting between academic and religious worlds, for both audience and speaker. Despite having delivered hundreds of talks to secular and religious audiences across the theological spectrum, this was Dowd's first presentation to an academic audience.

We closed the conference by addressing foundational questions about the naturalistic study of religion, as well as questions about the economic, spiritual, and political benefits and costs of religious belief and practice. Biologist and religious scholar, Jeffrey Schloss (Westmont College), closed the conference by detailing the various threads of argumentation linking naturalistic (generally functionalist) inquiry about religion to wider theological questions. Schloss also used the example of laughter—which he skillfully induced frequently in his audience—to illustrate an important theme of the conference: the role of commitment signals in authenticating genuine religious commitments. The talk stimulated much discussion over the relationship of religious commitment to science and morality, the reliability of religious signaling, and the role of religious feeling in its evolutionary history.

In addition to the research sessions and evening talks, there were three scheduled afternoon workshops aimed at assessing recent advances in the evolutionary study of religion, and setting an agenda for areas of progress and integration. The three sessions were distinguished by their focus on anthropology, psychology, and overall reactions to the evolutionary study of religion. Popular demand initiated a fourth workshop on group selection and cultural evolution, which was gratefully organized by David Sloan Wilson (SUNY Binghamton) and Peter Richerson (UC Davis). This workshop afforded an opportunity for conference participants to ask questions about selectionist theories and their application to the study of religion.

There were numerous healthy debates that permeated discussions throughout the conference. One of the most constructive debates concerned whether or not religion should be considered an adaptation or a by-product. While no consensus was reached in this debate, various positions were clearly articulated, and future research that will be necessary to resolve this issue was discussed. There were also sustained discussions on the applicability of various evolutionary models to religious phenomena, including sexual selection and signaling models, cultural group selection, and meme theory. One of the livelier debates centered on defining religion, and the claim that if we cannot define it, then it is incoherent to claim we can develop its evolutionary study, for there is no stable "it" to study.

This volume offers many of the excellent talks that were presented in Hawaii. Chapters are intentionally short, at least shorter than the authors would have wished. Our task was to keep the volume affordable, while capturing the full range of conference presentations. Nevertheless, we are impressed by the clarity, scope, and precision consistently displayed throughout this volume. During the conference there were significant theoretical and methodological disagreements among scholars, but we think that all would agree that the new interdisciplinary study of evolution and religion is off to an outstanding start, and its future looks very promising. We hope this volume attests to that.

References

Atran, S. 2006. The cognitive and evolutionary roots of religion. In P. McNamara Ed., *Where God and science meet: How brain and evolutionary studies alter our understanding of religion*, Vol. 1, 181-207. Westport, CT and London: Praeger Publishers.

Barrett, J. 2000. Exploring the natural foundations of religion. *Trends in Cognitive Sciences, 4,* 29-34.

Bering, J. 2006. The folk psychology of souls. *Behavioral & Brain Sciences, 29,* 453-493.

Boyer, P. 2003. Religious thought and behavior as by-products of brain function. *Trends in Cognitive Sciences, 7,* 119-124.

Bulbulia, J. 2004. The cognitive and evolutionary psychology of religion. *Biology & Philosophy, 18,* 655-686.

Bulbulia, J. 2007. Evolution and religion. In R. I. Dunbar & L. Barrett Eds., *Oxford handbook of evolutionary psychology*. New York, NY: Oxford University Press.

Dow, J. W. 2006. The evolution of religion: Three anthropological approaches. *Method & Theory in the Study of Religion, 18,* 67-91.

Sosis, R., & Alcorta, C. 2003. Signaling, solidarity and the sacred: The evolution of religious behavior. *Evolutionary Anthropology, 12,* 264-274.

PART I

Evolutionary Scenarios

Evolution and Religion

The Transformation of the Obvious

David Sloan Wilson

In his autobiography, Darwin (1887/1958) describes a fossil-hunting expedition to a valley in Wales that he took as a young man with Adam Sedgwick:

> We spent many hours in Cwm Idwal, examining all the rocks with extreme care, as Sedgwick was anxious to find fossils in them; but neither of us saw a trace of the wonderful glacial phenomena all around us; we did not notice the plainly scored rocks, the perched boulders, the lateral and terminal moraines. Yet these phenomena are so conspicuous that…a house burnt down by fire did not tell its story more plainly than did this valley. If it had still been filled by a glacier, the phenomena would have been less distinct than they are now (70).

Darwin and Sedgwick couldn't see the evidence for glaciers because the theory of glaciation had not yet been proposed. With the theory in mind, the evidence was so overwhelming that the glaciers might as well have still been present. This phenomenon can be called *the transformation of the obvious*. It illustrates the need for a theory to organize the facts that lay all around us. A similar transformation of the obvious occurred with Lyell's theory of geology and Darwin's theory of evolution.

Can there be a transformation of the obvious for the study of religion? Certainly we do not lack facts, which lay all around us like the rocks of Cwm Idwal. In addition to a sizeable social scientific literature on religion, there is a much larger body of traditional scholarship on religions around the world and throughout history. This information is descriptive, but so was most of the information about geological formations, plants, and animals available to Lyell and Darwin. What we lack is a comprehensive framework for *organizing* the facts about religion.

Evolutionary theory can provide this framework, as it has for the natural world and increasingly for other human-related subjects. However, this enterprise is still in its infancy, comprising perhaps a few dozen individuals, with the most important developments taking place within the last ten years. In this article I will attempt to provide a brief tutorial and progress report.

Major evolutionary hypotheses about religion (or any other trait)

Evolutionary theory offers a number of major hypotheses for the study of any trait, which can be applied to the study of religion. Perhaps the most important question is whether the trait counts as an *adaptation* that evolved by enhancing survival and reproduction, as opposed to the many non-adaptive products of evolution. If so, then we need to know the *unit of selection*. Did it evolve by enhancing the fitness of whole groups, relative to other groups in the total population (between-group selection), or by enhancing the fitness of individuals, relative to other individuals in the same group (within-group selection). With cultural evolution there is a third possibility. A cultural trait can potentially evolve to increase its own transmission, like a disease organism, without benefiting human individuals or groups (Dawkins 2006; Dennett 2006).

If the trait is not an adaptation, it can nevertheless remain in the population for a variety of reasons. Perhaps it was adaptive in the past but not the present, like our eating habits, which make excellent sense in a world of food scarcity but have become a major cause of death in today's fast food environment. Perhaps it is a byproduct of another adaptation—a spandrel, to use an architectural metaphor made famous by Gould and Lewontin (1979). Or perhaps it is merely neutral and entered the population by genetic or cultural drift.

Table 1: Major evolutionary hypotheses for any trait, which can be applied to the study of religion.

RELIGION AS AN ADAPTATION	RELIGION AS NONADAPTIVE
Group-level adaptation (benefits groups, compared to other groups) Individual-level adaptation (benefits individuals, compared to other individuals within the same group)	Adaptive in small groups of related individuals but not in modern social environments. Byproduct of traits that are adaptive in non-religious contexts.
Cultural parasite (benefits cultural traits without regard to the welfare of human individuals or groups)	Neutral traits (drift)

These six major hypotheses provide an excellent framework for the study of religion, as shown in Table 1. One indication of its utility is that it can classify past theories of religion that were formulated without evolution in mind, in aify past theories of religion that were formulated without evolution in mind, in addition to more recent efforts based on contemporary evolutionary theory.

As one example, consider Durkheim's (1912/1995) definition of religion: "[A] unified system of beliefs and practices relative to sacred things...which unite into one single moral community called a Church, all those who adhere to them" (44). Durkheim and the tradition of functionalism that he helped to initiate clearly imagine religion as a system that is adaptive at the level of whole groups. Nevertheless, it was not classified as "evolutionary" at the time because cultural evolution was associated with a linear progression from savagery to civilization. From a modern evolutionary perspective, Durkheim might well have been on the right track, but his theory of group-level functionalism requires an explanation in terms of group-level selection.

As a second example, modern sociologists tend to rely upon economics as their theoretical framework for explaining religion. According to Rodney Stark and William Bainbridge (1987; Stark 1999), the human mind is designed to formulate explanations that are good at obtaining benefits in a non-religious context. Some benefits cannot be had, such as rain during a drought or everlasting life. That does not prevent us from wanting them, so we invent gods with whom we bargain for that which we can't have. This is clearly a byproduct theory of religion as something that is not adaptive by itself but connected to something else that is adaptive. Evolutionists such as Pascal Boyer (2001), Scott Atran (2002) and Kirkpatrick (2004) have a different conception of the mind than Stark and Bainbridge, based on evolutionary psychology rather than economic theory, but they also envision the elements of religion as byproducts of mental "modules" that evolved in non-religious contexts. More generally, it is gratifying that the evolutionary framework can accommodate all naturalistic theories of religion, past and present, without requiring additional major hypotheses.

At this point, it is worth asking whether the evolutionary framework has added anything new, especially if it can assimilate all past theories. If there is no alternative to evolutionary theory, doesn't it become a vacuous term for any kind of change? In biology, evolution is defined as any kind of genetic change, whether by selection, mutation, drift, linkage, or any other process. It is important for the definition to include everything, or else it would not function as a complete accounting system. The theoretical framework is not vacuous because it includes specific categories of change. Progress is made when we assign particular traits to particular categories—that the spots on guppies evolve primarily by selection, rather than drift; that many genetic polymorphisms are selectively neutral and evolve by drift, rather than selection; that juvenile features of domestic dogs are byproducts of selection for tame behavior, and so on.

The study of human-related subjects such as religion from an evolutionary perspective is much the same. Human behavioral change is often based upon psychological and cultural processes that are rudimentary or absent in other species, but we still must begin with a complete accounting system for any kind of change, which is not vacuous because it includes a number of meaningful categories for classifying particular examples of change. This is the sense in which the evolutionary framework outlined above represents an important advance for the study of religion.

Another point to make is that "non-evolutionary" theories of religion were never truly imagined as non-evolutionary. To pick the example of Stark and Bainbridge's economic theory, they are not creationists and do not invoke supernatural intervention. When pressed to explain why the human mind is designed for cost-benefit reasoning in non-religious contexts, they would surely invoke evolution. In this fashion, Stark and Bainbridge rely upon evolution, *but think they can proceed without knowing much about evolution*. The same can be said for every other theory of religion that rejects the possibility of supernatural intervention. What's new is that the italicized assumption has proven false for the study of religion and virtually all other human-related subjects. Not only do naturalistic explanations require assumptions about evolution, but they also require a sophisticated knowledge of contemporary evolutionary theory.

A current lack of consensus among evolutionists

Once we have a general theoretical framework, we need to determine the relative importance of the major hypotheses for particular elements of religion. Evolution is a messy, multifactorial process and all of the major hypotheses might be relevant to some degree—otherwise they would not be worth including as categories within the general framework. Still, for any given religious trait, some hypotheses will be more relevant than others and it should be possible to reach a consensus, based on the empirical evidence. With the accumulation of studies, a more general assessment of the major hypotheses becomes possible. Until the field of evolutionary religious studies is operating in this mode, it cannot be considered a fully mature scientific discipline.

Unfortunately, the field is *not* yet operating in this mode. Evolutionists interested in religion agree on the major hypotheses, but there is no consensus whatsoever on their relative importance. Each has its champions as the primarily explanation of religion. In my opinion, there can be much more agreement among evolutionists on the basis of current information. For example, there can be a consensus on the plausibility of group selection, especially for human cultural evolution, despite the heretical status of group selection in the past (Wilson 2002, 2007). There can also be a consensus about byproducts turning into adaptations. In particular, authors such as Kirkpatrick (2004) might be right that most elements of religion are based on genetic psychological adaptations that evolved in non-religious contexts, but authors such as Richerson and Boyd (1999, 2005) might be right that cultural evolution turned these "exaptations" into adaptations for collective action. Even though the nascent field of evolutionary religious studies comprises only a few dozen people, in the past they have worked largely in isolation. Workshops such as the one that led to this volume and other mechanisms of coordination are required to turn these individuals into a coherent scientific discipline worth the attention of the wider community of scientists and scholars interested in religion.

A natural history foundation

Evolution is fundamentally about the relationship between organisms and their environments. That is why detailed field studies of plants and animals are so important and provide the foundation for more controlled laboratory experiments. For religion, the analog of a field study is a careful ethnography of a particular religious system in a particular location and time. Fortunately, this kind of information exists in abundance for religions around the world and throughout history. Religious scholars are the natural historians of religion, and the field of evolutionary religious studies needs to collectively play the role of Darwin in organizing this information from an evolutionary perspective.

In *Darwin's Cathedral* and a subsequent article (Wilson 2002, 2005) I made a humble beginning by conducting a study of 36 religions, chosen at random from Eliade's (1987) *Encyclopedia of Religion*. The encyclopedia was used to *select* the religions, which were then *evaluated* with respect to the major hypotheses using the wider literature. Because the religions were chosen without respect to any particular hypothesis, the sample can be used to assess the relative importance of the major hypotheses for religious systems in general, as defined by the editors of the encyclopedia. The details are provided by Wilson (2005), but the general conclusion is that most religions in the sample are clearly designed to define groups, coordinate behavior within the group, and solve the all-important problem of cheating. Their *secular utility*, as Durkheim would put it, is unmistakable. Elements of religion that appear irrational and dysfunctional often make perfectly good sense when judged by the only appropriate gold standard as far as evolutionary theory is concerned—by *what they cause people to do*. This conclusion emerges so strongly that it begins to qualify as a transformation of the obvious. Space permits only a single example of what I mean by this bold claim.

Jainism: an example of the transformation of the obvious

One of the religions in the sample is Jainism, which has been practiced by a small fraction of the Indian population for thousands of years. It is one of the most ascetic religions in the world. Jain renouncers are homeless and without possessions. They filter the water that they drink, the air that they breathe, and sweep the path in front of them to avoid killing unseen creatures. They even occasionally fast themselves to death in a practice called Santhara, which is celebrated by the entire community. How can such a religion be adaptive for either individuals or groups? Jainism appears to be a good candidate for the cultural parasite hypothesis—until one reads the scholarly literature.

It turns out that the renouncers comprise a tiny fraction of the religion, whose lay members are among the wealthiest merchants of India. The Jains occupy an economic niche similar to the Jews of Western Europe and other merchant societies around the world (Landa, 2007), which requires cooperation over long distances and is correspondingly vulnerable to exploitation. The religion provides an elaborate set of mechanisms for insuring cooperation. The renouncers even serve as a moral police force, entering the houses of the lay Jain families and inspecting their devoutness before accepting their food (see Wilson, 2005 for a more detailed discussion). Here is how one natural historian of religion, a Jain scholar named James Laidlaw, describes the secular utility of Jainism in a book whose title says it all: *Riches and Renunciation: Religion, Economy, and Society among the Jains* (Laidlaw 1995):

> How then, is it possible to live by impossible ideals? The advantage for addressing this question to Jainism is that the problem is so very graphic there. The demands of Jain asceticism have a pretty good claim to be the most uncompromising of any enduring historical tradition: the most aggressively impractical set of injunctions which any large number of diverse families and communities has ever tried to live by...This directs our attention to the fact that yawning gaps between hope and reality are not necessarily dysfunctions of social organization, or deviations from religious systems. The fact that lay Jains make up what is—in thoroughly worldly material terms—one of the most conspicuously successful communities in India, only makes more striking and visible a question which must also arise in the case of renouncers themselves (7).

With a little information, such as the sight of an emaciated ascetic or beliefs and practices that appear bizarre and irrational when taken out of context, Jainism appears obviously dysfunctional for both individuals and groups. The same religion becomes obviously functional based on more information. As for Jainism, so also for most of the religions in the random sample. As for the random sample, so also for most of the religions in the *Encyclopedia of World Religions*.

Humans as a largely group-adapted species

Evolutionary theory was confined to the biological sciences and excluded from most human-related subjects for most of the 20th century. Now virtually all human-related subjects are being approached from an evolutionary perspective, with the most important developments occurring during the last ten or twenty years. There will be many transformations of the obvious, including but not restricted to religion. In retrospect, we will wonder how we could have missed the degree to which we are genetically and culturally adapted to function at the level of groups.

References

Atran, S. 2002. *In gods we trust: The evolutionary landscape of religion*. New York, NY: Oxford University Press.

Boyer, P. 2001. *Religion explained: Evolutionary origins of religious thought*. New York, NY: Basic Books.

Dawkins, R. 2006. *The God delusion*. London, UK: Bantam Press.

Darwin, C. 1958. *The autobiography of Charles Darwin, 1809-1882, with original omissions restored*. Ed. Nora Barlow. New York, NY: Harcourt Brace. Original work published 1887.

Dennett, D. C. 2006. *Breaking the spell: Religion as a natural phenomenon*. New York, NY: Viking.

Durkheim, E. 1995. *The elementary forms of religious life*. New York, NY: The Free Press. Original work published 1912.

Eliade, M. Ed. 1987. *The encyclopedia of religion*. New York, NY: MacMillan.

Gould, S. J., & Lewontin, R. C. 1979. The spandrels of San Marco and the panglossian paradigm: A critique of the adaptationist program. *Proceedings of the Royal Society of London, Series B, 205* (1161), 581-598.

Kirkpatrick, L. A. 2004. *Attachment, evolution, and the psychology of religion*. New York, NY: Guilford Press.

Landa, J. T. 2007. The bioeconomics of homogenous middleman groups as "adaptive units." *Journal of Bioeconomics*.

Laidlaw, J. 1995. *Riches and renunciation: Religion, economy and society among the Jains*. Oxford, UK: Oxford University Press.

Richerson, P. J., & Boyd, R. 1999. Complex societies: The evolutionary origins of a crude superorganism. *Human Nature, 10*, 253-290.

Richerson, P. J., & Boyd, R. 2005. *Not by genes alone: How culture transformed human evolution*. Chicago, IL: University of Chicago Press.

Stark, R., & Bainbridge, W. S. 1987. *A theory of religion*. New Brunswick, NJ: Rutgers University Press.

Stark, R. 1999. Micro foundations of religion: A revised theory. *Sociological Theory*, 17, 264-289.

Wilson, D. S. 2002. *Darwin's cathedral: Evolution, religion and the nature of society*. Chicago, IL: University of Chicago Press.

Cognitive Evolution and Religion; Cognition and Religious Evolution

Harvey Whitehouse

Explaining religion it is not a matter of accounting for a single trait; it involves explaining a very *complex* and interconnected repertoire of patterns of thinking and behavior. Many early attempts to account for the origins and spread of religion (e.g., Freud 1938/1913; Durkheim 1964/1915; Marx & Engels 1976/1888; Tylor 1871) sought the solution in a single core process (repression of guilt, symbolization of the social order, exploitation by a ruling class, intellectual curiosity, etc.), giving rise to theories that were either untestable or, if rendered more precisely, quite easily refuted. Partly as a consequence of this failure, many scholars of religion in recent decades have abandoned explanatory projects in favor of purely descriptive and interpretive/ hermeneutic activities.

The new 'cognitive science of religion' (CSR) offers a fresh approach. Its aim is to fractionate religion into numerous different traits, each of which must be explained on it own account. The CSR proceeds from evidence that human minds develop in fundamentally similar ways the world over, even though cultural settings differ widely; it proposes that these recurrent features of our minds evolved under natural selection to deal with problems that don't *necessarily* have anything to do with religion; it postulates, however, that these universal features of cognition can help to explain widespread patterns of religious thinking and behavior.

Valuable as the contributions of the CSR have been, it should be acknowledged that they constitute only a modest starting point in explaining religion. For the field to mature it must expand its horizons to take into account the role of ecological variables in processes of religious evolution.

Explaining Recurrent Features of Religion

Figure 1 lists a number of traits that might be associated with the category 'religion'.[1] These traits are probably found, in some shape or form, in all hu-

1 Problems of defining 'religion' can be set aside here – what matters is that we find an explanation for specific traits; whether or not those traits happen to be classified as 'religious' at certain times and places is if little importance for explanatory purposes.

man societies – or at least are very widespread and historically recurrent. The CSR has attempted to account for this recurrence in terms of the shaping and constraining effects of universal cognitive mechanisms.

Figure 1: Cross-culturally recurrent religious repertoire

Afterlife
Beings with special powers
Signs and portents
Creationism
Spirit possession
Rituals
Ritual exegesis
The Sacred
Deference
Moral obligation
Punishment and reward
Revelation

For instance, *afterlife beliefs* have been explained in terms of our inability to simulate the elimination of mental states (Bering 2006); notions of *beings with special powers* have been explained in terms of the cognitive salience of concepts that violate intuitive ontological knowledge (Boyer 2001); *creationism* has been explained in terms of a predisposition toward teleological reasoning (Evans 2001; Kelemen 2004); various properties of *ritual* have been explained in terms of universal features of action representation systems (Lawson & McCauley 1990); and so on. In the last few years new books in the CSR, developing these and other (related) ideas, have been appearing at an astonishing rate (see http://www.iacsr.com/index.html).

Evolution and Religion

Based on these kinds of theories in the CSR, we might reasonably ask how cognitive evolution is implicated in the rise and spread of religion – and vice versa. One possibility is that religious thinking and behavior is a spandrel, a set of traits arising from cognitive capacities that evolved in response to adaptive challenges quite unrelated to religion *per se* (e.g., Atran, 2002; Boyer 2001). Another possibility is that at least some aspects of religious thinking and behavior contribute to inclusive fitness, constituting adaptations that arose under natural selection (e.g., Bering 2006; Bloom 2004). The arguments on both sides are complex and engrossing, as these conference proceedings amply demonstrate. It is too early, however, to say much with confidence about the relationship between cognitive evolution and religion because of the paucity of evidence in evolutionary psychology generally and in its claims about religious phenomena in particular. A more neglected question, but ironically one that we are in a much stronger position to address with the backing of empirical evidence, is how *cognition* might impact on processes of *religious evolution*.[2] One of the most compelling arguments of the CSR has been that cultural phenomena can be understood within a *selectionist* framework, one that couches its predictions in terms of statistically meaningful tendencies that are at least partly determined by cognitive dispositions and susceptibilities.[3] Much remains to be done in order to expand the empirical foundations of this approach and to refine its theoretical models accordingly. Nevertheless, there is much more to explain about religion than a set of statistically recurrent features. Herein lies the key to developing new perspectives on processes of religious evolution. Two possible strategies immediately present themselves:

Strategy 1: look for variables that amplify/suppress universal features

One strategy is to focus on the differential emphasis on core features of the recurrent religious repertoire from one tradition to the next. For instance, some Afro-Brazilian cults postulate a vast pantheon of supernatural beings and there is a very heavy emphasis on spirit possession (Cohen, 2007). All the other features of the religious repertoire are present as well but some of those features (e.g., moral obligation and revelation), although everyone would recognize them, are under-emphasized, when compared with other religious traditions. Conversely, some versions of Christianity show little interest in the idea of spirit possession and/or take a somewhat dim view of ritualization, but may place great emphasis on moral obligation or notions of supernatural punishment (eternal damnation) and other features (Malley 2004).

Could there be factors that predictably influence which kinds of cognitively attractive concepts occur in which kinds of religious traditions? Even allowing for a considerable degree of random innovation, this seems eminently possible. That is, even though we may still be dealing with explanatory strategies tracking on relative frequencies rather than the particularities of given cases, we stand to increase the specificity and predictive power of our models by introducing additional contextual variables. Consider the following candidates.

Biological variables

A wide variety of population-level biological variables could influence religiosity, including genetically influenced personality differences, ageing, sexual

2 This neglect in modern times results in part from the failure of Victorian theories of religious evolution to convince (in large part because of their flawed Lamarckianism but also because of their association with colonial imperialism).

3 The paradigmatic statement of this approach remains Dan Sperber's (1985) account of the 'epidemiology of representations'.

dimorphism, diet, drug abuse, and many other factors. Gender-based differences, to take one example, could prove to be a profitable area for investigation. Women, at least at a population level, exhibit more highly developed 'Theory of Mind' (ToM) capacities than men, and serious pathologies involving ToM deficits (mostly notably autism) are much less common in women than in men (Baron-Cohen 2003). It follows that those parts of the religious repertoire that rely on sophisticated ToM operations might be expected to feature more prominently in the thinking and behavior of women than men (all else being equal). Of our list of recurrent features in the religious repertoire the one that places the heaviest burdens on our ToM capacities is undoubtedly the complex of behaviors surrounding 'spirit possession'. This complex involves keeping track of at least two mental entities (the possessing spirit and the host) at the same time, and typically a number of such entities if (as is commonly the case) the host is possessed by several spirits in rapid succession. Moreover, since spirit possession frequently occurs in group settings (such as the séance), observers and participants alike would need to keep track of what is happening in the minds of many other persons as well, if they are to grasp the social implications of the information divulged by possessing spirits. The upper limit on such tracking for normal adults is 'level 4' (e.g., Dick knows that Mary thinks that Harry has persuaded Lucy to come to the party). Spirit possession phenomena make heavy demands at this ceiling level. We might therefore predict that spirit possession will be a domain of religious activity that will tend to involve higher levels of participation from women than from men. That is potentially quite an interesting line of enquiry because the evidence from ethnography and historiography does seem to point in that direction.

Technological variables.

The level of technological development is likely to be a key ecological factor influencing religiosity. For instance, particular modes of subsistence could serve to prime our Agency-Detection System in specific ways. Even under normal conditions, humans readily perceive agency in the most unlikely places (Guthrie 1993). We are especially likely to think that agents are lurking when we are in spooky or dangerous situations (like a darkened tomb or a haunted forest). Over-attribution of agency may be greatly heightened by living in communities where predators and pests pose a significant threat to health and livelihood. Historically, the precious livestock of farmers have been threatened (to a greater or lesser extent) by carnivorous predators. Crops have been at risk from disease and pestilence, and buildings and storehouses have been compromised by burrowing insects and other menaces. In conditions where these kinds of problems are most acute people are especially vigilant—continually on the alert for signs of harmful agency. It seems quite possible, in principle at least, that this habitual *priming* of the Agency-Detection System might give rise to relatively high levels of perceived encounters with supernatural agents. Are stories about encounters with spirits and goblins more prevalent under these conditions, as compared with populations that have less to fear from predators and pests? At present we do not know but this topic could certainly be investigated.

Sociopolitical variables

Sociopolitical structure and ideology has long been recognized by anthropologists to influence religious beliefs.[4] This is appreciated too by some contributors to the CSR field. For instance, Boyer (2005) has suggested that in any coalition where the pressure to defect is relatively great, we will tend to find ritual groupings that impose particularly high entry costs. An obvious example would be traumatic initiation rites. The ethnographic record does indeed seem to show that the most horrifying initiatory ordeals occur mostly in warlike societies where the temptation to abandon one's fellows on the battlefield would be exceptionally acute. By undergoing especially grueling tests of initiation, group members might be publicly demonstrating their trustworthiness—in other words showing that they can be relied upon to stay at their posts, even in the face of great danger and suffering. Again this raises major empirical questions. Is the intuition that high membership costs demonstrate loyalty to the coalition truly widespread across a range of cultures? Does the ethnographic record show that the incidence and severity of initiation rites correlate directly with defection pressures, assuming we can find appropriate measures for these variables (see Sosis, Kress & Boster, in press)?

Cultural variables

Cultural schemas could also influence the activation of universal cognitive mechanisms in ways that help to shape patterns of religious innovation and transmission. Consider, as a simple example, the difference between group recruitment based on ideals of ascription and achievement respectively. In kinship-based societies, recruitment to corporations is *ideally* based on *ascribed* traits, for instance the ability to trace lines of descent to fictive primordial ancestors. In liberal democracies, by contrast, recruitment to corporations is *ideally* based on meritocratic selection, along competitive lines. The members

4 Well-known arguments from anthropology include the alleged causal connection between hierarchy and patriarchy, on the one hand, and ritual inversion or 'rites of rebellion' on the other (Gluckman 1963), the thesis that accusations of witchcraft tend to be directed at transgressors of difficult-to-prosecute social or moral (rather than legal) infractions (Douglas 1970), or the thesis that beliefs about procreation and the inheritance of spiritual characteristics are shaped by descent ideology and methods of corporate group recruitment (e.g., Fortes 1945).

of both types of society may share the same basic essentialized construals of the person category and may agree on basic moral principles (e.g., that people should, ideally, get what they deserve in terms of punishments and rewards). Nevertheless, in many traditional societies these intuitions are exploited by pervasive cultural schemas that see individual identity as mapping closely onto *group* identity; *whereas*, in contemporary Western societies, the same basic intuitions are exploited by schemas that emphasize the discreteness of individual and collective identity—and by valuing (at least ideally) not who you are, but what you can do. These kinds of pervasive tendencies in cultural schemata, taken together with a universal predisposition to essentialize the person category, might in turn bias religious thinking in predictable ways. So, for instance, cultural schemata emphasizing descent ideology typically postulate the sharing of essentialized properties between *deities* and particular *groups* of human beings. (We could call this the 'totemic principle.') By contrast, in more individualistic cultures we would expect deities to be construed as sharing essentialized properties with all other persons (as an undifferentiated category) but at the same time construing each person in terms of unique qualities that are presumed not to be shared with anybody else (i.e., being in possession of a unique spirit or soul). (We could call this the principle of 'universalistic individualism.') In other words, the same kinds of essentializing biases could be put to work in doctrinally distinctive ways that are shaped and constrained by wider cultural assumptions. Some schemas might be pervasive in a given society, without necessarily being particularly *religious*. But, equally, we could focus on the shaping effects of more specifically religious schemas. So we could ask, for instance, how the presence of particular kinds of religious beliefs might make the invention and transmission of other kinds of religious beliefs more or less likely.

Strategy 2: Look for mechanisms that transcend the recurrent repertoire

A major limitation with CSR research has been its somewhat narrow emphasis on the issue of how universal cognitive biases shape and constrain patterns of religious transmission. Although that is clearly a valuable starting point, it only helps to explain variations on a theme. That is, it may help us to explain why certain features of religious thinking and behavior are especially widespread and may even help us to explain why some aspects of the universal repertoire are more heavily emphasized in one place rather than another—for instance, if (as I've suggested) we build in sufficiently detailed information about various contextual factors (that is, the sorts of ecological variables we've been looking at). But religious traditions are much more than just the sum of various universal themes. Some religions involve highly elaborated and distinctive cosmologies, for example. Others incorporate extensive ethical systems that run against the grain of intuitive moral reasoning. And what we find, on the ground, is that all these gloriously diverse ideas are often linked together in ways that might be described as systemic. So we talk quite reasonably about *religious systems* rather than simply about loose assemblages of catchy concepts.

Religious systems, as such, are not particularly catchy and, indeed, are often extremely difficult to acquire. Consider, for instance, how much labor and energy, around the world, is invested in processes of missionization, proselytism, and education. Thus, although religion has recurrent and intuitive features, it also encompasses ideas that are extremely hard to learn and pass on. And it is in the complex balance between these two sets of features that we must look if we want to understand the evolution of religious systems.

The relationship between intuitive and hard-to-acquire aspects of religion may be productively understood as a 'ratchet effect' (Tomasello 1999).[5] A ratchet does two things: it holds a bolt in place so that the ratchet retains its grip and of course it turns the bolt so that it grinds its way into a threaded hole. The *retaining* function of a ratchet corresponds to our recurrent religious repertoire. Some aspects of religion never change – or, more to the point, they never *evolve*. By contrast the *turning* function of the ratchet corresponds to those aspects of religion that build up, cumulatively, over time. This is essentially an evolutionary process.

The cumulative evolution of religion depends in part on patterns of *innovation* (the creation of new ideas and novel connections between previously unrelated ideas, e.g., through processes of inference, extrapolation, deduction, analogical reasoning, etc.) and *storage* (the retention of novel connections, e.g., by means of explicit memory, distributed cognition, external mnemonics, etc.).

Religious innovation is often construed as a process of revelation, understood in terms of miraculous intervention via dreams, trance, visitations, callings, and such like. Revelations are sometimes associated with altered states of consciousness, e.g., induced by epileptic seizures, hallucinogenic drugs, schizophrenia, or prolonged deprivation or abstinence. Personality differences can play an important role in all of this too - some people may be naturally more susceptible to revelatory experiences than others and people also differ in the extent to which they are prone to *interpreting* their revelatory experiences and passing the details on to other people. Nevertheless, there are also various ways in which patterns of revelation can be *socially regulated*. Rituals that are especially arousing tend to be remembered with particular vividness. Since rituals of this kind are deeply puzzling and disturbing experiences, they

5 The term "rachet effect" is used rather differently here from the way Tomasello intended, insofar as he understood the holding function of the ratchet in terms of the preservation of cultural innovations rather than the intrusion of panhuman biases.

tend to set off subjective experiences of *revelation*. My own research team has made a start at investigating this hypothesis experimentally (Richert, Whitehouse, & Stewart 2005). But we also have considerable evidence from ethnography suggesting that people who participate in traumatic or ecstatic rituals tend to develop highly elaborate bodies of personal, idiosyncratic exegetical knowledge, based on deep and enduring conscious reflection (Whitehouse 1995, 2000; Whitehouse & Laidlaw 2004). I refer to this complex as the *imagistic* mode of religiosity. Imagistic practices provide a highly effective way of generating religious innovations. Nevertheless, if religious innovations are to be *transmitted* effectively then the conscious schemas that bind them together must somehow be stored as a body of explicit knowledge.

The *storage of religious innovations* depends extensively on *semantic memory* (often augmented by external mnemonics, distributed cognition, and other forms of cognitive support). Semantic memory, however, can only store large bodies of information through processes of regular rehearsal. Any religious tradition that draws on this method of transmission must adopt a somewhat routinized regime of doctrinal reiteration. I refer to this pattern as the *doctrinal* mode of religiosity. As with the imagistic mode, the doctrinal mode involves a complex clustering of features. The key thing to note here, though, is that the doctrinal mode is based around *frequently repeated teachings and rituals*. Much of the religious knowledge is codified in language and transmitted primarily via recognized leaders and authoritative texts. Routinized transmission allows cognitively challenging ideas to be learned and stored in semantic memory. But heavy repetition also makes it possible for religious ideas to become rather rigidly systematized and standardized in a population. If the religious concepts, and the authoritative logical and interpretive connections that bind them together, are frequently reiterated, then it becomes easier to spot deviations from the standard account.

The theory of 'modes of religiosity' maintains that all these cognitive features are causally linked to a set of contrasting sociopolitical arrangements, thus hoping to provide at least a preliminary explanation for long-recognized patterns of religious variation—one that is commensurate, however, with the finding that religions *also* encompass relatively unchanging, universal dynamics. According to the modes theory, there are really just three ways of acquiring and transmitting religion. The first is species-typical and more or less invariable, consisting of naturally 'catchy' concepts.[6] The second seems to have emerged in relatively recent human prehistory and is associated with the establishment of highly cohesive ritual groupings and the emergence of cognitively complex and typically esoteric religious revelations (the imagistic mode).

---

6 These aspects of religion are sometimes referred to as 'cognitively optimal beliefs' (Boyer 2001; Whitehouse 2004).

The third is a more recent pattern, emerging alongside the earliest large-scale settlements and proto-states and involving the transmission of more systematized religious teachings (the doctrinal mode). Nowadays, all three ways of acquiring and transmitting religion are widely distributed in the world's religious traditions.

Of course, we still have to ask *why* doctrinal and imagistic modes of religiosity emerged in the order that they did. Why, in other words, is this long-term transformation a process of evolution? The answer, I suggest, lies in understanding the impact of ecological variables on human cognition.

The imagistic mode generates extremely cohesive coalitions – and for this reason helps to guarantee co-operation in circumstances where there are strong incentives to defect. A likely trigger for the emergence of the imagistic mode would have been increasing competition for scarce resources. Many contemporary hunter-gatherer societies have extraordinarily flexible social groupings and high levels of personal autonomy. But what happens when the survival of human populations in technologically simple societies suddenly depends upon higher levels of co-operation? The answer is that weak coalitions either die out or become assimilated into stronger coalitions. The imagistic mode was probably an adaptation to such conditions. It provided the cohesion necessary to work together in increasingly dangerous pursuits – the hunting of larger game animals and, most likely, territorially-driven predation and warfare against neighbouring bands (Sosis, Kress & Boster, in press).

The emergence of imagistic cults (e.g., based around initiations, ancestor worship and fertility rites) provided a sociopolitical adaptation but also a means of generating ever more complex cosmologies and esoteric revelations. The doctrinal mode, by contrast, emerged when relatively large-scale patterns of cooperation became routinized, probably as a result of the seasonal rhythms associated with the domestication of animals and plants and the establishment of the first townships. The doctrinal mode provided, for the first time in human history, the mnemonic scaffolding (based around regular public reiteration of religious creeds) for the transformation of imagistic revelations into more standardized bodies of doctrine. From that point onwards, we find that all three modalities of transmission *influence* each other, producing distinctive patterns of religious transformation over time (Whitehouse 2004).

Conclusion

All human populations share a common set of religious concepts and behavioral patterns that derive from relatively implicit, intuitive patterns of thinking. Such phenomena are, we might reasonably assume, as old as our species (possibly older even than that). They are part of the human condition, like the capacity for language or the ability to track several intentional states at one time. This recurrent religious repertoire constitutes the *holding* function associated with the so-called 'ratchet effect'. Meanwhile, however, modes dynamics provide an insight into the *turning* function of the ratchet, and hence the *evolution* of religion. Many religious concepts require considerable cognitive, social, and technological resources to create, remember, and pass on. Cross-culturally variable aspects of religion arise in part from the evolution of cognitive systems devoted to connecting concepts (e.g., through the formation of novel analogies) and storing them (e.g., in semantic memory) and in part from the historically changing sociopolitical conditions in which such systems can be exploited. Only a coordinated, interdisciplinary effort that takes into account the role of both evolved cognition and human ecology in religious innovation and transmission will be sufficient to provide the broad empirical and theoretical base necessary for explaining religion.

References

Atran, S. 2002. *In gods we trust: The evolutionary landscape of religion*. New York, NY: Oxford University Press.

Baron-Cohen, S. 2003. *The essential difference: The truth about the male and female brain*. New York, NY: Basic Books:

Bering, J. M. 2006. The cognitive psychology of belief in the supernatural: A by-product of the ability to reason about the minds of others may offer evolutionary advantage. *American Scientist*, 94, 2, 142-149.

Bloom, P. 2004. *Descartes' baby: How the science of child development explains what makes us human*. New York, NY: Basic Books.

Boyer, P. 2001. *Religion explained: The evolutionary origins of religious thought*. New York, NY: Basic Books.

Boyer, P. 2005. A reductionist model of distinct modes of religious transmission. In H. Whitehouse & R. N. McCauley. ,Eds., *Mind and religion: Psychological and cognitive foundations of religiosity*, 3-29. Walnut Creek, CA: AltaMira Press.

Cohen, E. 2007. *The mind possessed: The cognition of spirit possession in an Afro-Brazilian religious tradition*. New York, NY: Oxford University Press.

Douglas, M. 1970. *Witchcraft, confessions, and accusations*. London, UK: Tavistock.

Durkheim, E. 1964. *The elementary forms of religious life*. London, UK: Allen and Unwin. Original work published 1915.

Evans, E. M. 2001. Cognitive and contextual factors in the emergence of diverse belief systems: Creation versus evolution. *Cognitive Psychology*, 42, 3, 217-266.

Fortes, M. 1945. *Dynamics of clanship among the Tallensi*. Oxford, UK: Oxford University Press.

Freud, S. 1938. *Totem and taboo*. A. A. Brill, Trans. Harmondsworth, UK: Penguin Books. Original work published 1913.

Gluckman, M. 1963. *Order and rebellion in tribal Africa*. New York, NY: Free Press.
Guthrie, S. E. 1993. *Faces in the clouds: A new theory of religion*. New York and Oxford: Oxford University Press.
Kelemen, D. 2004. Are children "intuitive theists"? Reasoning about purpose and design in nature. *Psychological Science, 15*, 295-301.
Lawson, E. T., & McCauley, R. N. 1990. *Rethinking religion: Connecting cognition and culture*. Cambridge, UK: Cambridge University Press.
Malley, B. 2004. *How the Bible works: An anthropological study of evangelical biblicism*. Walnut Creek, CA: AltaMira Press.
Marx, K., & Engels, F. 1976. *Manifesto of the Communist party*. In K. Marx & F. Engels, Eds., *Collected works*. Vol. 6, 476-519. New York, NY: International Publishers. Original work published 1888.
Richert, R. A., Whitehouse, H., & Stewart, E. 2005. Memory and analogical thinking in high-arousal rituals. In H. Whitehouse & R. N. McCauley, Eds., *Mind and religion: Psychological and cognitive foundations of religiosity*, 127-145. Walnut Creek, CA: AltaMira Press.
Sosis, R., H. Kress, , & J. Boster, 2007. Scars for war: Evaluating alternative signaling explanations for cross-cultural variance in ritual costs. *Evolution & Human Behavior, 28*, pp. 234-247.
Sperber, D. 1985. Anthropology and psychology: Towards an epidemiology of representations. The Malinowski Memorial Lecture, 1984. *Man N.S., 20*, 73-89.
Tomasello, M. 1999. *The cultural origins of human cognition*. Cambridge, MA: Harvard University Press.
Tylor, E. B. 1871. *Primitive culture*. London, UK: John Murray.
Whitehouse, H. 1995. *Inside the cult: Religious innovation and transmission in Papua New Guinea*. Oxford, UK: Oxford University Press.
Whitehouse, H. 2000. *Arguments and icons: Divergent modes of religiosity*. Oxford, UK: Oxford University Press.
Whitehouse, H. 2004. *Modes of religiosity: A cognitive theory of religious transmission*. Walnut Creek, CA: AltaMira Press.
Whitehouse, H., & Laidlaw, J. 2004. *Ritual and memory: Toward a comparative anthropology of religion*. Walnut Creek, CA: AltaMira Press.

From Apes to Devils and Angels
Comparing Scenarios on the Evolution of Religion

Armin W. Geertz

Introduction

Cognitive studies of religion today are rife with evolutionary scenarios informed by cognitive archaeology, evolutionary psychology, developmental psychology, comparative religion, ethology and many more. Some of the scenarios seem to ring more true than others. This paper will briefly explore why evolutionary scenarios of religion are so difficult to achieve.

There are two main difficulties. The first is that much of the struggle involved in developing evolutionary theories of religion resides in battles between two apparently incompatible paradigms. The most dominant paradigm, which is under serious attack these days, is the metaphor of the brain as a kind of computer, and those aspects that make us human are conceived in terms of brain modules. Culture is unimportant, genetic endowment entrenches thought, whatever the cultural variance. During the past decade, a paradigm based on the biological metaphor perceives human consciousness as situated in a web of neurobiological processes, cultural symbols and social mechanisms. Here, culture is indispensable to the construction of mind, the ultimate cause of which is a mixture of genetic and epigenetic factors.

The second is that much of the debate on evolution is based upon assumptions we happen to have about what is and is not characteristically human. This often leads to a kind of roller-coaster science: someone decides what is human and claims that the apes don't have it. This is followed by a wave of publications proving the opposite, sometimes even arguing that not only apes have it, but so do dolphins or elephants or birds.

The Cognitivist Paradigm

The cognitivist paradigm, called CRUM (Computational-Representational Understanding of Mind) by one of its critics (Thagard 1996, 10), assumes that the mind is a computer, based on algorithmic rules that compute information like a formal grammar. Furthermore, the paradigm assumes a scientistic, objectivist position rejected by the philosophy of science decades ago.

The formalistic systems of the 1950s provided a much needed alternative to straightjacket behaviorism. In many ways, however, the cognitive revolution introduced a more sophisticated behaviorism. The following 40 years witnessed a large number of formalistic and componential analyses producing universal grammars of natural language (Noam Chomsky), cultural grammars (Ward H. Goodenough), lexical folk-taxonomies (Harold C. Conklin, Mary Black), color terminology (Paul Kay), universal structures in human narrative (Claude Lévi-Strauss) and complex schemes of kinship systems (Floyd G. Lounsbury). See the papers by many of these names in the reader edited by Stephen A. Tyler (1969) and the collection on color edited by Gumperz & Levinson (1996). The assumption was that many of these systems and grammars were hardwired in the human brain through evolutionary selection processes. Thus, when the second cognitive revolution hit the 1990s scene, many of the pioneers of the cognitive science of religion who were publishing at the time assumed that modules, domains and prototypes were at the core of human cultural and religious universals. Thus, Steven Mithen (1996) developed his Fodorian Swiss-army-knife mentality theory to account for a highly modular history of the mind (cf. Fodor, 1983), E. Thomas Lawson & Robert N. McCauley developed their Chomskian ritual representation theory (1990), and Pascal Boyer (1994) investigated how religious ideas tweak default cognitive domains.

There are a number of reasons why these approaches are problematic. The evidence they offer, as my colleague Uffe Schjødt (2005, 50) has argued, is based on a modular theory of social cognition in which children are assumed to develop full theory of mind competence around the age of three. By then, they are able to hold meta-representations of other's motivations based on propositional inference processes. But there are strong arguments against this interpretation that do not require the separation of affection and connation from cognition. Behavior seen from this perspective is causally linked to affective states and motives and not to propositional representations independent of the somatosensoric systems (Barsalou, 1999; Barsalou, Niedenthal, Barbey, & Ruppert, 2003; Damasio, 1994, 1999; Hobson, 1993; Stern, 2000; Trevarthen, 1998).

A second important problem is the claim that the inference systems hypothesized by these scholars are task specific. This claim, however, is not supported by the neurological evidence which on the contrary shows that brain regions are multi-purpose. A series of task specific modules or systems would be costly and ineffective in day to day brain tasks.

The third main problem is that culture is assumed to be epiphenomenal to more basic psychological processes. Two of the most strident champions of this assumption are Pascal Boyer (1994 & 2001) and Scott Atran (2002). I will not go into a detailed critique of their work, but will concentrate in the next section on the assumption itself.

Solipsistic Models

Evolutionary psychologist Merlin Donald has eloquently argued that a solipsistic model of human cognition is wrong. His biocultural model emphasizes the evolution of human cognitive communities as one of the most significant revolutions in the history of the world. These cognitive communities, which by the way, arose before language, involve what he calls knowledge networks, feeling networks, and memory networks:

> The first priority was not to speak, use words, or develop grammars. It was to bond as a group, to learn to share attention and set up the social patterns that would sustain such sharing and bonding in the species. (Donald 2001, 253)

Language arose later out of a "communicative universe that was much larger than one contained inside a single brain and was instead provided by a community of brains" (Ibid.). Just as the physical environment drove the evolution of perceptual mechanisms, Donald claims, "so cultural energy drove the evolution of sophisticated communicative capacities. It also generated forward pressure on the developing mind" (Donald 2001, 254). The truly human mode of consciousness, he argues, is defined by our immersion in culture. The human mind is a hybrid mind.

A good colleague of mine and I were arguing once about the relationship between culture and cognition. Sharing the assumptions of the epiphenomenalists, my colleague quipped, "If there were no brains, there would be no culture." But this is the wrong way of putting it, mainly because it is a moot question, like the chicken and egg. But I think that we can be sure of one important thing, namely that whenever consciousness happened to have arisen, perhaps with the increase in brain size evidenced by *Homo habilis* or *Homo ergaster*, hominids were already living in highly social and cultural environments. There is no way one can separate culture and cognition, and I am convinced that there is no foundation for maintaining a solipsistic model of human cognition.

Deleting culture from human cognition and claiming that what remains are universal processes and default inference systems is poor philosophy and questionable heuristics. Humans without culture are not humans. End of story. What could possibly be left after the cultural equation is deleted? Australopithecus? They evidently had no culture, no material culture at any rate. If we also include social, immaterial culture, then even the Australopithecus might still be candidates. Even baboons are candidates according to recent studies on primate culture (Sapolsky, 2006). Without culture we would be wombats.

Imagining humans without culture may be a good exercise in off-line cognition, but it is also clearly off-the-wall. We need to take culture into account.

There is plenty of evidence for adjusting our assumptions on this point (Clark, 1997; Clark & Chalmers, 1998; Deacon, 1997; Hutchins, 1995; Richerson & Boyd 2005; Rowlands, 2003; Tomasello, 1999; West-Eberhard, 2003).

From Apes to Devils and Angels

The British biological anthropologist Robert Foley called most of our evolutionary scenarios "the evolutionary Catch 22":

> The difficulty in coming to any clear conclusions and the inability to put the finger on a single characteristic represents the tactical problem of investigating human evolution, and of unraveling the ape from the angel. In many of the arguments there is in fact a Catch 22 that is liable to unsettle simple discourse (Foley 1995, 46).

The catch, as Foley puts it, is that as soon as we identify a particular trait as being uniquely human, we assume that it isn't found among other animals. However, before too long, someone claims that chimps have it too:

> No sooner was Kenneth Oakley's *Man the Toolmaker* published than Jane Goodall reported chimpanzees using tools. When hunting was popular, then chimpanzees and baboons were found to hunt. When humanness withdrew to language, all the studies of language acquisition in apes were produced. The catch comes full circle when it is then pointed out that as these features occur in other species, they cannot be what made us human. A further knot is sometimes added, as in the case of human hunting, when it can also be shown that humans do not really do what they are supposed to do anyway. This circle of evolutionary fallibility can be repeated for virtually any trait, and it serves to prevent the breakdown of the ape and angel ideals that have dominated the imagery of human evolution (Foley 1995, 46).

Robin Dunbar noted that even though we share a number of features with our ape cousins, there are also differences. We share traits with them because of our common ancestry. But both we and they have developed during the past six million years, which may account for the differences. As he wrote:

> We share both the good and the bad habits of our primate (and especially ape) cousins, but it would be only a slight exaggeration to say that, on both counts, we simply do them on a grander scale (Dunbar 2004, 104).

The anatomical evidence seems to indicate that spoken language at the earliest could only have appeared somewhere between 300,000 (Foley) and 500,000 (Dunbar) years ago. Significant cultural change did not occur until that time, which indicates that spoken language was incremental to it. But it is probably also a fact that the reconfigurations of the brain that eventually led to language occurred in a primate brain, as Ursula Goodenough and Terrence Deacon (2003) have argued. Our brain still remains very much a primate brain. This is why we need to push our psychological speculations, analogies and homologies much further back than to the archaic hominids of the Pleistocene.

What makes things even more complicated is the fact that even though we have a very close connection to chimpanzees and bonobos—we share for instance 98% of our DNA, another more startling way of putting it: only some 50 genes separate us—there are 200 more distantly related primate species with whom we share many characteristics. As primatologist Karen B. Strier (2002) argued, the problem with thinking in anthropocentric terms and focusing exclusively on chimpanzees and bonobos is that all three are thus artificially set off from the rest of the primate world:

> In contrast, where we consider the behavioral diversity of primates other than apes, the social tendencies that humans share with chimpanzees or bonobos are situated along a continuum defined by common responses to common ecological challenges. Our history as hominoids predisposes us to act like apes, but underlying these predispositions is an even longer past as socially adaptable primates (74).

I cannot go into more detail here. Certainly we need to investigate the primate origins of our violent nature (Wrangham & Peterson, 1996). This would be the devilish line of inquiry. But such an investigation must also take into account that not all primates have the same inclination to violence. The bonobos, for instance, seem to practice a different social model than their chimpanzee cousins. Second, we need to investigate the primate origins of our moral nature (de Waal, 1996). This would be the angelic line of inquiry. Such an investigation of course hinges on how we define morality. It is without doubt a topic of crucial importance to the study of religion.

Conclusion

Any theory of the evolution of religion needs to reevaluate the relationship between cognition and culture. This requires abandoning the computer model, the solipsistic model and the epiphenomenalist position. Furthermore, the time scale of our evolutionary model must reach beyond the brief history of *Homo sapiens* into the very depths of our primate lineage.

References

Atran, S. 2002. *In Gods we trust: The evolutionary landscape of religion*. Oxford, UK: Oxford University Press.

Barsalou, L. W. 1999. Perceptual symbol systems. *Behavioral & Brain Sciences, 22*, 577-660.

Barsalou, L. W., Niedenthal, P. M., Barbey, A. K., & Ruppert, J. A. 2003. Social embodiment. In B. H. Ross, Ed., *The psychology of learning and motivation: Advances in research and theory*, Vol. 43, 43-92. San Diego, CA: Academic Press.

Boyer, P. 1994. *The naturalness of religious ideas: A cognitive theory of religion*. Berkeley, CA, Los Angeles, CA, and London, UK: University of California Press.

Boyer, P. 2001. *Religion explained: The evolutionary origins of religious thought*. New York, NY: Basic Books.

Clark, A. 1997. *Being there: Putting brain, body, and world together again*. Cambridge, MA: The MIT Press.

Clark, A., & Chalmers, D. J. 1998. The extended mind. *Analysis, 58*, 10-23.

Damasio, A. R. 1994. *Descartes' error: Emotion, reason, and the human brain*. New York, NY: Avon Books, Inc.

Damasio, A. R. 1999. *The feeling of what happens: Body, emotion and the making of consciousness*. London, UK: Heinemann.

Deacon, T. 1997. *The symbolic species: The co-evolution of language and the human brain*. London, UK: Penguin: Allen Lane.

Donald, M. 2001. *A mind so rare: The evolution of human consciousness*. New York, NY: W. W. Norton & Company.

Dunbar, R. 2004. *The human story: A new history of mankind's evolution*. London, UK: Faber and Faber Ltd.

Fodor, J. 1983. *The modular theory of mind*. Cambridge, MA: The MIT Press.

Foley, R. 1995. *Humans before humanity*. Oxford, UK: Blackwell Publishers Ltd.

Goodenough, U., & Deacon, T. W. 2003. From biology to consciousness to morality. *Zygon: Journal of Religion & Science, 38* (4), 801-819.

Gumperz, J. J., & Levinson, S. C. Eds. 1996. *Rethinking linguistic relativity*. Cambridge, UK: Cambridge University Press.

Hobson, P. 1993. Understanding persons: The role of affect. In S. Baron-Cohen, H. Tager-Flusberg, & D. J. Cohen, Eds., *Understanding other minds: Perspectives from autism*, pp. 204-227. Oxford, UK: Oxford University Press.

Hutchins, E. 1995. *Cognition in the wild*. Cambridge, MA: The MIT Press.

Lawson, E. T., & McCauley, R. N. 1990. *Rethinking religion: Connecting cognition and culture*. Cambridge, UK: Cambridge University Press.

Mithen, S. 1996. *The prehistory of the mind: A search for the origins of art, religion and science*. London, UK: Thames and Hudson Ltd.

Richerson, P. J., & Boyd, R. 2005. *Not by genes alone: How culture transformed human evolution*. Chicago, IL: University of Chicago Press.

Rowlands, M. 2003. *Externalism: Putting mind and world back together again*. Chesham, Buckinghamshire: Acumen Publishing Ltd.

Sapolsky, R. M. 2006. Social cultures among nonhuman primates. *Current Anthropology, 47* (4), 641-656.

Schjødt, U. 2005. *Homøostasis & religiøs adfærd: Om kognitivismens begrænsninger og simulationsteoriens forklaringskraft i et religionsvidenskabeligt perspektiv* "Homeostasis and Religious Behavior: On the Limits of Cognitivism and the Explanatory Power of Simulation Theory from the Perspective of the Study of Religion". Master's thesis, University of Aarhus, Aarhus, Denmark.

Stern, D. N. 2000. *The interpersonal world of the infant: A view from psychoanalysis & developmental psychology*. New York, NY: Basic Books.

Strier, K. B. 2002. Beyond the apes: Reasons to consider the entire primate order. In F. B. M. de Waal, Ed., *Tree of origin: What primate behavior can tell us about human social evolution*, 2nd ed, 69-93. Cambridge, MA: Harvard University Press.

Thagard, P. R. 1996. *Mind: Introduction to cognitive science*. Cambridge, MA: The MIT Press.

Tomasello, M. 1999. *The cultural origins of human cognition*. Cambridge, MA: Harvard University Press.

Trevarthen, C. 1998. The concept and foundation of infant intersubjectivity. In S. Bråten, Ed., *Intersubjective communication and emotion in early ontogeny*, pp. 15-46. Cambridge, UK: Cambridge University Press.

Tyler, S. A. 1969. *Cognitive anthropology*. Prospect Heights, IL: Waveland Press, Inc.

de Waal, F. B. M. 1996. *Good Natured: The origins of right and wrong in humans and other animals*. Cambridge: Harvard University Press.

West-Eberhard, M. J. 2003. *Developmental plasticity and evolution*. Oxford, UK: Oxford University Press.

Wrangham, R., & Peterson, D. 1996. *Demonic males: Apes and the origins of human violence*. New York, NY: Houghton Mifflin Company.

Why People Believe (What Other People See As) Crazy Ideas

William Irons

This brief note suggests a theoretical explanation of a conspicuous feature of religion: contra-empirical beliefs. This idea is offered as a refinement of the commitment theory of religion (Bulbulia 2004a, 2004b; Cronk 1994; Irons 1996, 2001; Sosis 2000, 2003, 2005; Sosis & Bressler 2003; Sosis & Ruffle,2003) which suggests that religion has served in human evolution as both a commitment device and a hard-to-fake signal of commitment. As such, religion functioned to establish reciprocal altruism and social cohesion (Wilson 2002, 2005). This function was especially valuable because inter-groups competition was the main driving force in recent human evolution (Alexander 1987; Dunbar 1996; Irons 1991).

The commitment theory of religion is an expansion of Schelling's idea that commitment has a strategic advantage in social interaction (1960). Hirschleifer (1987) and Frank (1988) expanded this idea by exploring many types of commitments and arguing that human emotions are commitment devices and their visible symptoms are hard-to-fake signals of commitment. Cronk (1994) and Irons (1996) further extended commitment theory by suggesting that religion had enhanced cooperation and social cohesion in recent human evolution by serving as a hard-to-fake signal of commitment. A recent volume edited by Nesse (2001) further expanded commitment theory by exploring many of the ways in which human social life is dependent on commitment.

Commitment theory is very similar to the costly signaling theory or handicap theory developed by Zahavi (1975) which was developed for the study of non-human animal behavior. Commitment theory however is a bit broader. This theory focuses on a range of reasons why signals may be hard-to-fake. Cost is certainly one reason but ease of monitoring is another. Further, some commitments are enforced by what can be called commitment devices, things such as feelings of guilt which punish us for not keeping to a commitment, or romantic love which motivates loyalty and altruism to a spouse or significant other. Some commitment devices are external to the committed individual, i.e. punishment clauses in contracts, laws backed up by police and courts; but some, like guilt or love, are subjective, that is, built into the psychology of the committed individuals.

Religion fits the commitment model in numerous ways. It is costly; it is easy to monitor; and, as I will argue here, it is by its very nature a commitment device and a hard-to-fake signal at the same time. Both religious beliefs and participation in religious ritual activities are irrational and their special value lies in the fact that they are irrational commitments to specific groups. There is good empirical evidence supporting the commitment theory of religion and the closely related multi-level-selection theory of religion (Cruz, this volume; Johnson 2005; Johnson & Krüger 2004; Roes & Raymond 2003; Sosis 2000, 2005; Sosis & Bressler 2003; Sosis & Ruffle 2003; Wilson 2002, 2005).

Crazy Beliefs Have the Advantage of Being Irrational and Specific.

In his 1988 classic book *Passions within Reason*, Frank emphasized that commitments need to be irrational to work. His distinction between rational and irrational is one commonly made by economists and game theorists. Rational behavior is self-interested and guided by cost-benefit analysis. It changes as the costs and benefits change. Irrational behavior is not subject to change as cost and benefits vary. When behaving irrationally, one is simply committed to a set course of action regardless of consequences. Defined in this way irrational behavior allows people to do things they could not do by behaving rationally. Falling in love is one example of such useful irrational behavior which Frank used to illustrate this point. Marriage requires a large investment of time and resources that will not payoff if a partner is deserted. Consider the difference between an irrationally committed marriage partner and a rational one. The rational one is convinced the marriage at hand may be the best he can find at the moment, but will keep an eye out for a better partner should one come along and, if one does, he will desert his current spouse. On the other hand, the person who has gone through the highly irrational experience of falling in love is committed to stay with the current partner regardless of who he encounters in the future. This commitment cannot stand up to rational cost-benefit evaluation. In fact, some people have compared falling in love to temporary insanity. However, a marriage is possible only if one can safely invest energy and resources in the union and forego other opportunities without fear of desertion. Thus the irrational partner, the one in love, is the preferable one by far. This has been true through much of human history and natural selection has favored psychological architecture facilitating the irrational experience of falling in love as a way to commit to a specific mate.

As with marriage, committing oneself to make sacrifices for the welfare of one's social group works best if the other members of the group are also irrationally committed to the group and can signal this commitment in a hard-to-fake way. This commitment device and signal can take the form of really believing that one is being continuously watched by a supernatural being that rewards behavior supportive of the group and punishers behavior not supportive of the group, or really believing that one's sacrifice will be rewarded in a future life and one's sins will be punished in a future life. Such beliefs constitute a dramatic and irrational commitment to a specific group. One has to believe in a specific supernatural being with a specific name and a specific set of characteristics who has issued a specific set of commandments or made a specific set of promises to a specific group. Religious beliefs also typically entail disdain or outright repugnance for different beliefs which identify people with different groups in competition with one's own group (Bulbulia 2004a).

In a way this parallels the experience of falling in love. A person falls in love with a specific person with specific characteristics. Other potential partners with different characteristics lack the attraction of the specific love interest. For example, a person in love can find the potential partner's brown hair has a special sheen not found in any other. Her blue eyes can be true windows to soul unlike those of any other. Her smile can convey a depth of meaning not found in any other smile, and so on. The more special characteristics the person in love sees in his love interest, the better the signal. A man who is in love with all women would be a lousy partner, as would a woman in love with all men. The object of love needs to be specific, reflecting commitment to a specific person.

Group loyalty is the same. One needs to be committed to one's own specific group, not to groups in general. Most religious belief systems convey this specific loyalty by being distinct from other belief systems. The more elaborate the belief system the better, since an elaborate system of beliefs can easily be distinguished from other belief systems at many points.

The fact that the belief system is irrational is also an essential quality. To be effective as a commitment device and signal, it needs to be irrational. Just as the basis of marriage is best found in an irrational evaluation of the marriage partner, so loyalty to a specific group is best served by an irrational belief in the group's religion. As with other counter-factual messages that human beings communicate to one another, this message is more effective if the message sender actually believes the message (Trivers 1971).

Why is an integrated system of rituals, taboos, and other costly signals not sufficient to serve as a hard-to-fake signal of commitment without also entailing contra-factual beliefs? Empirical work by Sosis and Bressler (2003) suggests an answer to this question. They took the longevity of American communes as a measure of their effectiveness in creating cooperation and social cohesion. They found that religious communes survived on average four times longer than secular communes. They also discovered that among religious communes there was a correlation between the number of costly rituals and taboos imposed on members and the longevity of the commune. However, this was true only for the religious communes. Secular communes did not improve their survival chances by imposing more costly requirements. This result suggests that cost alone is not what makes religion effective at encouraging social cohesion. Religion appears to be better at engendering cooperation because it is more effective as a commitment device than secular ideologies. Why are religions more effective as commitment devices? I suggest it is because they consist of irrational commitments to specific groups.

It should also be noted that beliefs that express irrational commitments to specific groups are not limited to religion. Patriotism is a conspicuous example of a non-religious commitment. Commitments to an alma mater, to a football team, to a club, to a social class, a political party, or even to an academic discipline can also be signaled by irrational beliefs. Religions are not the only hard-to-fake signals of commitment and the only commitment devices; however, they are the most elaborate and enduring of such signals and devices.

Human psychology is complex and capable of subtle distinction. People need to be rational about some things—wresting food, for example, from the natural environment and tending to basic survival needs (Bulbulia 2004a). Somehow people distinguish between rational messages about the natural world and irrational messages that signal group loyalty. Messages falling in the first category are subjected to logical and empirical scrutiny and if a message does not pass muster, it can harm the reputation of the message sender. Messages falling in the second category are judged by a different standard. Does the message express commitment to the in-group or not? Logic and evidence are irrelevant and irrationality is not a problem. In fact, irrational messages are preferable because they are not subject to rational evaluation; they are true commitments. (Modern scientists, who are committed to understanding all phenomena including human behavior and beliefs in completely natural terms, may have trouble with such social signals, but their problem is historically novel.) What I am suggesting here with the distinction between rational beliefs about the natural world and irrational social signals is basically the same as D. S. Wilson's (2002) distinction between practical realism and adaptive realism.

I have given extensive attention to irrational beliefs because many of the scientists currently studying the evolution of religion are convinced this is one of the hardest features of religion to explain. I do not intend by this to imply that belief is the most important element of religion. Rituals, taboos, sacred stories, group-specific codes of behavior, and special religious experiences such as trances or other altered states of consciousness are also important as commitment signals and devices and different religions place different emphases on various of these elements. Christianity has defined belief as central and Christians have argued about, and even spilled blood over, the precise wording of creeds. Other religions put rituals or taboos or codes of behavior at the center and argue or fight over these. The fact that Christianity is the religion most familiar to most scientists studying religion may be one of the reasons why belief has received so much attention. Nevertheless, the practices of rituals, observance of taboos and so on also serve as irrational commitments to specific groups.

It is important to note that I am not suggesting that social cohesion is the only function of religion. Religions no doubt serve many functions. However, I suggest that forming and communicating commitment to social groups has been the primary function of religion and is responsible for the evolution of specialized psychological mechanisms that make it easy to learn and practice the particular religion of one's community while holding other religions in disdain. It should also be noted that, while religion has an evolved psychological component, it is largely a cultural institution which rests on this psychological foundation. The psychological foundation is universal among human populations but very flexible. It consists of elements of the human mind which make it easy to learn the local religion and other local commitment devices and signals. Much of the definition of specific competing local groups and local signals of commitment is cultural in nature and represents the collective decision of large numbers of people over many generations.

It is further important to note that the commitment theory of religion does not say that religion is good. Whether religion is good or bad is irrelevant to questions of how and why it evolved. Evolution has produced numerous things that are very bad and numerous things that are very good. How the balance sheet comes out for religion in general or for any specific religion has nothing to do with whether religion evolved as a commitment device producing social cohesion.

Summary

1. The main driving force in recent human evolution was inter-group competition.
2. Inter-group competition made it advantageous for human beings to be committed to their own social groups and to signal this commitment in a hard-to-fake way.
3. Commitments to one's social group need to be irrational and clearly specific to that group. Counter-factual religious beliefs accomplish this. This is only one of many ways in which religion serves as a signal of commitment. Religion also serves as a hard-to-fake signal by being costly and easy to monitor.

References

Alexander, R. D. 1987. *The biology of moral systems.* Hawthorne, NY: Aldine De Gruyter.

Bulbulia, J. 2004a. Religious costs as adaptations that signal altruistic intention. *Evolution & Cognition, 10,* 19-38.

Bulbulia, J. 2004b. The cognitive and evolutionary psychology of religion. *Biology & Philosophy, 18,* 655-686.

Cronk, L. 1994. Evolutionary theories of morality and the manipulative use of signals. *Zygon: Journal of Religion & Science, 29,* 81-101.

Dunbar, R. I. M. 1996. *Grooming, gossip, and the evolution of language.* Cambridge, MA: Harvard University Press.

Frank, R. H. 1988. *Passions within reason: The strategic role of the emotions.* New York, NY: W. W. Norton.

Hirschleifer, J. 1987. On the emotions as guarantors of threats and promises. In J. Dupré, Ed., *The latest on the best: Essays in evolution and optimality,* 307-326. Cambridge, MA: The MIT Press.

Irons, W. 1991. How did morality evolve? *Zygon: Journal of Religion & Science, 26,* 49-89.

Irons, W. 1996. In our own self image: The evolution of morality, deception, and religion. *Skeptic, 4* (2), 50-61.

Irons, W. 2001. Religion as a hard-to-fake sign of commitment. In R. M. Nesse, Ed., *Evolution and the capacity for commitment,* 292-309. New York, NY: Russell Sage Foundation.

Johnson, D. D. P. 2005. God's punishment and public goods: A test of the supernatural punishment hypothesis in 186 Cultures. *Human Nature, 16,* 410-446.

Johnson, D. D. P., & Krüger, O. 2004. The good of wrath: Supernatural punishment and the evolution of cooperation. *Political Theology,* 5, 159-176.

Nesse, R. M. Ed.. 2001. *Evolution and the capacity for commitment.* New York, NY: The Russell Sage Foundation.

Roes, F. L., & Raymond, M. 2003. Belief in moralizing gods. *Evolution & Human Behavior, 24,* 126-135.

Schelling, T. 1960. *The strategy of conflict.* Cambridge, MA: Harvard University Press.

Soler Cruz, Monserrat. 2007. Commitment cost and cooperation: Evidence from Candomblé, an Afro-Brazilian religion. This volume.

Sosis, R. 2000. Religion and intragroup cooperation: Preliminary results of a comparative analysis of utopian communities. *Cross-Cultural Research, 34* (1), 70-87.

Sosis, R. 2003. Why aren't we all Hutterites? Costly signaling theory and religious behavior. *Human Nature, 14,* 91-127.

Sosis, R. 2005. Does religion promote trust? The role of signaling, reputation, and punishment. *Interdisciplinary Journal of Research on Religion, 1,* 1-30.
Sosis, R., & Bressler, E. 2003. Cooperation and commune longevity: A test of the costly signaling theory of religion. *Cross-Cultural Research, 37,* 211-239.
Sosis, R., & Ruffle, B. 2003. Religious ritual and cooperation: Testing for a relationship on Israeli religious and secular Kibbutzim. *Current Anthropology, 44,* 713-722.
Trivers, R. L. 1971. The evolution of reciprocal altruism. *Quarterly Review of Biology, 46,* 35-57.
Wilson, D. S. 2002. *Darwin's cathedral: Evolution, religion, and the nature of society.* Chicago, IL: University of Chicago Press.
Wilson, D. S. 2005. Testing major evolutionary hypotheses about religion with a random sample. *Human Nature, 16,* 382-409.
Zahavi, A. 1975. Mate selection: A selection for a handicap. *Journal of Theoretical Biology, 53,* 205-214.

PART II

Whose Adaptation? Individuals, Groups, Cultural Variants

Religion Is Not An Adaptation
Some Fundamental Issues and Arguments

Lee A. Kirkpatrick

The first question to be addressed by any evolutionary approach to religion is whether religion is an *adaptation* or a *byproduct* of adaptations designed for other purposes. Although byproduct theories currently are in vogue, their proponents have generally failed to delineate clearly the reasons for rejecting the alternative. The purpose of this contribution is to outline briefly a set of such arguments (see Kirkpatrick, 2005, 2006, for more thorough discussions).

My thesis that religion is not an adaptation can be stated in numerous ways at various levels of analysis: for example, (1) religion is not the direct result of natural selection owing to its beneficial effects on survival and reproductive success (inclusive fitness) during our species' evolutionary history; (2) we possess no genes specifically "for" religion, in the sense of producing belief or behavior unique to religion; (3) we possess no evolved psychological mechanisms whose primary adaptive function is (was) to produce religion in that sense. I hasten to add that I do *not* mean to suggest that religion cannot have beneficial effects on individuals or groups, or that it cannot have "adaptive" qualities in the context of *cultural* evolution or memetics. Most important, I do not mean to suggest that evolutionary biology and psychology are therefore irrelevant to understanding religion. Indeed, such an approach is essential to determine those psychological mechanisms of which religion is a byproduct and how it emerges from these.

To make this case, I first examine some of the empirical observations that have led many researchers to suspect that religion *is* an adaptation, and show that they do not in fact constitute persuasive evidence for that conclusion. I then outline a set of general arguments that must be faced, and theoretical problems that must be resolved or avoided, by any extant or prospective religion-as-adaptation hypothesis.

Purported Evidence for the Religion-as-Adaptation Hypothesis

Perhaps the most obvious hint that religion might be a biological adaptation is its apparent universality across time and cultures. This claim is easily overstated, however, given its reliance on definitions of terms. Religion probably is universal if defined sufficiently broadly or abstractly, but not according to most narrower definitions. Similarly, it surely is not universal if *universal* is taken literally to refer to all people at all times, but it probably is in the sense of appearing in all cultures at some point in their respective histories. Note that this latter claim actually is more consistent with a *cultural evolution* model than a biological one. An analogy might be made to reading and writing, for which – in contrast to spoken language – most researchers agree humans do not possess specialized evolved mechanisms. It might well be the case that all human cultures, given sufficient time, develop a written language, not because we have evolved specialized psychological systems or genes "for" this purpose.

A second set of observations that has led many scholars to speculate about religion-specific adaptations comes from neuroscience. If we can identify particular patterns of neurobiological activity or brain regions that are correlated with religious phenomena, doesn't that lead naturally to the question of what such "God modules" are *for*? The answer is no, for several reasons. First, there is no reason to expect that the functional organization of evolved psychological systems necessarily maps onto the physical organization of the brain in any simple isomorphic way, in much the same way that a particular software program or document cannot be located in any one particular place in your computer's hard drive. Second, it simply does not follow that because a brain region or process is reliably associated with a particular psychological or behavioral correlate that the region or process is designed to produce that effect. All thinking and behavior involve particular patterns of brain activity, but not necessarily because they are designed to do so. Tapping your knee in the right place with a hammer reliably produces a sequence of neuronal and muscular activity culminating in a knee-jerk, but not because the circuitry is designed specifically to do this. The evidence is equally consistent with the hypothesis that such knee-jerks are a byproduct (in this case, a *spandrel*) of functional (for other purposes) knee design.

Much has been made of evidence from behavioral genetics demonstrating that religion is at least moderately *heritable* and thus influenced by genes. However, such evidence speaks only to questions about *individual differences* in religion, and not at all to the question of universal design. Natural selection generally has the effect of reducing genetic variability as less adaptive variants are winnowed out; the genetic variability that natural selection has allowed to remain is often precisely the variability that did *not* have strong adaptive consequences over evolutionary history. Humans display a wide range of variation on personality dimensions, for example, but it is difficult to speak of these traits as adaptations except with respect to their entire ranges of values. Indeed, it isn't even clear whether we should be looking for the adaptive value of *introversion*, for example, or its bipolar opposite *extraversion*. Should we be speculating about the adaptive value of religion—or of nonreligion?

All three kinds of evidence are equally consistent with both adaptationist and byproduct explanations. We would all agree, I think, that humans possess no genes or psychological mechanisms specifically "for" playing soccer (*football* to everyone other than Americans), yet (1) the game might reasonably be construed as "universal" given some definitional latitude; (2) there undoubtedly are specific brain regions and neurobiological processes involved when one plays the game; and (3) ability for and interest in the game (and other sports) are probably both at least modestly heritable. An evolutionary approach to soccer would involve identification of the various psychological systems—evolved for other, nonsoccer functions – that systematically are employed when one plays the game, ranging from basic processes of perception to motivations related to such adaptive problems (and evolved psychological systems) as intrasexual competition and coalitional psychology. Religion, I submit, should be approached similarly.

Problems with Religion-as-Adaptation Hypotheses

A common (though often unfair) criticism of evolutionary explanations is that they are merely post-hoc speculations. To rise above such criticism, it is incumbent upon theorists to ensure that their hypotheses meet higher standards. Here I review a few such criteria that seem particularly problematic for adaptationist theories of religion.

Identifying the Phenomenon

No one studying the evolution of the human eye has any difficulty identifying what exactly constitutes the adaptation in question. In contrast, religion is notoriously difficult to define, with hundreds of years of scholarship having yet to lead to any kind of consensus on the questions of what common thread runs through all things denoted religion or of what distinguishes religion from nonreligion. Given the extreme fuzziness of the construct, it is reasonable to ask whether religion is in fact a thing that could be an adaptation in the first place. At best, an adaptationist hypothesis might address one or two specific elements common to many religions, but explaining religion writ largely seems a dubious proposition.

Part of this definitional fuzziness is the fact that the class of "religious" phenomena shades rather gradually around the edges into other phenomena —e.g., superstitions, beliefs in ESP or clairvoyance, and UFO belief—that are equally puzzling and in need of explanation. Moving still further from religion, we find common biases in everyday thinking, such as the animism we display when we curse at our computer or car. If religion is an adaptation, then how will we explain these apparently related (to various degrees) phenomena? Are these, too, adaptations? A simpler and more plausible explanation is that all of these phenomena, including religion, are spandrel-like byproducts of evolved psychological systems designed for other purposes.

Identifying the Adaptive Function

It usually is fairly easy to think of potential adaptive benefits that any particular behavior might have had for our ancestors, but the task of identifying the adaptive function of religion requires a good deal more work. First, one must be able to explain the many apparently maladaptive consequences of religion. For every example of a belief that seems comforting, one can easily find another that is terrifying; for every belief that seems well designed to increased reproduction, one can find examples of prohibitions that would seem to decrease it. Similarly, computations of adaptive value are incomplete without considering all of the potential *costs* as well as postulated benefits of a given adaptation. Turning one's fate over to God might be comforting, for example, but then reduce direct problem-solving efforts; suggestibility or gullibility might facilitate shamanic healing but creates vulnerabilities to exploitation by those with more nefarious goals. That the postulated benefits outweigh the correlated costs is hardly a *fait accompli*.

Another oft-overlooked problem is that of demonstrating how purported psychological benefits to individuals or groups actually translate into the hard currency of inclusive fitness. How increased group cohesion or individual happiness ultimately results in more copies of certain genes (alleles) than others is a much more complex question than it seems, but requires a clear answer because natural selection is blind to purely psychological effects. Related problems arise in considering physical health benefits associated with religion because, for example, a longer (post-reproductive) life is not necessarily fitness-enhancing.

Specifying the Design

A good theory about religion as an adaptation should go beyond delineating benefits (and costs): It should also specify the design of the adaptive system to show not only *why* it works, but *how*. For psychological adaptations, this involves outlining the cognitive architecture of the postulated system, including identification of the inputs to which the system is sensitive, the inferential rules by which it processes these inputs, and the outputs it generates to other psychological systems and/or in behavior. Such a design specification should be capable of explaining, among other things, how individual and cultural differences are generated and maintained through the interaction of a species-universal psychology with variable environments.

Perhaps most important, such a theory should explain why the postulated design was favored by natural selection over alternative designs that might have evolved instead to solve the adaptive problem at hand -- especially *simpler* designs that are more easily evolvable. Were it generally adaptive for human groups to be cohesive and cooperative, for example, it would have been relatively easy for natural selection to tweak a parameter or two of existing adaptations (e.g., related to kinship or love) to make people generally more committed to their groups and neighbors; if it were adaptive to feel secure or happy, a simple recalibration of one or more extant emotion systems would do the trick.

Williams (1996) argued that adaptations should be identifiable by clear evidence of "special design," such that they should do what they are designed to do with a reasonable level of economy, precision, reliability, efficiency, and so forth. To me, religion does not look like a precise, economical, reliable solution to any particular problem but rather a cobbled-together patchwork of psychological systems not particularly well suited to any adaptive task.

Conclusion

Such a cobbled-together patchwork is precisely what we would expect if religion is not an adaptation as such but rather a complex tapestry of byproducts of a diverse collection of psychological mechanisms and cultural evolution. In my own view, religion is (1) a spandrel-like byproduct of basic psychological mechanisms for understanding the natural world – e.g., folk physics and folk biology as per Boyer (1994), Atran (2002), and others; (2) an exaptation-like byproduct of evolved social-cognitive mechanisms for negotiating specific, functionally distinct types of relationships such as attachment, kinship, social exchange, coalitions, and dominance hierarchies (Kirkpatrick, 1999, 2005); and a product of cultural (Boyd & Richerson, 1985; Wilson, 2002) and memetic (Dawkins, 1993) evolutionary processes for which this domain-specific evolved psychology provides a rich pool of conceptual building blocks.

This multiple-byproducts perspective offers straightforward solutions to the various problems discussed in previous sections of this paper. It circumvents the thorny problem of defining religion because it provides a highly general theoretical approach that can be applied to any particular aspect of religion or related phenomena; indeed, it provides a way to carve the diversity of religious phenomena at its natural joints. It can deal equally well with both adaptive and maladaptive instances of religion, as indeed both are equally expectable, and it avoids the many theoretical problems of identifying the adaptive "function" of religion. A fresh perspective on individual differences derives (in part) from the idea that different people or different cultures, at different places and times, construct beliefs emphasizing or drawing upon various combinations and permutations of the numerous psychological systems underlying them.

I make no claim that the arguments presented in this paper render religion-as-adaptation theories entirely implausible or disproved in principle. Although I endorse a (multiple) byproduct view, I encourage those who disagree to continue to pursue religion-as-adaptation theories. I hope, however, that such attempts will regard these arguments as a set of important challenges to be addressed.

Author's Note

Preparation of this chapter was facilitated by a Faculty Semester Research Leave from the College of William and Mary.

References

Atran, S. 2002. *In gods we trust: The evolutionary landscape of religion*. New York, NY: Oxford University Press.

Boyd, R., & Richerson, P. J. 1985. *Culture and the evolutionary process*. Chicago, IL: University of Chicago.

Boyer, P. 1994. *The naturalness of religious ideas: A cognitive theory of religion*. Berkeley, CA: University of California.

Dawkins, R. 1993. Viruses of the mind. *Free Inquiry, 13* (3), 34-41.

Kirkpatrick, L. A. 1999. Toward an evolutionary psychology of religion. *Journal of Personality, 67*, 921-952.

Kirkpatrick, L. A. 2005. *Attachment, evolution, and the psychology of religion*. New York, NY: Guilford.

Kirkpatrick, L. A. 2006. Religion is not an adaptation. In P. McNamara Ed., *Where God and Science meet: How brain and evolutionary studies alter our understanding of religion*. Vol. 1, 159-179. Westport, CT and London: Praeger Perspectives.

Williams, G. C. 1966. *Adaptation and natural selection: A critique of some current evolutionary thought*. Princeton, NJ: Princeton University Press.

Wilson, D. S. 2002. *Darwin's cathedral: Evolution, religion, and the nature of society*. Chicago, IL: University of Chicago.

Religious Attachment Theory and the Biosocial Evolution of the Major World Religions

Stephen K. Sanderson

The phrase "evolution of religion" can refer to the biological evolution of religious concepts in the brain, but also to the social evolution of religion, or religious transformations over long periods of time. I use the phrase to refer to both forms of evolution, and thus this paper is an exercise in both Darwinian biological evolutionism and social evolutionism. It tries to show how both the evolution of religious concepts in the brain and a range of forces in social evolution are closely intertwined in producing important changes in religious beliefs and rituals.

Anthony Wallace (1966) has distinguished four major types of what he calls religious cult institutions. *Individualistic* cult institutions are those in which people perform their own private rituals; *shamanic* institutions involve a part-time religious practitioner (a shaman) who performs special rites for others in return for a fee; *communal* institutions involve bodies of laypersons who collectively perform calendrical and other religious rites; and *ecclesiastical* institutions are ones in which there are full-time priests who monopolize religious knowledge and perform highly specialized rituals before audiences of laypersons.

Combinations of cult institutions yield four major stages of religious evolution: shamanic, communal, Olympian, and monotheistic. *Shamanic religions* contain only individualistic and shamanic cult institutions; religious practice beyond the level of the individual focuses solely on the conduct of a shaman and there are no calendrical or other collective rites. *Communal religions* contain individualistic, shamanic, and communal cult institutions, and religious practice focuses primarily on the conduct of laypersons engaged in collective calendrical and other rites, although shamanic rituals still exist and remain important. *Olympian or polytheistic religions* contain all four cult institutions, especially specialized priesthoods; they have numerous gods, usually organized in a hierarchical pantheon, and worship is led by full-time priests. *Monotheistic religions* are like polytheistic religions, except that worship focuses on a single god rather than a pantheon of specialized gods.

Wesley Roberts and I have carried out a multiple regression analysis of the main predictors of religious evolution using an operationalized version of Wallace's typology and the Murdock and White Standard Cross-Cultural Sample of 186 preindustrial societies (Roberts & Sanderson, 2005). The two best predictors were the mode of subsistence technology and the presence or absence of writing and records. Together, just these two variables explained 65 percent of the variance in stage of religious evolution. Ecclesiastical religions with professional priesthoods are not really possible until a society has developed a fairly intensive form of agriculture because large economic surpluses are needed to support specialized religious functionaries. We found that many polytheistic religions are located in societies without writing, but the vast majority of monotheistic religions are found in societies with true writing. Priests are religious literati who form themselves into guilds and who monopolize religious knowledge and ritual.

However, Roberts and I regard our study as identifying only the *social prerequisites* or *preconditions* of more advanced religions. It does not give us the deep explanation that we are seeking. To achieve such an explanation, we need to consider two kinds of conditions: first, the evolved psychology of religious belief, and second, the entire social ecology in which particular communities and societies find themselves at particular points in human history. By social ecology I mean the total technological, economic, political, social, cultural, and natural environments in which people are located. Because of space limitations, here I discuss only one aspect of religious evolution, the transition from polytheistic religions to the monotheistic world salvation religions in the first millennium BCE.

The world's first monotheism was Zoroastrianism, which arose in Persia about 1200 BCE. This religion had a significant impact on Judaism, which was polytheistic until about 600 BCE, when it became monotheistic. Slightly later Buddhism and Hinduism arose in India, and Taoism and Confucianism in China. Then in the first century CE, of course, Christianity emerged, and in the seventh century CE Islam developed as a movement out of Christianity. The philosopher Karl Jaspers (1953/1949) has called the period of the emergence of these major world religions the Axial Age because it represented a major philosophical and religious transformation – indeed, probably the greatest religious transformation in all of human history and prehistory. Most of the developments are concentrated in the period between 600 BCE and the first century CE.

Polytheistic religions constitute a universal, or at least a very widespread, stage in religious evolution. They existed all over the world in very ancient times and were found much more recently in such New World civilizations as the ancient Maya, Aztecs, and Incas. These religions had the following primary characteristics:

1. professional priesthoods who monopolized religious knowledge and who led elaborate rituals for a lay audience;
2. a pantheon of highly specialized gods, who were
3. almost invariably very much like humans in their nature; some were considered good, others evil; some were highly competent at what they did, whereas others were considered fools; they usually ate and drank and often had great banquets; they generally liked sex and often had orgies; they also fought and went to war; like humans, these polytheistic gods were finite and mortal; they could be killed and even eaten
4. widespread animal (and sometimes human) sacrifice.

How did the new monotheistic religions that emerged during the Axial Age differ from their polytheistic predecessors? What was new in the major world religions, and how may these new features have been adaptive under the altered socioecological conditions of the day? There were many important novelties, but I restrict myself here to three critical developments.

1. *The emergence of single omnipresent, omniscient, omnipotent, and transcendent God.* In the polytheistic religions, the various gods were conceived very much along human lines, but the God of the monotheisms was a *transcendent* god that was little like humans.
2. *An emphasis on salvation from this world and on God's love and mercy.* It was Max Weber (1978/1923) more than anyone who emphasized that the core feature of the major world religions was their focus on *salvation*, which often took the form of a desire for *release from suffering.*
3. *A dramatic increase in the controlling, demanding, and potential punitiveness of God.* Virtually all religions have had evil spirits and gods who could cause harm, but the major world religions, especially the West Eurasian ones, constructed a God who, although loving and compassionate, had the power to inflict enormous punishment on those who failed to acknowledge Him and to live up to His demands. Thus we find the Ten Commandments, concepts of sin and eternal damnation for the failure to make amends for sin, and, for the

> damned, an afterlife filled with eternal pain and suffering on an unprecedented scale—hell. Indeed, God can inflict all sorts of horrible punishments *in this world* for failure to acknowledge and obey Him.

How can we explain this polytheism-to-monotheism shift? First, let's consider the necessary evolved psychology. Lee Kirkpatrick (2005) has recently applied John Bowlby's classic attachment theory to explain certain features of religious belief and behavior. Bowlby assumed that the human infant is primed to form a strong bond with its parents, its mother in particular, because parents are needed for nurturance and protection in an ancestral environment filled with predators. Kirkpatrick argues that many religious notions are extensions or generalizations of the parent-child bond. Supernatural agents are seen as protectors from harm in much the way that parents are. Kirkpatrick points out that people in modern societies often turn to religion in times of psychological distress and crisis, such as personal catastrophes, serious illness or injury, and death and grieving. Kirkpatrick stresses that God or gods are primarily *substitute attachment figures* for natural attachment figures, i.e, fathers, mothers, and other close kin. The feeling of a relationship with God or gods is most likely to be activated, therefore, when an individual's sense of security, safety, and freedom from anxiety falls below a certain threshold as a result of natural attachments being inadequate to life's challenges.

Kirkpatrick's attachment theory provides us with a critical component to understand some of the features of religion, including the long-term evolution of different types of religion. But what of the social ecological side of this momentous religious transformation? Something must have been changing in the social ecology of the Axial Age peoples to create the conditions that favored new types of religion. I suggest that two major social transformations were critical, one political and military and the other economic. First, there was a massive increase in the scale of war. Between the sixth and first centuries BCE, global war deaths increased from 15,000 to 762,000, or 51-fold. This increase was due to both an increase in the size of political empires and a revolution in military technology involving the development of iron weapons. Iron weapons helped to intensify warfare and greatly increased the killing power of combatants, resulting in a significant rise in war casualties.

It was this dramatic increase in warfare, I think, that was one of the crucial factors in the creation and spread of monotheistic religions. Here is where the Bowlby-Kirkpatrick notion of the need for attachment must be brought back into the picture. As we know, war is a tremendously socially disruptive and psychologically anxiety-producing phenomenon. It is not difficult to see how a dramatic increase in the scale of war casualties would create new needs for security and comfort. Not only do people die and live with an intensified anticipation and fear of death, but many are uprooted and displaced from their homes, which reduces security and creates a greater need for a substitute attachment figure.

The second major change in this time period is urban growth. Tertius Chandler (1987) has estimated that in 2250 BCE there were only 8 cities in the world with a population of about 30,000, or a total urban population of about 240,000. By 650 BCE, there may have been some 20 cities ranging in population from 30,000 to 120,000, with a total urban population of approximately 1 million. That represents about a four-fold increase in 1600 years. But in the 220 years between 650 and 430 BCE, the number of cities between 30,000 and 200,000 increased to 51, with a total population of almost 3 million, a three-fold increase in a much shorter period of time; between 430 BCE and 200 BCE, there were 55 cities of 30,000 or more totaling almost 4 million people; and between 200 BCE and 100 CE, the number of cities between 30,000 and 450,000 increased to 75 and a total population of over 5 million. So in the centuries of the Axial Age urbanization occurred on a far greater scale than in the previous two millennia. The vast majority of these cities were located in those very regions where the Axial Age proper was shortly to begin: Greater West Eurasia, Greater South Asia, and Greater East Eurasia (100% in 650 BCE, 98% in 430 BCE, 93% in 200 BCE, and 92% in 100 CE). And 62 percent of the population of these cities in 650 BCE lived in or around the very small region that produced both Judaism and Christianity.

How, exactly, would an increase in urbanization create new religious needs? The answer, I think, is much the same as what was said regarding the huge increase in warfare: rapid and large-scale urbanization was tremendously socially and psychologically disruptive. But what was it that was being disrupted? My answer: primarily *people's attachments to kin and other social intimates*. People were increasingly living in a world of strangers. People turn to God, Kirkpatrick says, as a substitute attachment figure, especially when there has been some sort of disruption in their attachments to parents, and God functions psychologically as a safe haven and secure base. This, I submit, is what was happening to encourage the formation of the Axial Age religions of compassion, love, and mercy. Humans evolved to live in small groups of kin, which nearly all of them did throughout most of human history and prehistory. They did not evolve to live in densely packed cities in which most of their social relations occurred with nonkin and strangers. The monotheistic religions of human compassion, and with an all-powerful and loving God, were an excellent prescription for people's new sense of threat and danger.

But how can we make sense of one and the same transcendent supernatural power being simultaneously compassionate and loving on the one hand and demanding and extremely punitive on the other? Kirkpatrick provides an answer based on attachment theory. Pointing to research showing that, other things equal, children attach more strongly to parents the more authoritarian they are, more punitive and demanding gods will produce greater attachment than less punitive and demanding ones. This is a plausible argument, but let me suggest an argument based on Sosis's (2003) costly signaling theory of religious ritual. The punitive and demanding gods of monotheism constituted new forms of costly signaling—new ways of assessing an individual's degree of religious commitment—under circumstances in which the major form of polytheistic costly signaling, animal or human sacrifice, was in dramatic decline. An extremely powerful God must also be a demanding God. To reap the benefits that this God can provide, individuals must be willing to pay high costs.

Whether religion is a true Darwinian adaptation or a byproduct of other cognitive adaptations, there is little doubt that it is an adaptation in a more general sense. Religion is complex and multifaceted, but much of it is devoted to dealing with existential anxiety and ontological insecurity, and there is considerable evidence that it is effective in dealing with these fundamental human problems.

References

Chandler, T. 1987. *Four thousand years of urban growth.* Lewiston, NY: St. David's University Press.

Jaspers, K. 1953. *The origin and goal of history* M. Bullock, Trans. New Haven, CT: Yale University Press. Original work published 1949.

Kirkpatrick, L. A. 2005. *Attachment, evolution, and the psychology of religion.* New York, NY: Guilford Press.

Roberts, W. W., & Sanderson, S. K. 2005. The evolutionary forms of the religious life: A cross-cultural study of the social origins of the gods. Paper presented at the annual meetings of the American Sociological Association, Philadelphia.

Sosis, R. 2003. Why aren't we all Hutterites? Costly signaling theory and religious behavior. *Human Nature, 14,* 91-127.

Wallace, A. F. C. 1966. *Religion: An anthropological view.* New York, NY: Random House.

Weber, M. 1978. *Economy and society,* Vol. 1, G. Roth & C. Wittich, Trans. Berkeley, CA: University of California Press. Original work published 1923.

Is Religion Adaptive?

Yes, No, Neutral, but Mostly, We Don't Know

Peter J. Richerson and Lesley Newson

We argue that the question "Is Religion Adaptive?" has no simple answer. We will use evolutionary theory as a tool to outline a theory of adaptation and maladaptations as regards religion. Evolutionary theory gives us access to concepts and theoretical and empirical tools that have been very successful in explaining biological diversity. Of course the tools of evolutionary biology have been mostly developed through the study of non-human living organisms with the assumption that it is *genes* that are evolving. The evolutionary study of human behavior adds an important wrinkle. In all living things, information is transmitted down the generations coded in genes. But humans also pass on a vast amount of information down the generations through culture.

Just as evolutionary theory can help us understand genetically inherited diversity, it can help us understand diversity that is inherited through culture. Only in the last quarter of the 20th Century did scholars begin to turn their minds to developing a quantitative, mechanistic theory of cultural evolution and most of the pioneers were biologists, not mainstream social scientists (Cavalli-Sforza & Feldman 1981; Lumsden & Wilson 1981). Most twentieth century social scientists saw little use in trying to derive a basic theory of human behavior from biology or evolution. An important exception was the psychologist Donald Campbell (1965; 1975). Today Darwinian social science is perhaps as mainstream as any other variety in this unfortunately fragmented field of inquiry (Gintis 2004; Laland & Brown 2002).

That religions are part of culture can be seen by the way they are inherited. If a baby, whose parents were Buddhist, is adopted by a Christian family in the United States, she will grow up to know about Christianity and will perhaps consider herself to be a Christian. Just as a child of Chinese speaking parents adopted by English speakers in an English-speaking community receives no knowledge of Chinese words from her genes, neither will she have Buddhist teachings coded in her genes. On the other hand, the *capacity* to learn a language *is* inherited genetically. Might it be that some capacity to "be religious" is also inherited genetically?

Richard Dawkins (2006) argues that religious ideas are maladaptive cultural elements (memes), typically transmitted to children at young ages when their minds are impressionable and their decision-making powers not yet fully functional. He subscribes to a by-product hypothesis to explain most if not all of religion. Young minds have to be impressionable so as to rapidly and accurately acquire essential information from parents. Parasitic religious memes take advantage of this impressionability.

Dawkins' analysis is too simplistic. Nevertheless, one doesn't have to follow Dawkins in suggesting that *all* religious ideas, institutions, and organizations are maladaptive to realize that some probably are. Theory tells us that cultural variants that are transmitted non-parentally can readily evolve pathological properties. Extreme examples of religious sects espousing maladaptive ideas do certainly exist. The cult led by Jim Jones that committed mass suicide in 1978 is one example.

Let's pick apart the question: "Is Religion Adaptive?" Are we asking if religion as a whole is adaptive, or some particular religion? Or do we want to examine some aspect of religion? Every religion is an amalgam of beliefs, practices, institutions, and organizations. These are webbed up with other domains of culture—art, social and political organization, family life, practical knowledge, and so on. And, of course, religions are diverse in a multiplicity of dimensions. There are polytheisms, monotheisms, and a-theistic spiritual, ethical, and mystical systems. Some insist that adherents maintain a proper set of beliefs, some consider carrying out proper ritual to be all-important, and some emphasize common commitment to ethical ideals. Some restrict entry to a select few. Others are evangelical and open to all who want to join. Some religions are bureaucratic and authoritarian and others are the product of egalitarian local groups. We know that some societies are successful and some fail and collapse. Religions, given their importance, complexity, and diversity, certainly contribute to both success and failure.

Dawkins' parasitic meme explanation gives us a first cut at a theory of religious maladaptations. Now let us turn to how religion might evolve adaptations. Religion—or "a" religion—or some aspect of religion might be adaptive for an individual human, or it might be adaptive for a group of individuals, a congregation, a tribe or a nation. In the case of the individual, we use "adaptive" to mean helping its survival and reproductive success. Religions seem to have individually adaptive benefits. For example, Hill and Pargament (2003) review the literature on the connection between religion and spirituality and physical and mental health. In the case of the group of individuals, we use "adaptive" to mean helping the group to continue and grow by recruiting new members and by helping the long-standing members to prosper and reproduce. Most adaptive accounts of religion focus on adaptations at the group level.

Let us see how such an account might be built. Richerson and Boyd (2005) have developed what they call the "tribal social instincts hypothesis" to explain human cooperation. The hypothesis argues that the evolution of culture set in motion a process of group selection on cultural variation. Populations in semi-isolation rapidly evolved cultural differences. Symbolic boundaries limited the flow of ideas between groups. Individual members were inclined to copy the behavior most common within their group and this decreased the differences within the groups and increased differences between the groups. Individuals who failed to conform were punished and fared badly within the group. Groups with superior culturally transmitted social institutions prosper in competition with ones with poorer institutions.

As these processes continued for generation after generation in the remote past, primitive cooperative institutions arose, forming a social environment that selected for innate social instincts that enabled humans to live in moral communities. The humans successful in this environment were relatively docile, prepared to conform to social norms and institutions, and prepared to cooperate, especially with members of a symbolically marked in-group. The societies in which our social nature was shaped were tribes comprising only a few hundred to a few thousand people, but in size and degree of cooperation they far surpassed the societies of other apes. These instincts don't force us to cooperate with just anyone, but enable us to learn to cooperate when appropriate. Thus human tribes and their modern successors came to be adapted units. Religions are candidates to have furnished some of the institutions that make tribes, and eventually large social systems, adapted systems.

Note that an adaptation at any one level is often maladaptive at other levels; religions that organize congregations tend to lead to sectarian strife among congregations. Sonya Salamon (1992) provides a concrete example from her comparisons of farming communities in the American state of Illinois. British ancestry communities in the state typically have a number of small Protestant churches. Congregations preach incompatible dogmas and compete for members. Religion is a divisive influence at the community level. German ancestry communities tend to have a single church in each community, either Catholic or Lutheran, but not both in any one community. In these communities the churches foster community-level solidarity.

Common features of religions are plausible community level adaptations (D.S. Wilson, this volume). Most religions teach a moral code that requires its members to help one another. They also provide the means for identifying "true" members (those who have taken the teachings to heart) from those who are not. Many elements of religion serve to mark the members in good standing. Iannaccone (1994) argues that strict faiths can generate higher levels of cooperation and mutual help than lax ones because the practices of strict churches are too costly for cheaters to fake. The beliefs of strict churches are complex and difficult to learn. The ongoing expenditures of time and resources to conform to the practices of strict faiths are high. Subscribing to outlandish beliefs handicaps members from reasonably considering the evidence and judging what might really be in their best interest. Belonging to a strict faith is a conspicuous commitment that makes it difficult for members to maintain strong ties with members of other belief systems. Few are willing to pay such high costs unless their commitment to the religious community is genuine. The group is therefore protected from invasion by parasitic impostors.

Still, the higher the costs members of a religion must pay, the lower their net benefit in being a member. The congregation might be so engaged in maintaining rituals and ritual objects that they can devote no effort left to helping one another. Furthermore, the levels of practical commitment that might sometimes be required of devout faith group members may be detrimental to their welfare. The net adaptive benefits of a religion may fall below zero well short of an extreme case like Jonestown.

When religion promotes welfare because it unifies a community under a common set of customs, institutions, and organizations, it is most effective when most, if not all, people in the population are members of the religious community. At the tribe and village scale, such uniformity may arise spontaneously, but the evolution of state-level societies was typically accompanied by the formation of more formal religious systems. Throughout the history of civilization, many conquerors and leaders have attempted to unify a population by declaring one form of religion to be official, often with themselves as the official leader or even as a living god. As ancient empires like Rome grew, they often incorporated the gods of newly won communities into the imperial pantheon. The teachings in the Qur'an unified Arab clans and eventually many different national groups despite the schisms that soon developed. Many societies, be they historically Buddhist, Christian, or Islamic, were and still are hostile to unofficial ideologies.

The fact that so many civilizations throughout history have had official religions suggests that religions are often a net advantage to a large population. Perhaps religion is most advantageous when everyone subscribes to a single one. A "universal" religion can promote cooperation on a wide scale and coordinate larger groups, bringing important benefits to the whole society (Wilson 2002). On the other hand, established churches often become hidebound, bureaucratic, and corrupt. Sometimes they are the handmaidens of predatory elites. Sociologists of religion Roger Finke and Rodney Stark (Finke & Stark 1992) contrast the feeble established churches of Western Europe with America's vibrant religious economy based upon a plethora of entrepreneurial churches and sects.

Culture is commonly adaptive in part because human actors shape them to be so. David Wilson (2002) provides a number of examples of religious ideas being adopted because they provided fitness benefits. The formation and spread of Calvinism is his central example. He describes in some detail how the problem of corruption in the Catholic Church led Calvin and his colleagues to propose, and the people of Geneva eventually to adopt, a religiously inspired code of conduct that effectively ended the disruptive factionalism in the city. Calvin's model inspired much imitation based on its success in Geneva. Karen Armstrong (1991) gives a similar account of Muhammad's religiously inspired code aimed at regulating the intertribal anarchy of the Arabs. Stephen Lansing (1993) shows how Balinese Water Temples function to organize scarce water and coordinate rice planting on Bali so as to optimize rice yields.

However, cultural-evolutionary mechanisms may generate specific sorts of maladaptive behaviors and, again, religion is as vulnerable as any other part of culture. For example, symbolic culture can evolve maladaptively exaggerated traits by a mechanism much like sexual selection (Richerson & Boyd 1989). Exaggerated, costly, religious rituals could be examples. The Protestant Reformation's charge that the Roman Catholic Church's lavish expenditures for buildings and ornaments were dysfunctional is a potential example. Perhaps costly religious behavior sometimes has little or nothing to do with guaranteeing honest signals and is mostly or entirely costly competitive exaggeration.

Conclusion

In the face of biological and cultural complexity and diversity, phenomena like religion are unlikely to support sweeping generalizations about adaptation versus maladaptation. Theory tells us that many things are possible and the empirical cases seem to agree. Any generalizations will have to be based upon careful empirical work. The basic task is to total up the various kinds of costs and benefits that accrue to religious variants at all the relevant levels of organization. This project has barely begun in any domain of culture.

References

Armstrong, K. 1991. *Muhammad: A western attempt to understand Islam.* London, UK: Victor Gollancz.

Campbell, D. T. 1965. Variation and selective retention in socio-cultural evolution. In H. R. Barringer, G. I. Blanksten, & R. W. Mack, Eds., *Social change in developing areas: A reinterpretation of evolutionary theory,* 19-49. Cambridge, MA: Schenkman Publishing Company.

Campbell, D. T. 1975. On the conflicts between biological and social evolution and between psychology and moral tradition. *American Psychologist, 30* (12), 1103-1126.

Cavalli-Sforza, L. L., & Feldman, M. W. 1981. *Cultural transmission and evolution: A quantitative approach, monographs in population biology, 16*. Princeton, NJ: Princeton University Press.

Dawkins, R. 2006. *The God delusion*. London, UK: Bantam.

Finke, R., & Stark, R. 1992. *The churching of America, 1776-1990: Winners and losers in our religious economy*. New Brunswick, NJ: Rutgers University Press.

Gintis, H. 2004. Towards the unity of the behavioral sciences. *Politics, Philosophy & Economics, 3* (1), 37-57.

Hill, P. C., & Pargament, K. I. 2003. Advances in the conceptualization and measurement of religion and spirituality: Implications for physical and mental health. *American Psychologist, 58* (1), 64-74.

Iannaccone, L. R. 1994. Why strict churches are strong. *American Journal of Sociology, 99* (5), 1180-1211.

Laland, K. N., & Brown, G. R. 2002. *Sense and nonsense: Evolutionary perspectives on human behaviour*. Oxford, UK: Oxford University Press.

Lansing, J. S. 1993. Emergent properties of Balinese Water Temple networks: Coadaptation on a rugged fitness landscape. *American Anthropologist, 95* (1), 97-114.

Lumsden, C. J., & Wilson, E. O. 1981. *Genes, mind, and culture: The coevolutionary process*. Cambridge, MA: Harvard University Press.

Richerson, P. J., & Boyd, R. 1989. A Darwinian theory for the evolution of symbolic cultural traits. In M. Freilich Ed., *The relevance of culture*, 124-147. Boston, MA: Bergin and Garvey.

Richerson, P. J., & Boyd, R. 2005. *Not by genes alone: How culture transformed human evolution*. Chicago, IL: University of Chicago Press.

Salamon, S. 1992. *Prairie patrimony: Family, farming, and community in the midwest, studies in rural culture*. Chapel Hill, NC: University of North Carolina Press.

Wilson, D. S. 2002. *Darwin's cathedral: Evolution, religion, and the nature of society*. Chicago, IL: University of Chicago Press.

Is Religiousness a Biocultural Adaptation?

Erica Harris and Patrick McNamara

In this paper, we argue that religiousness satisfies minimal criteria to be considered a biocultural adaptation. Why should anyone care whether religiousness is an adaptation? To establish religiousness as an adaptation will help to rule out some old and tiresome misconstruals of religiousness. If, for example, religiousness is an adaptation, then it is not likely to be a mere cognitive delusion as has been argued for centuries by anti-religious ideologues (and more recently by Dawkins 2006). Adaptations evolve to solve pressing fitness-related problems. Religiousness may have evolved to solve problems that our ancestors faced, but it still may be 'solving' similar problems in modern environments. For example, if religiousness promoted healing in some individuals in ancestral populations, it may still be doing so now. Similarly, if religiousness promoted outgroup antagonisms in ancestral populations, it may still be doing so now. Thus, evaluating potential adaptive properties of religiousness may help us to discover potential functions of religiosity.

To conclude that a trait is an adaptation, we must establish specific criteria that any trait must satisfy in order to be considered an adaptation and then test the evidence for each of these criteria. In this paper, we lay out what we believe to be the minimal criteria any trait must satisfy to be considered a biocultural adaptation. We use 'bio-cultural' instead of 'biological' because we are discussing human beings, who are shaped by both biologic and cultural forces.

We define religiousness as composed of two fundamental abilities: (1) the positing of belief in supernatural agents and (2) the tendency to perform rituals to relate to those agents. It is important to note that we are not asking whether religiousness itself is an adaptation but whether the capacity for religiousness is an adaptation.

What are the minimal criteria for a biocultural adaptation?

Most evolutionary scholars would posit the following three necessary (but not sufficient) criteria for the classification of a human trait as an adaptation: (1) universality across cultures; (2) relative effortless-ness of acquisition of the trait (the trait is not merely learned); and (3) an associated 'biology', which refers to a consistent set of physiologic systems that reliably support, mediate and produce the trait or behavior in question (Andrews, Gangestad, & Matthews 2002). A 'biology' of a human trait that functions as an adaptation would, in turn, likely include a) a genetic component as evidenced by gene-behavior correlations and heritability studies; b) a brain component as evidenced by classical neuropsychology and neuroimaging studies; and c) a chemistry component as evidenced by pharmacologic studies.

The 'specific biology' criterion speaks to the 'proximate mechanisms' by which the capacity or trait in question is implemented in the real world. Details on the proximate mechanisms of an adaptive trait, in turn, can give us vital clues both as to the function of the trait and the design complexity of the trait. If the proximate mechanisms involved in support of the trait in question evidence enough complexity and enough indications of 'design', then details on the proximate mechanisms can help us to decide that the trait in question is indeed an adaptation as most biocultural adaptations must be complex enough and 'designed enough' to solve some fitness-related problem the ancestral population faced. So, in addition to the criterion of universality and of 'effortless acquisition', there needs to be some evidence of design; that is, the trait's design had to solve some crucial survival-related or reproductive-fitness related problem faced by our ancestors in the ancestral environment. We get evidence of design from the 'specific biology' criterion.

It is important to note that the design may not be 'optimal' from an engineering perspective for purposes of solving the adaptive problem it was supposed to solve, but it is sufficient. Often sexual selection drives functional traits into seemingly maladaptive or wasteful spaces (like the secondary sexual organs). Instead, by design, we mean that it can draw a reasonable link between the properties of the trait in question back to the original problem it was supposed to solve.

Because the purpose of an adaptation is to solve some problem posed by the ancestral environment, in the case of human traits, that environment must include the primary ancestral social group, which has been estimated to be about 150 individuals (Aiello & Dunbar 1993). Humans evolved in an intensely social context. Biocultural adaptations, therefore, are likely to address problems of living in tightly knit social groups.

We now review the evidence that religiousness satisfies the minimal criteria to be considered a biocultural adaptation.

Universality

The practice of religious rituals and belief in supernatural agents occurs in virtually all human cultures (Brown 1991; Murdock 1965). When human universals have been carefully studied, religiousness is always found in the list of human universals, with Brown's compendium *Human Universals* (1991) being the most recent. In addition, when Murdock chose a sample of 186 societies to represent the full-range of human experience in various types of societies, religious rituals and beliefs in supernatural agents occurred in all of them (Johnson 2005; Murdock & White 1969).

Effortless acquisition of religiousness

Children do not need to be force-fed religiousness to posit supernatural beliefs. They do so spontaneously. Children even appear to spontaneously posit an omniscient supernatural agent. Developmental psychologists have found that children spontaneously ascribe omniscience to God—He can see all, can know all and cannot be fooled by standard theory of mind and false belief tasks (Barrett, Richert, & Driesenga 2001; Bering & Bjorklund, 2004; Kelemen 2004). Although these authors do not claim that religiouness is an adaptation, we interpret their work to be consistent with the claim that religiousness is an adaptation.

Specific biology

As we mentioned above, a human trait that functions as an adaptation should exhibit some evidence of design. This evidence of design boils down to evidence that the trait in question, religiousness in this case, is supported by selective biologic systems. If the biologic systems supporting the trait are dedicated to support of that trait alone and no others (a rarity in brain physiology), then we say that the system exhibits signs of modularity and to some extent 'encapsulation'. It is too early to tell whether the cognitive systems supporting religiosity exhibit any signs of automaticity or encapsulation. They nevertheless appear to be acquired relatively effortlessly by children—even children who have received no overt instruction in religion. In these cases, the rich conceptual world concerning supernatural agents developed by the children can be contrasted to the poverty of the stimulus they are exposed to in their environment. That contrast hints at an innate contribution to development of God concepts in children.

We turn now to the evidence that religiousness is associated with a specific biology.

Heritability

Does religiousness have a genetic component? Is it heritable? This question is important as heritability implies that several sets of genes contribute to the trait in question and thus that the trait is complex and may exhibit evidence of design. Evidence that the capacity for religiousness is heritable comes from a number of classical twin studies, particularly monozygotic twins who have been reared apart. The logic in using such studies is that these twins share the same genes but different childhood environments. For example, D'Onofrio and colleagues (1999) and Koenig and Bouchard (2006) have reviewed the literature on the heritability of religiousness and found that religiousness exhibits a moderate to high heritability coefficient (h^2 = 0.28-0.72; a 0.72 heritability coefficient refers to religious fundamentalists). It may even be that some people have higher doses of the relevant genes that promote this trait which in turn increases the likelihood they that will be more religious than someone with lower amounts of the gene (Hamer, 2004). These individual differences in aspects of religiousness suggest that it may, like many other heritable traits, be normally distributed in the population. Furthermore, the fact that religiousness is partially heritable suggests that it may be associated with a specific neurobiology—there should be brain systems that are consistently implicated in support of the trait religiousness.

Neuropsychology and neuroimaging studies

How might genes support the development of religiousness as an adaptive trait? If we have a gene, which in turn codes for a protein like the dopamine transport molecule (DAT), the genetic production of this molecule increases dopamine (DA) production. The availability of DA allows for increased released in the central nervous which has the effect of proliferating DRD4 receptors in areas of the brain that are rich in those receptors, namely the prefrontal cortex (PFC). If the gene codes for religiousness and levels of dopamine are high, then a person is more apt to have higher levels of religiousness.

Consequently, there should be selective areas of the brain that will be more involved in support of religiousness than other areas of the brain – namely those that have many DA receptors. The prefrontal cortex in particular is densely innervated by dopaminergic efferents ascending from dopamine synthesizing nuclei in the nigrostriatal and ventral tegmental regions of the brain. Thus, we should expect the dopaminergic prefrontal cortex to be involved in support of religious experience.

Beauregard & Paquette (2006) and Azari and colleagues (2001) have conducted neuro-imaging studies of brain activation patterns in religious people as they engage in religious activities. Beauregard & Paquette studied 15 Carmelite nuns and asked them to recall the most intense mystical experience of their lives and imaged their brains using fMRI. Azari and colleagues imaged the brains of six religious subjects who recited the first verse of Psalm 23 using PET. Both studies found overlap of activated brain regions on the right-side of the forebrain, including the prefrontal cortex and corresponding activation in the left-side subcortical sites. These areas contain the highest number of DA receptors, particularly in the right dorsolateral and orbito-frontal cortices. The most striking result of these neuro-imaging studies is that the right-side of the PFC is consistently activated during intentional and private religious practices. As mentioned above, the prefrontal lobes are densely innervated by dopaminergic fibers ascending from the substantia nigra (SN) and the ventral tegmental area (VTA) in the brainstem. If the prefrontal lobes are especially implicated in the mediation of religious experiences, then religiousness should be influenced by pharmacologically-induced changes in dopaminergic activity.

Pharmacology

Drugs that enhance DA transmission can induce religious experiences in persons who are well-disposed to religiousness or spirituality. Drugs that block DA transmission can reduce religiously-tinted delusions in various psychiatric populations (Nichols & Chemel 2006). It is important to note that drugs that influence other transmitters, like acetylcholine, do not have as strong an effect on religiousness as do drugs that influence DA.

To further support the hypothesis that religiousness has a specific biology that is especially influenced by dopaminergic systems, we can look at patterns of religiousness in patient populations that exhibit dramatic alterations in dopaminergic functioning such as Parkinson's disease (PD). Levels of dopamine are 40% below normal in these patients (Agid, Javoy-Agid, & Ruberg 1987). McNamara and colleagues (2006) recently reported that these patients do in fact report lower levels of religiousness than their age-matched counterparts.

If dopamine is in fact functionally implicated in the mediation of religiousness, then genes that code for construction of proteins that construct the dopamine molecule should be associated with scores on religiousness scales, and that is in fact what we find. The DRD4 gene in the brain was found to correlate positively with different religious tests; higher levels of this gene were linked to higher levels of religiousness (Comings, Gonzales, Saucier, Johnson, & MacMurray 2000).

To sum up, we find that 1) religiousness is associated with moderate to high heritabilities; 2) there are genes that are correlated with religiousness; 3) these genes code for neurotransmitters that promote DA activity in specific regions of the brain that are high in DA receptors; 4) the PFC is high in DA receptors; 5) different neuroimaging techniques have demonstrated high (relative to baseline condition) activation levels in the right PFC during religious activity; and 6) religiousness varies in patient populations according to levels of dopaminergic activity in the brains of these patients. All of these data suggest that religiousness is supported by a fairly specific biologic system and that it exhibits a fair degree of biocultural complexity. In short, the proximate mechanisms that support the trait religiousness likely involve right-sided prefrontal dopaminergic activity. This biology of religiousness in turn supports the claim that religiousness exhibits design complexity and therefore could be adaptive.

If religiousness is an adaptation, what problem did religiousness solve for our ancestors? Evolutionary scholars have offered several possibilities, such as health promoting effects and facilitating cooperation. Although additional research is currently being done to evaluate these possibilities, we feel that more research into the biology of religiousness is necessary.

Claims about the potential adaptive functions of religiousness need to be treated with great caution and tested against the evidence that it is not an exaptation or a spandrel. From the evidence presented, religiousness is a trait that is universal in all cultures, is effortlessly acquired, and has a specific biology which includes genetic heritability, activation of brain structures, and a drug-modulating effect. There is also evidence of design that supports the trait. However, do our findings concerning a specific biology help us decide between the adaptive possibilities of religiousness? We know that activation of the pre-frontal dopaminergic cortex is associated with placebo responding and social cooperation tasks. But, work in this area is still in its infancy. The evidence as it currently stands, while intriguing, does not yet help to constrain existing hypotheses on the adaptive function of religiousness.

References

Agid, Y., Javoy-Agid, M., & Ruberg, M. 1987. Biochemistry of neurotransmitters in Parkinson's disease. In C. D. M. S. Fahn, Ed., *Movement disorders 2*, pp. 166-230. London, UK: Butterworth.

Aiello, L. C., & Dunbar, R. I. M. 1993. Neocortex size, group size, and the evolution of language. *Current Anthropology, 34* (2), 184-193.

Andrews, P. W., Gangestad, S. W., & Matthews, D. 2002. Adaptationism – how to carry out an exaptationist program. *Behavioral & Brain Sciences, 25*, 489-553.

Azari, N. P., Nickel, J. P., Wunderlich, G., Niedeggen, M., Hefter, H., Tellmann, L., et al. 2001. Neural correlates of religious experience. *European Journal of Neuroscience, 13*, 1649-1652.

Barrett, J. L., Richert, R. A., & Driesenga, A. 2001. God's beliefs versus mother's: The development of nonhuman agent concepts. *Child Development, 72* (1), 50-65.

Beauregard, M., & Paquette, V. 2006. Neural correlates of a mystical experience in Carmelite nuns. *Neuroscience Letters, 405*, 186-190.

Bering, J. M., & Bjorklund, D. F. 2004. The natural emergence of reasoning about the afterlife as a developmental regularity. *Developmental Psychology, 40* (2), 217-233.

Brown, D. E. 1991. *Human universals.* Philadelphia, PA: Temple University Press.

Comings, D. E., Gonzales, N., Saucier, G., Johnson, J. P., & MacMurray, J. P. 2000. The DRD4 gene and the spiritual transcendence scale of the character temperament index. *Psychiatric Genetics, 10* (4), 185-189.

D'Onofrio, B. M., Eaves, L. J., Murrelle, L., Maes, H. H., & Spilka, B. 1999. Understanding biological and social influences on religious affiliation, attitudes, and behaviors: A behavior genetic perspective. *Journal of Personality, 67* (6), 953-984.

Dawkins, R. 2006. *The God delusion.* New York, NY: Houghton Mifflin Company.

Hamer, D. 2004. *The God gene. How faith is hardwired into our genes.* New York, NY: Anchor Books.

Johnson, D. D. P. 2005. God's punishment and public goods. A test of the supernatural punishment hypothesis in 186 world cultures. *Human Nature, 16* (4), 410-446.

Kelemen, D. 2004. Are children "intuitive theists"? *Psychological Science, 15* (5), 295-301.

Koenig, L. B., & Bouchard, Jr., T. J. 2006. Genetic and environmental influences on the traditional moral values triad – authoritarianism, conservatism, and religiousness – as assessed by quantitative behavior genetic methods. In P. McNamara, Ed., *Where God and science meet: How brain and evolutionary studies alter our understanding of religion,* Vol. 1, 31-60. Westport, CT and London: Praeger Perspectives.

McNamara, P., Durso, R., Brown, A., & Harris, E. 2006. The chemistry of religiosity: Evidence from patients with Parkinson's disease. In P. McNamara, Ed., *Where God and science meet: How brain and evolutionary studies alter our understanding of religion,* Vol. 2, 1-14. Westport, CT and London: Praeger Perspectives.

Murdock, G. P. 1965. *Culture and society.* Pittsburgh, PA: University of Pittsburgh Press.

Murdock, G. P., & White, D. R. 1969. Standard cross-cultural sample. *Ethnology, 8,* 329-369.

Nichols, D. E., & Chemel, B. R. 2006. The neuropharmacology of religious experience: Hallucinogens and the experience of the divine. In P. McNamara, Ed., *Where God and science meet: How brain and evolutionary studies alter our understanding of religion,* Vol. 3, 1-33. Westport, CT and London: Praeger Perspectives.

Cultural Evolution of Intense Religiosity

The Case of "Sankirtan Fever" in the Hare Krishna Movement

Kimmo Ketola

Intense religiosity

There are two things in religion that regularly provoke outsiders' puzzlement, and often even ridicule and hostility. The one involves actions that seem to stem from "blind faith," that is, willfully ignoring, or at least temporarily suspending the ordinary criteria of interpreting and justifying the reasons for action. The other consists of behaviors that are obviously harmful for the actor. The recent cases of suicide terrorism come easily to mind as examples of cases involving both of these features: they seem to stem from blind faith and they end in the actors' self-destruction. But there are also cases of blind and self-negating behaviors that are not at all sinister. The lives of the most admired saints are also often typified by self-negating altruism stemming from invulnerable convictions. Asceticism and self-mortification are perhaps the most typical cases of such intense religiosity between these extremes. However, it seems to be a universal feature of such behavior that it tends to provoke either passionate adulation or equally passionate disgust or ridicule. Expressions of intense religiosity are seldom left without an emotionally tinged comment.

It is important to keep in mind that not all religious thinking or behavior involves these features, much of the commonplace religiosity does not deviate all that far from ordinary criteria of rationally self-interested behavior. As countless anthropologists and scholars of religion have tried to emphasize, many religious behaviors can be readily appreciated as being quite reasonable —at least once all the cultural beliefs behind such behavior are made explicit and examined. Thus, we may speak of a continuum of religious intensity, where the more commonly accepted forms of religious expression lie at the one end, while the extreme and extraordinary behaviors lie at the other. It appears that this continuum can be found in all cultures.

Not all intense religiosity involves only the behaviors of exceptional or deviant individuals. Blindly followed self-deleterious behaviors may become institutionalized in religious traditions in the form of intensive and resource-wasteful collective rituals. By the above definition, rituals are, in fact, "blind" by their very nature, and they often involve huge expenditures of time and resources with no evident pay-off in terms of calculative rationality. Lavish and spectacular rituals of sacrifice seem to have evolved independently in countless religious traditions.

Cognitive theories of ritual (see Lawson & McCauley 1990; McCauley & Lawson 2002; Whitehouse 1995, 2000, 2004) explain how the combined effects of ritual frequency and levels of emotional arousal affect the cultural transmission of religion. They also explain what kind of social forms are likely to form around different types of ritual systems. But these theories have not provided us with a fully developed account of the evolutionary forces behind the dynamics of ritual life cycles. Here I shall propose that the perspective of cultural evolution developed by Robert Boyd and Peter J. Richerson (1985; Richerson & Boyd 2005) can be usefully combined with the cognitive perspective to provide a fuller picture of the evolutionary forces behind intense rituals and intense religiosity in general.

Boyd and Richerson argue that cultural transmission is often affected by biases of various sorts (1985 8-11; Richerson & Boyd 2005, 68-80). Transmission biases may be caused by universal characteristics of the human mind, but they may also stem from other cultural variants. An example of the former type of bias is the tendency to imitate successful and prestigious individuals, which is labeled as "prestige bias." Prestige bias belongs to a larger set of "model-based biases" (Richerson & Boyd 2005, 69).

It is evident that an innate bias towards imitation of successful models may be adaptive and therefore selected for by natural selection. However, under some conditions model-based transmission may lead to a runaway process closely resembling that of runaway sexual selection. It has often been pointed out that sexual selection can cause wildly exaggerated features that may be maladaptive from the point of view of natural selection, such as the peacock's tale. Under certain conditions there may arise a process in which both the tail size and the tail size most preferred by females start to increase in a self-reinforcing feedback loop. In the same way, prestige bias may cause a similar dynamic in cultural evolution leading to exaggerated displays of status.

However, since no value can really go on increasing indefinitely in the real world, the process may either reach some stable equilibrium or become inherently unstable, leading to permanent oscillations (Boyd & Richerson 1985, 267). In the following analysis, I shall try to show that such a self-reinforcing process can indeed be detected in the development of religious ritual behavior.

The specific case I will use to illustrate such a runaway cultural evolution is a ritual practice known as *sankirtan* developed in a new religious movement called ISKCON (International Society for Krishna Consciousness), popularly known as the Hare Krishna movement. *Sankirtan* is a ritual practice that originates in 16th century Bengali devotional Vaishnavism. It primarily consists of publicly chanting God's holy names, which when chanted by pure devotees are believed to purify and bless everyone who happens to hear them. In the Hare Krishna movement, this was soon institutionalized as a practice; groups of devotees would visit public places to chant, preach, and distribute devotional literature in exchange for small donations. It became a means by which the Hare Krishna devotees could simultaneously attract new members and collect money.

However, this simple practice soon started to spiral into more and more intense forms, and by the mid-1970s, it began to invite considerable criticism and hostility from the general public. ISKCON soon came to be known as a "destructive cult" that uses deceptive forms of street solicitation and also exploits its members during the process by causing them to work over their capacity. In the following analysis, I shall try to show that the cultural evolution of its exaggerated forms can be explained as outcomes of a runaway process based upon prestige bias.

The evolution of *sankirtan* in ISKCON

The founder of the Hare Krishna movement, A. C. Bhaktivedanta Swami Prabhupada (1896-1977) came to New York in September 1965. By June 1966 he had managed to rent a small storefront for a temple in the Lower East Side and a month later he had managed to incorporate his religious society legally. Then, one day during the fall, Prabhupada decided to go for a chanting tour in one of the nearby parks with the devotees. They had done this once before, with not much response. This time they went to Tompkins Square Park, as the poet Allen Ginsberg had suggested.

They brought drums, cymbals and a harmonium along, and some of the disciples were bold enough to dance. This time they managed to get some of the onlookers to join in the singing. They handed out flyers explaining the meaning of the chant that started by saying: "STAY HIGH FOREVER. No More Coming Down. Practice Krishna Consciousness." The event was an instant success. Next week both *The New York Times* and *The East Village Other* reported very favorably on the occasion, printing large photographs of the swami sitting in the park (Dasa 1985, 82-85).

Prabhupada also saw the practice as a fair means of income. In India the students of a guru would go from door to door begging, but Prabhupada quickly understood that this was impossible in the West (Goswami 1993, 98). During the same October, Prabhupada instructed his disciples to start publishing a magazine called *Back to Godhead,* which the devotees could distribute in exchange for a small donation.

The next step was taken when some of the devotees started to realize that the best way to please their spiritual master was to excel in distributing his literature. So, in 1968 some devotees in Los Angeles took a large *sankir-*

tan party to downtown Los Angeles and distributed more than one hundred *Back to Godhead* magazines. When Prabhupada heard of these reports, he encouraged them to distribute even more. In 1970, some of the devotees in San Francisco had also begun to sell hardbound books from door to door. With the establishment of the publishing wing of the movement in 1971, the mass scale distribution of the hardback books was begun.

Following these events, young men began to travel for extended periods in order to distribute books. Thus, around 1973 there arose in the United States the idea of a traveling *sankirtan*-team. These teams, which usually consisted of about 10-15 male devotees, lived and traveled in big vehicles such as old Greyhound buses. At its most intense phase, the daily schedules of the traveling parties were arduous, lasting about 16 hours a day including the morning devotions. At the same time devotees began to also wear conventional clothes to conceal their identity (Goswami 1993, 168).

Finally, the teams started to compete with each other. It was easy to compare the success of each *sankirtan* party by simply keeping a close count of the books distributed by each zone. It was decided that traveling *sankirtan* parties were comparable to the temples, and so all ISKCON temples and traveling teams were lined up into competing teams. The race could begin.

During 1975, the number of books distributed started to increase significantly. One devotee's traveling team, consisting of several vans and buses, collectively distributed 14,500 books in July, 22,000 in October, and 33,000 in November (Goswami 1984, 558). The climax came in December with the so-called "Christmas marathon", when the same traveling *sankirtan* team distributed an unprecedented 65,000 big books and 225,000 magazines in a state that can only be described as religious frenzy. One New York devotee is reported to have danced and twirled down Fifth Avenue dressed as Santa Claus laughing like a madman and shouting: "We've got what you can't buy for all the diamonds in Tiffany's—love of Godhead!" (cited in Goswami 1984, 571).

The enthusiasm and book distribution peaked in 1976, when the devotees distributed over eighteen thousand books per week on average in Canada and the United States (Rochford 1985, 174). The decline started soon after that, at first slowly, but more seriously in 1979.

But some of the changes made during the process had changed the nature of the *sankirtan* in dramatic ways. By the middle of the decade, it was transformed from being an openly religious practice and recruitment technique to an aggressive and deceptive profit seeking technique with no intent of attracting new members. In contrast to chanting and book distribution, which provide opportunities to preach and attract people to the movement, a practice called "picking" was developed, which involves seeking straight donations for some vaguely determined worthy cause. In 1977, the devotees began to sell a variety of non-religious goods, such as candles, candy, prints of artwork, lapel pins, buttons, bumper stickers, and baseball caps. The low point was reached in 1979, when distributing religious literature was actively discouraged (Rochford 1985, 183).

Although economic factors clearly played a role in this series of events, the decisive factor behind the process of escalation and subsequent collapse was clearly the prestige bias. The people who chose to follow Prabhupada obviously found admirable religious qualities in him. They became his loyal devotees and soon started to model their behavior after him. If the guru danced and sung in public places, so did the disciples. Before long, the disciples started to compete with each other in trying to get their guru's attention. The competition led to a process whereby the practice started to consume more and more time and energy from the devotees. The most successful book distributors got rewarded not only with religious ecstasy, but also praise and appreciation from their spiritual master. The most enthusiastic book distributors became his closest disciples, and soon, Prahbupada chose them for the most prestigious positions in the movement. Many of them got to be chosen as initiating gurus after the demise of their spiritual master.

Conclusion

As Boyd and Richerson have argued, humans may possess an innate, adaptive bias towards imitation of prestigious individuals. While such innate biases may be generally adaptive, they may also fuel processes of runaway cultural evolution. The specific point I want to make here is that instances of intense religiosity can often be explained by these kinds of cultural evolutionary processes. The description of the development of the *sankirtan* practice presented here is meant to illustrate how cultural practices may show a pattern of self-reinforcing cycles, which end only when the actors' utmost limits of psychic and material resources are reached. In the case of religion, such cycles will typically end in a religious ecstasy of one sort or another. In the most extreme cases, such as the Peoples Temple, it may even end in collective self-destruction.

During 1975-1976, the Hare Krishna devotees in the United States reached extraordinary levels of bliss by exerting themselves to the utmost limits in distributing spiritual literature in public places. It is important to understand that *sankirtan* is fundamentally a religious ritual. Prabhupada seems to have been possessed of a special genius for pushing his disciples beyond themselves, to act in ways that were not governed by social conventions. The devotees must have felt a sense of ecstatic liberation from the ranks of common people and their concerns of propriety. But the same disregard of ordinary ethical concerns also resulted in extremely cynical and uncaring strategies of profit seeking. After the whole enterprise crashed down, the practice stabilized into more attenuated, reasonable, and routinized forms. The cycle, however, is likely to repeat itself under suitable conditions with new devotees who have not experienced the previous cycle.

References

Boyd, R., & Richerson, P. J. 1985 *Culture and the evolutionary process.* Chicago, IL: The University of Chicago Press.

Dasa, H. 1985 *The Hare Krishna explosion: The birth of Krishna consciousness in America 1966-1969.* n.p.: Palace Press.

Goswami, S. D. 1993 *Srila Prabhupada – lilamrta: A biography of his divine grace A. C. Bhaktivedanta Swami Prabhupada.* Vol 5. *Let there be a temple.* Juhu, Bombay: Bhaktivedanta Book Trust.

Goswami, T. K. 1984 *Servant of the servant.* N.p.: published by the author.

Lawson, E. T., & McCauley, R. N. 1990 *Rethinking religion: Connecting cognition and culture.* Oxford, UK: Oxford University Press.

McCauley, R. N., & Lawson, E. T. 2002 *Bringing ritual to mind: Psychological foundations of cultural forms.* New York, NY: Cambridge University Press.

Richerson, P. J., & Boyd, R. 2005 *Not by genes alone: How culture transformed human evolution.* Chicago, IL: The University of Chicago Press.

Rochford, E. B. 1985 *Hare Krishna in America.* New Brunswick, NJ: Rutgers University Press.

Whitehouse, H. 1995 *Inside the cult: Religious innovation and transmission in Papua New Guinea.* Oxford, UK: Clarendon Press.

Whitehouse, H. 2000 *Arguments and icons: Divergent modes of religiosity.* Oxford, UK: Oxford University Press.

Whitehouse, H. 2004 *Modes of religiosity: A cognitive theory of religious transmission.* Walnut Creek, CA: AltaMira Press.

Supernatural Niche Construction Incubates Brilliance and Governs the Ratchet Effect

David Kydd

Humans create the idea that gods create humans. In turn, gods 'build' specific features of human brains. This is the culture-gene coevolutionary model I propose, and hope to show how social, cognitive, and neuroscientists investigating religion stand to accelerate the ratchet of our own enterprise by implementing the niche perspective.

To begin, what exactly is "the ratchet effect"? Humans possess the unique ability to accumulate material artifacts, social institutions, behavioral traditions, languages, and information in brains (e.g., ideas). The snowballing of human culture is often referred to as the 'ratchet effect' because each behavioral modification stays in place in the group until further modifications are made (Tomasello, Kruger, & Ratner 1993). As used by primatologist and developmental psychologist Michael Tomasello, the ratchet effect puts special emphasis on imitative learning—the specific sequence of actions that an imitator uses in route to duplicating a goal. Although chimps and several other species possess rudimentary skill in true imitation, humans sprint ahead in this domain (Tomasello & Carpenter 2005). Since there are a number of factors that lead to the accumulation of culture, including population size, transmission biases, epidemiological dispersion of mental and public representations, and so on (Richerson & Boyd 2005; Sperber 1996), the use of the term *ratchet effect* is an instance of metonymy—one attribute of cultural transmission processes stands for the entire dynamic. The term, even though originally pivoting on "true imitation," is advantageous for scientists of religion for reasons that include:

a. imitative behavior is a prominent feature of ritual, where precise duplication of prior performance is often idealized, while in a broader sense religions the world over frequently blame misfortune as punishment by supernatural agents due to the failure of a society to faithfully replicate ancestral ways;

b. a broader category of imitative behavior known as *mimesis*—nonsymbolic, analogic event reenactment such as pantomime or rehearsal for skill activities like throwing or dance (Donald 1991; 2005)—may well have occupied the major duration of hominin life beginning c. 2,000,000 BP (years Before Present) and continues to undergird much of modern human behavior, including the repetitious nature of many components of religion;

c. imitative activity indexes the continuum of a larger framework of duplicative processes that place 'value' on fidelity in information transfer and include DNA replication, fixed action patterns, imprinting, modeling, identification, ritual, etc.;

d. the term *ratchet effect* enables us to differentiate a corresponding term, *the wretched effect,* that delimits a range of slips in the ratchet, poor rates or quality of information transfer, and even hypertrophied rates of transfer that usher in deleterious cultural and-or genetic effects.

How the Hominin-Carved Niches Sculpted our Genome

Niche construction refers to a common, simple twist of Darwinian evolution wherein an organism, for example a beaver building a lodge, proactively alters the environment and thereby shifts selection pressures, which in turn alter gene frequencies: those beavers with longer teeth and flatter tails will build better lodges (Odling-Smee 1988; Odling-Smee, Laland, & Feldman 2003). Humans are the niche constructors par excellence. A widely cited example is *the herding niche* wherein the domestication of cattle for meat c. 10,000 BP was eventually followed by dairying c. 7,000 BP in North Africa, Europe, and the Near East. During the dairying time span of approximately 300 generations, those individuals who had the genetic allele coding for a lactase enzyme to break down the otherwise indigestible lactose molecule in milk thrived in comparison to those who did not. Anthropologist William Durham (1991) provides compelling evidence that the lactase allele spread in populations with both: (a) high rates of drinking *fresh* milk—as opposed to processed milk products like cheese, yogurt, kefir, etc., that effectively minimize the necessity of lactase, and crucially, (b) traditions of ancient mythology that honor fresh milk consumption. The fact that people in these societies tended to imitate the behavior of mythic heroes associated with milk exemplifies a form of cultural transmission known as *prestige bias* (Henrich & Gil-White 2001). We tend to imitate the person of high status (Boyd & Richerson 1985). Thus the herding niche consists of both the dairy practices and the public evaluations of them, including those coded in myth.

Two prime examples of hominin niche-building brilliance underwrite the emergence of religious behavior: what I shall call *the fire niche* and *the handaxe niche.*

The earliest solid evidence for the hominins entering the fire niche is 1,640,000 BP (Bellomo 1994; Rowlett & Peters 1997). Archaeologists at the site Koobi Fora on Lake Turkana in Kenya document both the control and production of fire by *H. erectus* and possibly *H. ergaster*. Although evidence suggests that these hominins already began cooking, it is clear that over the next million years the cooking of tubers and meat had a major impact upon the evolution of the brain and gut: since cooking effectively externalizes the energetic load required for digestion, more energy was freed for brain metabolism (Aiello & Wheeler 1995; Wrangham, Jones, Laden, Pilbeam, & Conklin-Brittain 1999). Hence a lion's share of the variance for the balloon-like swelling of the hominin brain and decrease in gut size is due to the culture-gene coevolution involving pyro-techniques (Odling-Smee et al. 2003). Further, a preliminary cross-cultural study of children's behavior with fire suggests that there even may be a domain specific mechanism dedicated to 'fire cues' similar to the well documented predispositions toward snake detection in primates and humans (Fessler 2006). Obviously, hypotheses like this warrant caution.

Briefly, we find a similar coevolutionary trajectory in the use of the stone-tool handaxe. Like the production of fire, handaxe production required careful training at the individual level plus maintenance of the tradition at the group level. Among individual handaxe knappers, refinements in imitation due to longer sequential processing, along with increased demands on hand-eye coordination skill, likely explains a share of the variance in evolutionary modifications to the prefrontal cortex, hemispheric laterality, and the opposable thumb and power grip (Wynn 2002). These skills in turn would have served as a platform for the genes coding for the timing, accuracy, and mental rotation skills involved in throwing a variety of projectiles, again a skill that far surpasses any other animal.

In sum, by entering the fire and handaxe niches, a number of behavioral traditions were established at the group level that structured a novel evolutionary environment, which in turn generated selection pressure for modified genotypes. These colossal feedback loops and a cascade of downstream effects continued for over 1,640,000 years at a minimum.[1]

Ancestors Build Gods and Gods Modify Brains

A perennial head-scratcher for evolutionary anthropologists is the fact that hominins had the intelligence to build fire and chisel handaxes but did not advance the technological ratchet very much for an enormous span of time. What enabled *H. sapiens* to accelerate both the speed and volume of the ratchet effect?

I hypothesize that a portion of the variance which explains the unprecedented increase is that a small population of hominins learned to control

---

1 Suggestion: Scientists might inaugurate the first truly worldwide festival celebrating the hominin ancestors who gave us fire and the handaxe.

yet another natural resource, altered states of consciousness — dreams and trance-states induced by repetitive dancing, chanting, sensory deprivation, or hallucinogens. The pivot of this model is a supernatural niche comprised of *emotionally charged* schemas that are positioned in a hierarchy of ancestrally sanctioned values. These are affect-laden representations.

I illustrate the schema configuration in 3-D to underscore (a) how the template frequently exploits the metaphors of verticality such as 'higher is better' (Lakoff & Johnson 1980) in order to rank values, and (b) how spatio-temporal cognition helps to structure the imagination (Levinson, 2003). It is important to bear in mind that the multivalent schemas can be represented in a distributed neural network in terms of weighted nodes, or alternatively, they can be mapped onto a traditional cognitive framework like the Interacting Cognitive Subsystems model (Barnard & Teasdale 1991).

Two lines of evidence suggest a unique evolutionary footprint among *Homo sapiens*: (1) the cultural manipulation of biochemistry, especially the dopaminergic system, in the assigning of salience to ideas, and (2) specific cognitive endophenotypes. Dopamine is an ancient signaling system that assigns salience to sensory stimuli, e.g. hunger, sex, pain, and novel events (Berridge & Robinson 1998; Horvitz 2000). The dopamine footprint is most clearly seen when antipsychotic drugs—dopamine blockers—dampen the salience of hyperactive ideas like manic flights or depressive self-condemnations (Kapur 2003). The same mechanism applies in part to auditory hallucinations as sub-vocal talk writ large and to delusions, which are characterized less by bizarre reasoning than by unshakeable conviction. Hyper-salient ideas can also be found in other pathologies such as Cotard's syndrome, in which the person often feels immortal, or in personality facets like perfectionism that cut across the diagnostic categories of obsessive-compulsive disorder, obsessive-compulsive personality disorder, and narcissism. Importantly, the sub-clinical manifestations of attributes like a striving toward perfection can have adaptive significance (Flett & Hewitt 2002).

Vital to my hypothesis is the fact that overwhelming evidence now links sub-psychotic cognitive traits to components of creativity (Karlsson 1984; Nettle 2001). The curve that may describe part of the variance of this dynamic is the *cliff-edged fitness function* (Nesse 2004), applied here to mean that the traits assigning salience to ideas increase fitness steadily and then suddenly crash into psychosis. Indeed, the region of the curve nearing the apex I suggest we call the 'brilliant prone spectrum' to offset and balance the current pathocentric focus upon the 'psychosis prone spectrum.'

Returning to dopamine, a recent study (Reuter et al. 2005) showed its link to creativity, in particular to a variant of novelty-seeking. Another study found that a version of one class of dopamine receptor (the DRD4 7R allele), again linked to the novelty-seeking phenotype, first appears among *H. sapiens* at *c.* 40,000 BP (Ding et al. 2002). Finally, the traits along the brilliant-prone spectrum are also associated with components of religious ideation (Day & Peters 1999; Deeley 2004).

Taken together, I interpret the data to mean that a significant portion of the variance driving human brilliance is the promotion of relatively grand ideas under the watchful eyes of the ancestors. For the first time in history the salience of an idea—the immortals, the supernatural—displaced the salience of perception as 'the really real.' This holds both for dramatic cases like martyrs who hold fast to the theologically correct (Barrett 1999) and trade this very life for a promise, and for native Australians whose Dreamtime beings are superimposed upon all of nature. The inversion of salience enables the *presence of absence* to motivate behavior and channel the experience of meaning, thereby providing the platform upon which other functional attributes of religious systems build: intensified group cohesion (Bulbulia 2004; Sosis 2004; Wilson 2002), enhanced memory transmission (Boyer 2001; McCauley & Lawson 2002; Whitehouse 2000), intra-subjective relations with attachment figures (Kirkpatrick 2004), and plausibly the bootstrapping of protolanguage to fully symbolic language. Words presence absence, too.

The heart of supernatural niche construction is a "techne" that like a car engine combines the *heavy metal of tradition* symbolized most pervasively by ancestor-representations (Steadman, Palmer, & Tilley 1996) with the *volatile gasoline of ASCs* (Stephen 1979) in order to generate work—the work of innovative ideation. Though the mechanism accelerates the ratchet effect, it modulates the runaway potential of decoupled representation (Tooby & Cosmides 2001) by means of cognitive binding: indices of experiment such as new ideas are riveted to symbols of experience such as conformist and prestige bias transmitters in the form of supernatural agents. For example, shamans worldwide perform traditionally proscribed rites, enter trance, contact supernatural agents, and return with a creative solution. Similarly, the native Australian Yolungu feel immense pressure from supernatural presences to repeat ancestral ways, yet in dream and trance the agents suggest new songs, myths, or paintings. In both cases, credit for innovative ideas is given not to mortals but to ostensible immortals: the new enters through the door of the old. Thus the supernatural niche structures a dynamic, fast and frugal heuristic mediating stasis and change, experience and experiment, Zeusean wisdom and Promethean wit.

References

Aiello, L., & Wheeler, P. 1995. The expensive-tissue hypothesis: The brain and the digestive system in human and primate evolution. *Current Anthropology, 36,* 199-221.

Barnard, P., & Teasdale, J. 1991. Interacting cognitive subsystems. *Cognition & Emotion, 5,* 1-39.

Barrett, J. 1999. Theological correctness: Cognitive constraint and the study of religion. *Method & Theory in the Study of Religion, 11,* 325-339.

Bellomo, R. 1994. Methods of determining early hominid behavioral activities associated with the controlled use of fire at FxJj 20 Main, Koobi Fora, Kenya. *Journal of Human Evolution, 27,* 173-195.

Berridge, K., & Robinson, T. 1998. What is the role of dopamine in reward? *Brain Research Reviews, 28,* 309-369.

Boyd, R., & Richerson, P. 1985. *Culture and the evolutionary process.* Chicago, IL: University of Chicago Press.

Boyer, P. 2001. *Religion explained.* New York, NY: Basic Books.

Bulbulia, J. 2004. Religious costs as adaptations that signal altruistic intention. *Evolution & Cognition, 10,* 19-42.

Day, S., & Peters, E. 1999. The incidence of schizotypy in new religious movements. *Personality & Individual Differences, 27,* 55-67.

Deeley, P. 2004. The religious brain: Turning ideas into convictions. *Anthropology & Medicine, 11,* 245-267.

Ding, Y.-C., Chi, H.-C., Grady, D., Morishima, A., Kidd, J., Kidd, K., et al. 2002. Evidence of positive selection acting at the human dopamine receptor D4 gene locus. *Proceedings of the National Academy of Sciences of the USA, 99,* 309-314.

Donald, M. 1991. *Origins of the modern mind: Three stages in the evolution of culture and cognition.* Cambridge, MA: Harvard University Press.

Donald, M. 2005. Imitation and mimesis. In S. Hurley & N. Chater Eds., *Perspectives on imitation: From neuroscience to social science,* Vol. 2, 283-300 Cambridge, MA: The MIT Press.

Durham, W. 1991. *Coevolution: Genes, culture, and human diversity.* Stanford, CA: Stanford University Press.

Fessler, D. 2006. A burning desire: Steps toward an evolutionary psychology of fire learning. *Journal of Cognition & Culture, 6,* 429-451.

Flett, G., & Hewitt, P., Eds. 2002. *Perfectionism: Theory, research, and treatment.* Washington, D.C.: American Psychological Association.

Henrich, J., & Gil-White, F. 2001. The evolution of prestige: Freely conferred deference as a mechanism for enhancing the benefits of cultural transmission. *Evolution & Human Behavior, 22,* 165-196.

Horvitz, J. 2000. Mesolimbocortical and nigrostriatal dopamine responses to salient non-reward events. *Neuroscience, 96,* 651-656.

Kapur, S. 2003. Psychosis as a state of aberrant salience. *American Journal of Psychiatry, 160,* 13-23.

Karlsson, J. 1984. Creative intelligence in relatives of mental patients. *Hereditas, 100,* 83-86.

Kirkpatrick, L. 2004. *Attachment, evolution, and the psychology of religion.* New York, NY: Guilford Press.

Lakoff, G., & Johnson, M. 1980. *Metaphors we live by.* Chicago, IL: University of Chicago Press.

Levinson, S. 2003. *Space in language and cognition.* Cambridge, UK: Cambridge University Press.

McCauley, R., & Lawson, T. 2002. *Bringing ritual to mind.* Cambridge, UK: Cambridge University Press.

Nesse, R. 2004. Cliff-edged fitness functions and the persistence of schizophrenia. *Behavioral & Brain Sciences, 27,* 860-862.

Nettle, D. 2001. *Strong imagination.* Oxford, UK: Oxford University Press.

Odling-Smee, J. 1988. Niche constructing phenotypes. In H. Plotkin, Ed., *The role of behavior in evolution,* pp. 73-132 Cambridge, UK: Cambridge University Press.

Odling-Smee, J., Laland, K., & Feldman, M. 200.3 *Niche construction: The neglected process in evolution.* Princeton, NJ: Princeton University Press.

Richerson, P., & Boyd, R. 2005 *Not by genes alone: How culture transformed human evolution.* Chicago, IL: University of Chicago Press.

Reuter, M., Panksepp, J., Schnabel, N., Kellerhoff, N., Kempel, P., & Hennig, J. 2005. Personality and biological markers of creativity. *European Journal of Personality, 19,* 83-95.

Rowlett, R., & Peters, C. 1997. Burnt earth associated with hominid site FxJj 20 East. In G. Isaac & B. Isaac, Eds., *Koobi Fora Research Project,* 78-92 Oxford, UK: Oxford University Press.

Sosis, R. 2004. The adaptive value of religious ritual. *American Scientist, 92,* 166-172.

Sperber, D. 1996. *Explaining culture: A naturalistic approach.* Oxford, UK: Blackwell Publishers.

Steadman, L. B., Palmer, C. T., & Tilley, C. F. 1996. The universality of ancestor worship. *Ethnology, 35,* 63-76.

Stephen, M. 1979. Dreams of change: The innovative role of ASCs in traditional Melanesian religion. *Oceania, 50,* 3-22.

Tomasello, M., & Carpenter, M. 2005. Intention reading and imitative learning. In S. Hurley & N. Chater, Eds., *Perspectives on imitation: From neuroscience to social science,* Vol. 2, 133-148 Cambridge, MA: The MIT Press.

Tomasello, M., Kruger, A. C., & Ratner, H. H. 1993. Cultural learning. *Behavioral & Brain Sciences, 16,* 495-552.

Tooby, J., & Cosmides, L. 2001. Does beauty build adapted minds? *SubStance, 94,* 6-25.

Whitehouse, H. 2000 *Arguments and icons: Divergent modes of religiosity.* Oxford, UK: Oxford University Press.

Wilson, D. S. 2002. *Darwin's cathedral: Evolution, religion, and the nature of society.* Chicago, IL: University of Chicago Press.

Wrangham, R., Jones, J. H., Laden, G., Pilbeam, D., & Conklin-Brittain, N. 1999. The raw and the stolen: Cooking and the ecology of human origins. *Current Anthropology, 40,* 568-594.

Wynn, T. 2002. Archaeology and cognitive evolution. *Behavioral & Brain Sciences, 25,* 389-438.

PART III

TRIBES UNDER GOD

Pigeons, Foxholes, and the Book of Psalms

Evolved Superstitious Responses to Cope with Stress and Uncertainty

Richard Sosis

In a curious but classic article entitled *'Superstition' in the Pigeon*, B.F. Skinner (1948) described the results of an experiment in which pigeons, placed inside what we now refer to as a "Skinner box", developed superstitious ritual behaviors in response to an unpredictable feeding schedule. Legend has it that Skinner was so confident in the emergence of such behaviors that he would take a boxed pigeon to his undergraduate lectures at Harvard, dramatically uncover the box at the end of class, and invariably reveal a pigeon engaged in some ritualistic behavioral pattern, presumably in hope of securing food that was in fact being randomly dispersed. Since Skinner's pioneering work, various studies have documented how children and adults in analogous experimental conditions quickly generate novel superstitious practices (e.g., Ono 1987).

Years before Skinner's experiments, Bronislaw Malinowski (1925/1954) predicted that individuals would turn toward magic, i.e. superstitious acts, to exercise some control when faced with unpredictable conditions. Under conditions of certainty, however, Malinowski predicted that magical thought and behavior would not emerge. His hypothesis, which was consistent with the fishing activities of the Trobriand Islanders he studied, has been more recently dubbed the "uncertainty hypothesis" (Burger & Lynn 2005). Following Malinowski's insights, researchers have found support for his hypothesis in a variety of populations facing unpredictable conditions, including baseball players, test-taking students, craps shooters, and targets of war.

While anthropologists have long suggested that many religious practices and beliefs are superstitious responses to uncertain conditions, especially risk of death, most evolutionary accounts of religion have either ignored or dismissed the human tendency to turn to the supernatural world under conditions of uncertainty. However, folk wisdom (there are no atheists in foxholes) and the claims of anthropologists are now being supported by empirical research. Recent controlled experiments, for example, show that priming subjects with thoughts of death increases supernatural belief

(Norenzayan & Hansen 2006). Moreover, and particularly relevant to the project described below, studies indicate that increased religiosity is a common response to exposure to terror and that religion plays an important role in moderating the stress effects of terror (e.g., Shuster et al. 2001).

Beseeching a supernatural agent to save one from imminent danger appears to be cognitively distinct from many personal superstitions, such as carrying a rabbit's foot or walking backwards into the dugout after batting practice, although they do share some commonalities. For example, both types of superstitions reduce anxiety and enhance one's ability to cope with conditions of uncertainty. Furthermore, both assume that an unseen and unverifiable force will favorably influence an otherwise unpredictable outcome. Superstitious actors, however, have no relationship with the unseen forces that translate a rabbit's foot into a higher exam score or ensure that walking backwards into the dugout will result in a higher batting average. In contrast, when turning directly to a supernatural agent for assistance, one is addressing an omnipotent friend with whom one assumes a personal relationship. Indeed, similar to human social life, such superstitious actions are often accompanied by entreaties for some reciprocal exchange ("Get me out of this and I'll change my ways!").

Malinkowski and others have claimed that superstitious beliefs and practices reduce anxiety produced by uncertain conditions, thus allowing individuals to focus on and successfully complete the particular high-risk task they face. If such practices have adaptive significance, it must be shown that they do indeed positively influence task performance. Does the student who takes an exam clenching her lucky rabbit foot improve her exam score? Does the Trobriand fisher who relies on fishing magic increase his return rates? Do supplications to God in the foxhole reduce stress and allow the soldier to make clearer decisions, thus increasing his probability of survivorship? While many scholars assume that superstitious beliefs and practices must have functional consequences, empirical data supporting such assertions are lacking. Other researchers, with equally sparse data, maintain that superstitious behaviors are maladaptive, producing no discernable benefits but costing individuals significant time and energy.

To address these issues, I undertook a study that explored how women in the northern Israeli town of Tzfat used culturally and religiously defined superstitious beliefs and practices to cope with the stress of the Second Palestinian Intifada (SPI). Here I document these beliefs and practices, and discuss the scope of efficacy attributed to them. I then examine the demographic and socioeconomic determinants of the most frequently performed religious superstitious practice, psalm recitation. Lastly, I assess whether psalm recitation has functional consequences by examining its relationship to short- and long-term precautionary responses to the SPI. The results provide strong support for the uncertainty hypothesis and suggest that psalm recitation among this sample of women may have adaptive consequences.

Study Location: Tzfat, Israel

While throughout their history Israelis have been regularly exposed to threats of terror, in September 2000, which marks the beginning of the SPI, the frequency and severity of attacks began to escalate to new heights. Over the following three years there were thousands of attempted attacks, including drive-by shootings, stabbings, and suicide bombings. In the SPI's most prolific year, 2002, there were over 450 fatalities, whereas terror-related fatalities never exceeded 100 per year prior to the SPI. Studies by Klar and colleagues (1996, 2002) show that Israelis characterize terrorist attacks as both uncontrollable and unpredictable. In commenting on the Israeli experience, Noy notes that "while the expected number of casualties from a terrorist attack is not high, the prolonged effect of the uncertainty of when, where or how an attack will occur can result in disturbance to normal functioning and psychic life, leading to the development of an on-going and pervasive state of generalized anxiety and disruption of life" (2004, 31). Hence, the SPI created conditions of stress and uncertainty where superstitious practices and beliefs are expected to flourish.

Tzfat has over 30,000 residents, maintaining an eclectic mix of secular and religious Jews who peacefully coexist. While during the SPI the threat of terrorism was real and constant in Tzfat, no attacks ever occurred there. Its relative safety was a significant factor in the author choosing it as a field site to live with his family from June 2002 through August 2003.

Data Collection

All interviewees in this study were women. The survey instrument was developed following 16 open-ended interviews on religious responses to the SPI conducted by the author. Four local Israeli women were subsequently trained to conduct protocol-based interviews. 367 interviews were conducted in Tzfat's Ministry of the Interior between February and August 2003, a year which recorded the second highest terror-related fatality rate in Israeli history. To limit the effects of particular attacks influencing interviewee responses, no interviews were conducted for 48 hours following a terrorist attack in which there was at least one fatality. There were 12 such attacks during the seven month study period, and at least one attack occurred in six of those months.

Main Findings

Here I present a brief overview of the project's main findings. Detailed analyses and additional results will appear in subsequent publications (eg., Sosis 2007).

Superstitious Practices and Beliefs in Tzfat

Open-ended interviews revealed a variety of practices that were believed could improve what was known as the *matzav* (literally, "situation"), as well as directly protect one from a terrorist attack, including giving charity, checking the parchment inside phylacteries and *mezuzot* (which hang on the doorframes of Jewish homes), and doing *mitzvot* in general. Three practices, however, were mentioned significantly more than others: reciting psalms, wearing *tziztit* (a garment with fringes worn only by men), and carrying the picture of *tzaddik* (holy person). In the protocol-based interview, interviewees (N=367) rated the following three statements on a scale of 1 (really agree) to 10 (really disagree): Reciting psalms [wearing tzitzit, carrying a picture of a tzaddik] protects one from an attack. 58.6%, 49.9%, and 30.0% of interviewees really agreed (chose "1") that reciting psalms, wearing tzitzit, and carrying a tzaddik's picture respectively would protect one from an attack, and the mean response for reciting psalms was significantly lower than the mean responses for wearing tzitzit and carrying a tzaddik's picture.

Interviewees also rated the following statement: Reciting psalms can improve the matzav. 77.8% of the self-defined religious population and 35.7% of the self-defined secular population strongly believed (chose "1") that reciting psalms could improve the matzav, whereas 3.7% of the religious population and 28.6% of the secular population strongly disagreed with this statement (chose "10"). Remarkably, among secular interviewees there was no significant difference between the efficacy attributed to psalm recitation and government actions in improving the matzav. Among the religious, much greater efficacy was attributed to psalm recitation than to government actions.

While not mandated by Jewish law, many religious women in Israel regularly recite psalms as a spiritual practice. Given the strong beliefs in the power of psalms to protect one from an attack as well as improve the overall situation, it is not surprising that many women in the sample were reciting *additional* psalms in response to the SPI: 83.0% (n=270) of self-defined religious women, and 35.7% (n=56) of self-defined secular women.[1] While reciting psalms is generally a private ritual, during the SPI women through-

1 These percentages do not reflect psalm recitation throughout Israel. Had the research been conducted in a predominantly secular area, such as Tel Aviv, the rate of psalm recitation by secular residents would surely have been lower.

out Tzfat (and elsewhere in Israel) organized themselves to ensure that the entire Book of Psalms (150 psalms) was collectively recited at least once per day. Women were assigned five or more psalms to recite either at communal gatherings, or more commonly, in private at one's convenience.

What are the main determinants of psalm recitation?

Most demographic variables (age, education, native Israeli, ethnicity, and income) were not predictors of psalm recitation; the only exception was political preference (rightwingers are more likely to recite psalms than leftwingers). Experiential variables, however, such as knowing someone who was killed in the SPI, experiencing a decrease in income during the SPI, and believing that Tzfat will be attacked have strong positive impacts on the likelihood that self-defined secular Tzfat women will recite psalms. These variables have little effect on the probability that self-defined religious residents will recite additional psalms.

Is psalm recitation related to other behavioral responses?

If reciting psalms plays a role in reducing stress and increasing one's sense of control, it should be negatively correlated with other behavioral responses to the SPI, such as being cautious following an attack, and long-term responses like avoiding buses, restaurants, and crowded places. Those who recite psalms are expected to have a greater sense of control and lower anxiety concerning the SPI, and thus be more comfortable maintaining their daily routine. Among those who believe that Tzfat will be attacked (78.3% of the sample), reciting psalms is a significant negative predictor of short- and long-term precautionary behavioral changes, controlling for other significant variables (age, education, and income). There is a significant interaction effect between psalm recitation and secular/religious self-identity. Secular interviewees who are not reciting psalms are the most likely to make precautionary behavioral changes, whereas reciting psalms is largely unrelated to whether religious interviewees make precautionary behavioral changes. There is no difference between religious interviewees and secular interviewees who are reciting psalms with respect to their likelihood of making behavioral changes.

Conclusion

The results summarized here suggest that conditions of life-threatening stress, such as exposure to terrorism, may elicit evolved motivations to turn toward culturally learned rituals in order to gain some control of an otherwise uncertain situation. The greater the threat secular women perceived, the greater the likelihood they recited psalms. Furthermore, psalm recitation is negatively related to the likelihood that one will alter their normal routine in response to the SPI, suggesting functional consequences of psalm recitation; namely, increasing performers' ability to cope with the stress and uncertainty of the SPI.

Yet, if psalm recitation reduces stress and increases ones sense of control, why does it seem to be effective only among the secular and not the religious? I offer three possible non-mutually exclusive explanations. First, some religious women who do not feel a stress-related need to recite additional psalms may recite psalms nonetheless because someone has asked them to, which may explain why the experiential variables were largely unrelated to psalm recitation among religious women. Secular women are unlikely to face similar social pressure, thus those who decide to recite psalms must be particularly self-motivated. Second, the stress reducing benefits that superstitious rituals offer may face diminishing returns. Consequently, if one is reciting psalms and had not been doing so previously (as among the secular), the effects of such ritual practice are probably much greater than for those who had already been reciting psalms (as among the religious) and decided to recite additional psalms because of the SPI. Third, the data presented here may suffer from phenotypic correlation problems. For example, if religious women who are experiencing SPI-related stress are more likely to recite additional psalms than religious women who are not stressed, then it is possible that had these women *not* recited additional psalms they would have made more precautionary changes. By reciting psalms however, their behavioral responses were similar to women who were not stressed by the prospect of an attack.

While I have argued that psalm recitation likely has adaptive consequences, it is possible that refraining from precautionary behaviors is maladaptive. However, even during the height of the SPI Israelis were more likely to be killed in an automobile accident than a terrorist attack. Indeed, many authors have chided governments and citizens for overreacting to terrorism while ignoring much more common societal dangers. The actual likelihood of being killed by terrorists, even in Israel, is exceedingly low. Yet, because of the spectacular nature of terrorism, and its extensive media coverage, our perception of the threat is much greater than the actual threat. Obviously, more detailed studies are needed to assess whether or not superstitious responses to terror are adaptive, but hopefully it will be necessary to pursue such research through historical, rather than anthropological, methods.

References

Burger, J., & Lynn, A. 2005. Superstitious behavior among American and Japanese professional baseball players. *Basic & Applied Social Psychology, 27*, 71-76.

Klar, Y., Medding, A., & Sarel, D. 1996. . Nonunique invulnerability: Singular versus distributional probabilities and unrealistic optimism in comparative risk judgments. *Organizational Behavior & Human Decision Processes, 67,* 229-245.

Klar, Y., Zakay, D., & Shavrit, K. 2002. .'If I don't get blown up…': Realism in face of terrorism in an Israeli nationwide sample. *Risk Decision & Policy, 7,* 203-219.

Malinowski, B. 1954. *Magic, science, and religion.* Garden City, NY: Doubleday Anchor Books.

Norenzayan, A., & Hansen, I. 2006. . Belief in supernatural agents in the face of death *Personality & Social Psychology Bulletin, 32,* 174-187.

Noy, S. 2004. Minimizing casualties in biological and chemical threats war and terrorism. : The importance of information to the public in a prevention program. *Prehospital & Disaster Medicine, 19,* 29-36.

Ono, K. 1987. . Superstitious behavior in humans. *Journal of the Experimental Analysis of Behavior, 47,* 261-271.

Schuster, M., Stein, B., Jaycox, L., Collins, R., Marshall, G., Elliot, M., et al. 2001. A national survey of stress reactions after the September 11, 2001 terrorist attacks. *New England Journal of Medicine, 345,* 1507-12.

Skinner, B. F. 1948. .'Superstition' in the pigeon. *Journal of Experimental Psychology, 38,* 168-172.

Sosis, R. 2007. Psalms for safety: Magico-religious response to threats of terror. *Current Anthropology, 48.*

Gods of War

The Adaptive Logic of Religious Conflict

Dominic Johnson

"The attachment of the Roman troops to their standards was inspired by the united influences of religion and of honour. The golden eagle, which glittered in the front of the legion, was the object of their fondest devotion; nor was it esteemed less impious than it was ignominious, to abandon that sacred ensign in the hour of danger."

Edward Gibbon, *Decline and Fall* (1776-1778, 17)

I explore the hypothesis that religious beliefs and practices were adaptive in human evolutionary history because they improved combat performance in inter-group conflict (in addition to whatever other uses they may have had). The idea that group cohesion under a religious banner may be adaptive for group competition has a prominent heritage in Darwin himself (1871): "There can be no doubt that a tribe including many members who, from possessing in a high degree the spirit of patriotism, fidelity, obedience, courage, and sympathy, were always ready to give aid to each other and to sacrifice themselves for the common good, would be victorious over other tribes; and this would be natural selection" (166).

Darwin did not mention religion explicitly here, but the conceptual link was made a century later by R. D. Alexander (1987). Alexander suggested that the evolution of morality, achieved through religion, was essential for the solidarity necessary to protect against man's greatest natural enemy: other human groups. Inter-group competition is believed to have been a potent selective force in human evolutionary history, with significant male death rates arising from war (Bowles 2006; Chagnon 1988; Guilaine & Zammit, 2004; Keeley 1996; LeBlanc & Register 2003; Wrangham & Peterson 1996). A cross-cultural study by Roes and Raymond (2003), corroborating Alexander's theory, found that "moralizing" gods are associated with larger societies, implying that societies only attain a large size if they are bound together by a religiously inspired morality, reducing internal conflict and promoting group cooperation in the face of external enemies. Interestingly, the *Encyclopedia of Religion and War*, having reviewed the role of religion in war across a diverse range of societies, religions and historical periods, comes to an almost identical conclusion: the two purposes of religiously sanctioned conflict which stand out are: (1) external war with out-groups; and (2) the preservation of internal in-group order (Palmer-Fernandez 2004).

Across the world, religion is increasing in vitality, numbers of adherents, and influence on politics (Huntington 1997; Shah & Toft 2006). By virtue of globalization, we are faced with the prospect of expanding religious groups coming into ever closer contact and competition with each other over fundamental values and global ambitions. It is therefore more important than ever to understand the connections between religion and conflict.

The Adaptive Logic of Religious Conflict

What features of religion might make it effective for war fighting? Table I lists some basic characteristics that are desirable in soldiers but are hard to attain—indeed, they often violate social norms or individual genetic interest. They therefore pose special adaptive problems. Some of religion's solutions to these problems are listed in Table 1 and just two examples (given space limitations)—ritual and in-group/out-group rhetoric—are explored in detail below.

Ritual

If there is one common phenomenon of war across time and culture, it is an overt and deep connection with ritual. Rituals dominate not only war itself but military organizations in their entirety: initiations, oaths of allegiance, ranks, duty, training, drill, parades, indoctrination, standard operating procedures, combat tactics, memorials to the dead, and offerings to the gods prior to battle or after victory. Military effectiveness has long been attributed to precise, repetitive, and self-sacrificing rituals, which is the core reason for the draconian discipline that dominates both training and the battlefield (Diamond 1998; Hanson 2001; McNeill 1995).

The rituals of war are especially interesting in the light of the "costly signaling theory" of religion, which argues (and demonstrates) that religious rituals are *more* effective at achieving group cooperation than secular rituals (Irons 2001; Sosis 2004). Indeed, Sosis et al. (2007) found that across pre-industrial societies, those that suffered a greater incidence of between-group warfare had significantly more costly rituals, rites, and initiations, apparently as a response to overcome the enormous collective action problem of battle. Other work by Alcorta and Sosis (2005) suggests that human brains are highly sensitive to repetitive or emotionally charged rituals, especially if they occur at an early age. The immersion of young soldiers in military ritual may therefore be especially effective.

Table 1. Some desirable characteristics of warriors, the adaptive problems they pose, and solutions offered by religion.

Desirable Characteristics	Adaptive Problem	Religion's solution
• Strong unit cohesion	Unit cohesion is hard to cultivate but essential to combat effectiveness	• Ritual
• Not afraid of the enemy • Not afraid of danger (though not reckless) • Belief that victory is possible	One of military training's primary problems is how to overcome soldiers' fear in battle	• Faith • Confidence
• Belief that performance will be rewarded • Willing to endure great sacrifice • willing to die if necessary	Soldiers are often willing to fight, but not necessarily for an unlimited time, against great odds, or to die	• Supernatural punishment for cowardice • Supernatural reward for compliance • Martyrdom
• Belief that they are fighting for the forces of good • Belief that they are fighting against the forces of evil	Age old problems of: (1) how to maintain purpose, sacrifice for the group, hatred for the enemy; and (2) how to discourage defection, sympathy for the enemy, and reluctance to kill other human beings	• In-group/out-group rhetoric • Dichotomy of good and evil

In summary, the reason that religious rituals so often underlie the trappings of war in human history may reflect the fact that they are an effective motivator of group cohesion and combat effectiveness (and are better than secular methods). Indeed, we should perhaps be *least* surprised to see religious beliefs and practices associated with war than with other pursuits. This is, after all, one of few collective action problems that may demand the ultimate sacrifice from its participants—death. Religion may have been the best way to overcome this adaptive problem (MacNeill 2004).

In-group out-group rhetoric

The human bias favoring one's in-group and disfavoring out-groups is one of the most firmly established paradigms of social psychology (Fiske, 2002). "Social Identity Theory" builds on a mass of empirical evidence that people rapidly identify with even arbitrarily assigned groups, and systematically overvalue their own group's performance and qualities. Such beliefs appear to be related to group violence. A review of human aggression studies found that "collective violence tends to be linked to explicit beliefs in the superiority of the violent group" (Baumeister & Boden 1998, 115-116). Another study found that nearly all tyrants in modern history, and many of their subjects, held strong beliefs in their own cultural superiority (the Nazis being the most obvious example; Chirot, 1994). Jonathan Mercer called this "the double-edged sword of social identity—in-group identity promotes intergroup discrimination" (Mercer 1995, 245).

Religion is clearly a powerful promoter of in-group/out-group psychology, inspiring or directly claiming the superiority of one's own group over others (Dawkins, 2006). "Religious teaching", according to Matt Ridley, "has almost always emphasized the difference between the in-group and the out-group: us versus them; Israelite and Philistine; Jew and Gentile; saved and damned; believer and heathen; Arian and Athanasian; Catholic and Orthodox; Protestant and Catholic; Hindu and Muslim; Sunni and Shia. Religion teaches its adherents that they are a chosen race and their nearest rivals are benighted fools or even subhumans. There is nothing especially surprising in this, given the origins of most religions as beleaguered cults in tribally divided, violent societies" (Ridley 1996, 91).

In summary, Social Identity Theory and studies of human aggression predict that different groups—perhaps especially religious groups—will tend to isolate themselves from each other, assume that their own group is superior to other groups, derogate other groups' beliefs and qualities and, according to Baumeister & Boden, promote inter-group violence. All this sounds pretty nasty. But when engaged in life or death struggles with rival groups, these may be essential ingredients of survival.

Conclusions

In the light of an adaptive logic to religious conflict, the answers to many puzzling questions have good answers: Why do gods offer protection in battle?—because this is an effective method of overcoming fear. Why do gods promise victory?—because confidence is an essential ingredient of combat effectiveness. Why do so many societies have gods of war?—because war fighting is more effective when it has a religious patron, role model, and psychological ally.

A recent study concluded that wars themselves are not usually religious per se: "armed conflict is rarely, if ever, solely about religion or religious differences" (Austin, Kranock, & Oommen, 2006, 3). Rather, wars tend to *acquire religious overtones* because elites use religion as a tool to boost support, motivate soldiers, and to provide a justification and rationale for conflicts that are essentially political. This phenomenon of elite manipulation may operate: (1) subconsciously, because people naturally tend to do this in situations of crisis (and they can't help it); and/or (2) consciously, because it is very effective (and they know this). Either way, religion certainly seems to offer a powerful weapon in conflict, given that leaders so often appeal to it whenever war looms on the horizon.

Shah and Toft (2006) caution that we cannot pin all the blame on elites: "the marriage of religion with politics is often welcomed, if not demanded, by people around the world". The reason wars acquire religious overtones, they argue, is because it is especially salient to people. It works precisely because you *do not* have to ram it down people's throats. The disposition to religious beliefs and ideals in human nature is therefore a key part of the success of this strategy (MacNeill 2004). Human brains, especially in wartime, offer fertile ground for religious rationalizations and inspiration.

The importance of inter-group conflict in human evolutionary history suggests a role for the differential selection of groups, as Darwin originally proposed. Ironically, group-selection is often seen to champion the idea that human nature is altruistic, but the "dark side" of group-selection is that within-group cooperation may promote (and reflect) between-group competition, raising the specter of war as both a mechanism and outcome of natural selection (Bowles 2006). Lawrence Keeley noted that "warfare is ultimately not a denial of the human capacity for social cooperation, but merely the most destructive expression of it" (Keeley 1996, 158). Indeed, group-selection implies that if we are selected to cooperate with our in-group, then we must also be selected *not* to cooperate with out-group members (Hagen & Hammerstein 2006; Sosis 2003). Compared with the apparent selfishness of individual selection, threfore, group-selection may be even worse. As Matt Ridley put it: "Preferring the morality of group selection to the ruthlessness of individual struggle is to prefer genocide to murder ... the more cooperative societies are, the more violent the battles between them" (Ridley 1996, 193).

Three main conclusions can be drawn from the literature on religion and war: (1) conflict often *appears* to be about religion, but in reality arises from underlying political causes; (2) leaders nevertheless commonly *exploit* religion to drum up support for war; and (3) whether leaders use religion as a tool of manipulation or not, religion becomes a powerful *motivating force* (for soldiers, citizens, societies, and elites alike). Thus, wars may only sometimes initially be "about" religion, but they rarely proceed without its heavy influence.

If wars must be fought, as they were in the ruthless Darwinian struggle for survival in human history and pre-history, then an important question becomes what makes some humans better at war than their competitors? Religion turns out to have many properties that make it an excellent adaptation for war. Perhaps this is an accident. Alternatively, perhaps it is so effective because it was designed for exactly this purpose.

References

Alcorta, C. S., & Sosis, R. 2005. Ritual, emotion, and sacred symbols: The evolution of religion as an adaptive complex. *Human Nature, 16*, 323-359.

Alexander, R. D. 1987. *The biology of moral systems*. Aldine, NY: Hawthorne.

Austin, G., Kranock, T., & Oommen, T. 2006. *God and war: An audit and an exploration*. Bradford, UK: Department of Peace Studies, University of Bradford.

Baumeister, R. F., & Boden, J. M. 1998. Aggression and the self: High self-esteem, low selfcontrol, and ego threat. In R. G. Green & E. Donnerstein, Eds., *Human aggression: Theories, research, and implications for social policy*, 111-137. San Diego, CA: Academic Press.

Bowles, S. 2006. Group competition, reproductive leveling, and the evolution of human altruism. *Science, 314*, 1569-1572.

Chagnon, N. A. 1988. Life histories, blood revenge, and warfare in a tribal population. *Science, 239*, 985-992.

Chirot, D. 1994. *Modern tyrants: The power and prevalence of evil in our age*. New York, NY: Free Press.

Darwin, C. 1871. *The descent of man*. New York, NY: Penguin Classics.

Dawkins, R. 2006. *The God delusion*. New York, NY: Houghton Mifflin Company.

Diamond, J. 1998. *Guns, germs and steel*. London, UK: Vintage.

Fiske, S. T. 2002. What we know about bias and intergroup conflict, problem of the century. *Current Directions in Psychological Science, 11*, 123-128.

Gibbon, E. 1776-1778. *The history of the decline and fall of the Roman empire*. New York, NY: Modern Library.

Guilaine, J., & Zammit, J. 2004. *The origins of war: Violence in prehistory*: Oxford, UK: Blackwell Publishing.

Hagen, E. H., & Hammerstein, P. 2006. Game theory and human evolution: A critique of some recent interpretations of experimental games. *Theoretical Population Biology, 69*, 339-348.

Hanson, V. D. 2001. *Carnage and culture: Landmark battles in the rise of western power*. New York, NY: Anchor Books.

Huntington, S. P. 1997. *The clash of civilizations and the remaking of world order*. New York, NY: Touchstone.

Irons, W. 2001. Religion as a hard-to-fake sign of commitment. In R. Nesse, Ed., *Evolution and the capacity for commitment*, 292-309. New York, NY: Russell Sage Foundation.

Hanson, V. D. 2001. *Carnage and culture: Landmark battles in the rise of western power*. New York, NY: Anchor.

LeBlanc, S., & Register, K. E. 2003. *Constant battles: The myth of the peaceful, noble savage*. New York, NY: St. Martin's Press.

McNeill, A. 2004. The capacity for religious experience is an evolutionary adaptation to warfare. *Evolution and Cognition, 10*, 43-60.

McNeill, W. H. 1995. *Keeping together in time: Dance and drill in human history*. Cambridge, MA: Harvard University Press.

Mercer, J. 1995. Anarchy and identity. *International Organization, 49*, 229-252.

Palmer-Fernandez, G., Ed. 2004. *Encyclopedia of religion and war*. New York, NY: Routledge.

Ridley, M. 1996. *The origins of virtue: Human instincts and the origins of cooperation*. London, UK: Penguin.

Roes, F. L., & Raymond, M. 2003. Belief in moralizing gods. *Evolution& Human Behavior, 24*, 126-135.

Shah, T. S., & Toft, M. D. 2006. Why God is winning. *Foreign Policy, July/August*, 39-43.

Sosis, R. 2003. Why aren't we all Hutterites? Costly signaling theory and religious behavior. *Human Nature, 14*, 91-127.

Sosis, R. 2004. The adaptive value of religious ritual. *American Scientist, 92*, 166-172.

Sosis, R., Kress, H., & Boster, J. 2007. Scars for war: Evaluating alternative signaling explanations for cross-cultural variance in ritual costs. *Evolution & Human Behavior, 28*, 234-247.

Wrangham, R., & Peterson, D. 1996. *Demonic males: Apes and the origins of human violence*. London, UK: Bloomsbury.

One Species under God?

Sorting through the Pieces of Religion and Cooperation

Azim F. Shariff

In studying the evolution of religion, one misstep to avoid is treating "religion" as a seamless whole. Religions are complex. More than that, they are complexes, stitched together from many elements that have evolved at different times for different reasons. Some aspects of religion may be, or may have been, individually or culturally adaptive, whereas others may be more analogous to viruses. Asking whether religion, as a whole, is adaptive is a misleading question. For an answer complex enough to do justice to the packages of memes[1] called religions, one needs to look under the hood.

Memes within a meme

In an attempt at unpacking religion into its composite parts, I will outline three classes of memes which prove useful in understanding the evolution of religion. These are *foundation memes, social utility memes* and *scaffolding memes*. Following their brief description, I will use the example of how the fear of supernatural policing agents encourages cooperative behavior to demonstrate how these classes of memes interact and how understanding them can add to discussions in the area.

Foundation memes are aspects of religion that follow directly from the structure of the human mind. Our biologically evolved brains lead us to these inventions, making them exceedingly likely, almost inevitable (Atran & Norenzayan 2004) have called this *canalization*). Two examples that I explore below are belief in life after death and the tendency to imbue agency to natural phenomena. Though technically cultural ideas, these memes are expected to emerge quite naturally for all people in all cultures. Most importantly, foundation memes provide the canvas material upon which the more elaborate aspects of religion are drawn.

1 The concept of memes has been used extensively as a cultural analog to genes, but has also attracted much criticism (e.g., Atran & Norenzayan 2004). There is no consensus on what exactly fits the criteria of a meme, therefore it is unclear where one meme ends and another begins, or even at what level of analysis do memes exist. Is religion a meme? Is Islam? Is praying five times a day? Is each prayer? The imprecision of the definition leaves considerable freedom in its usage. As a consequence, the concept of meme can be useful as a low resolution word for a unit—any unit—of cultural information. At least for this essay, this soft definition suits my purposes.

Social utility memes are aspects of religions that serve an adaptive purpose to social living. Ultimately resulting in benefits to the viability of societies, these types of memes are most likely the product of random cultural group selection. Groups that stumbled upon these memes had selection advantages over groups that did not. Food taboos and hygiene rituals that have become codified into religious frameworks may qualify as social utility memes, as would the fear of omniscient, punishing supernatural agents.

The effectiveness of these social utility memes, however, depends upon the level of religious observance. Universal participation is best, with effectiveness falling steeply as noncompliance increases. Therefore, to preserve the utility, belief would need to be preserved as well. *Scaffolding memes* are those whose primary function is to keep afloat the religious package that hosts them. Developments that incentivized piety and disincentivized doubt (and doubters) would have supported the effectiveness of any social utility meme that relied on religious conformity. These memes are any that are primarily devoted to ensuring the 'stickiness' of the collection of memes that made up a religion.

The evolution of punishing supernatural agents: An example.

Foundation Memes

Guthrie (1993) has argued that humans have naturally evolved hyper-active-agency detection devices that liberally interpret natural phenomena as being authored by agents. As a direct consequence, humans developed a tendency to ascribe anthropomorphic characteristics to these phenomena, turning them, in the absence of any countering evidence, into supernatural agents. This is an example of a foundation meme; one would not say that humans had a biological, modular adaptation for imagining supernatural agents, but adaptations that do exist make such cognition extremely likely.

Another edifying example is the belief in a life after death. Conceptions of a life beyond death seem to come quite readily to the human mind, and are certainly easier both to grasp and to swallow than the reality of death's finitude. Bering (2006) has suggested that imbuing the time after death with living-like characteristics is a consequence of the cognitive constraints of the mind's ability to represent a complete and interminable unconsciousness. Unable to conceive of 'what it's like' to be dead, people work with what they know. Again, though belief in an afterlife is not, itself, a biological adaptation, our minds come heavily inclined to create one. Human biology has pulled out the chair for such beliefs.

The products of foundation memes, like supernatural agents and conceptions of a life after death, are the starting points of religion. The elaboration of these concepts turned otherwise personal beliefs into communal religions. Certain variations would have proved more conducive to replication. For instance, Morewedge (2007) has demonstrated what he calls a negative agency bias—a tendency to attribute negative events to external agents more so than neutral or good events. As a consequence of this mental bias, bad fortune would have been more intuitively attributed to supernatural agents than good, and cultural conceptions of a punishing supernatural agent would have been a more easily formed and apprehended meme.

Social Utility Memes

Other elaborations would have been spread not only because of their conduciveness to the structure of the human mind, but because of the utility that they offered. For example, many have speculated that certain aspects of religion evolved due to the benefits they provided to social cohesion. If elements of religion increased cooperative behaviour—especially that between unrelated strangers—this would have minimized defection among large groups of people, thereby allowing the massive population densities that have emerged in the last ten thousand years.

A recent spate of empirical evidence supports this hypothesis. Sosis and Bressler (2003) have shown that religious communes historically lasted longer than their secular counterparts. Sosis and Ruffle (2003) found members of religious, rather than secular, Israeli kibbutzim to exhibit more cooperation in cooperative-pool economic games. Shariff and Norenzayan (2007) showed that participants exposed to even implicit cues of religion behave more pro-socially towards anonymous strangers than did control participants.

While Sosis suggests that these cooperative effects derive from the costly signaling involved in religious rituals, Shariff and Norenzayan credit these effects to the imagined presence of supernatural policing agents. These two explanations are by no means mutually incompatible. However, I will maintain current focus on the punishing supernatural watcher.

Humans have evolved to be hyper-vigilant towards their reputations. With the emergence of indirect reciprocity as a viable support for cooperation, one's reputation became of critical concern. Defection—still a reality — was hidden in deception and anonymity. Reputations could be maintained, and costs of social distrust avoided, so long as one avoided 'being caught'. Hidden defection was still a viable option for the individual, and therefore still compromised the stability of the group.

The development of all-seeing, supernatural policing agents circumvented these problems, allowing wider and more complete cooperation. The fear of supernatural agents not only extended one's vulnerability to 'being caught' to everywhere visible by omniscient beings, but raised the price of being caught to that of divine punishment, either in this life or the next.

Punishment, it should be noted, is more powerful than reward for these ends (Johnson & Bering 2006). A large body of research demonstrates the utility of the stick over that of the carrot, at least with regards to promoting cooperation. Therefore, a meme that exploited people's fear of divine punishment, rather than their want of divine reward, would be the more effective.[2] In support of this hypothesis, Shariff and Norenzayan (2007) found that the same implicit religious cues that increased prosocial behavior aroused feelings of guilt, but not empathy, charity or positive affect. Taking into account Morewedge's negative agency bias, these findings suggest that punishing agents emerged as both an intuitive and useful meme.

Though the means might exploit negative emotions, the benefits of a cooperative society are manifold and palpable for its members. The difficulty is achieving such cooperation when it is within everyone's short-termed interests to defect. If the belief in supernatural watchers successfully curbed these selfish behaviors in most people, most of the time, then groups that had stumbled upon this belief would have enjoyed a level of cooperation beyond those without comparable beliefs. Groups with more internal cohesion, and thus larger potential populations, would have had comparative survival advantages leading to cultural selection for these groups and the memes they hosted.

Like with any selection process, cultural group selection does not demand that individuals understand or are even aware of the adaptive qualities of their cultural traditions. A moral tradition which fostered cooperation would remain and flourish among cultures because it *worked*, regardless of whether or not its adherents sought or even recognized these benefits. Hayek captured this well:

> [Cultural] group selection thus does not primarily choose what the individuals recognize as serving their own ends, or what they desire. It will elect customs whose beneficial assistance to the survival of men are not perceived by individuals. The group thereby becomes dependent for the very survival of its increased numbers on the observance by its members of practices which they cannot rationally justify, and which may conflict with both their innate instincts on the one hand, and their intellectual insight on the other. (Hayek 1984, 324)

Religious fear and guilt may have thereby promoted a sense of harmony better than any attempt at an intelligently designed moral system has managed, either before or since. Precisely by bypassing rational thinking, memes regarding omniscient, punishing supernatural agents fomented religion's initial social utility.

---

2 Using this logic, Heaven and Hell could be seen, not as flipsides of the same memetic coin, but as independent memes serving independent functions. Heaven might be better conceived as a comforting 'perk' of belief, with Hell serving the more utilitarian function of ensuring cooperation through fear of punishment.

Scaffolding memes

Certainly the irony will not be lost to those currently decrying the divisive, intolerant, and violent aspects that are associated with today's sectarian strife. More than irony, however, there may be explanation.

If people are driven to moral behavior because they fear the punishment of omniscient supernatural agents, they can assume that those who fear these same gods will face the same fears and be concerned with the same transgressions. That is, people with the same beliefs can be both predictable and trustworthy. People with different beliefs, or worse, *no* beliefs become highly suspect.

The success of most social utility memes depends on the ubiquity of belief. Scaffolding memes that ensure these beliefs also ensure that noncompliance and defection are kept to a tolerable minimum. The dogmatic elements of religion – resistance to alternate explanations for the way the world works, the indoctrination of the young, and the severe punishments for doubt - are all examples of scaffolding memes that serve to maintain the functioning of religions. So too are the attempts to minimize social interaction with those who hold different beliefs. Without the assurance that these people will cooperate, they should be treated with wariness, converted, ostracized, or worse.

This distrust of atheists and members of other religions is evident in both scripture and attitude polls. The Bible shows little love for pagans. Though the Qur'an demonstrates a notable tolerance for other People of the Book (Jews and Christians, who, after all, fear the same God as Muslims), idolaters face hellfire.

Ancient scripture is corroborated by modern surveys. Using a 10-nation poll of over 10,000 people and representing all the major world religions, Hansen and Norenzayan (in prep) found that people believing that their god was the only god were considerably more likely to blame members of other religions for the world's problems than those who believed in a god, but made no claims to exclusivity.

In a 2003 poll of over 2,000 Americans, 33.5% of the representative, predominantly Christian sample, said they would disapprove if their child wanted to marry a Muslim—a "standard measure of group prejudice" (Edgell, Gerteis, & Hartmann 2006, 217). In accordance with the theory presented here, the number was even higher—47.6%—for an atheist. In open-ended interview responses reproduced by the authors, most mention a connection between atheists and immoral behavior. The following response is typical of this long-held association:

> ...prisons aren't filled with conservative Republican Christians. The prisons are probably filled with people who don't have any kind of a spir-

ritual or religious core. So I don't have to worry about...a conservative Christian, you know, committing a crime against me, chances are. (228)

Conclusion

Some, though not all, aspects of religions may have, and may continue to serve socially beneficial ends. Social utility memes may have found ways to encourage prosocial behavior that individual reason could not, then or now. However, some, though not all, aspects of religion may serve ends that from the perspective of both the individual and group may be counterproductive. The existence of scaffolding memes brings with it the danger that religions may be sustained in absence of, or even when at odds with, adaptive ends. Although these aspects become tethered together in a collective, they evolved at different times for different reasons. Keeping these differences in mind will result in a nuanced and appropriately complex understanding of where religion came from. God, after all, is in the details.

References

Atran, S., & Norenzayan, A. 2004. Religion's evolutionary landscape: Counterintuition, commitment, compassion, communion. *Behavioral & Brain Sciences, 27*, 713-770.

Bering, J. M. 2006. The folk psychology of souls. *Behavioral & Brain Sciences, 29*, 453-498.

Edgell, P., Gerteis J., & Hartmann, D. 2006. Atheists as 'other': Moral boundaries and cultural membership in American society. *American Sociological Review, 71* (2), 211-239.

Guthrie, S. G. 1993. *Faces in the clouds: A new theory of religion*. Oxford, UK: University Press.

Hansen, I., & Norenzayan, A. in preparation. Does religious belief promote religious scapegoating? University of British Columbia.

Hayek, F. A. 1984. The origin and effect of our morals: A problem for science. In C. Nishiyama & K. R. Leube, Eds., *The essence of Hayek*, 318-330. Stanford, CA: Hoover Institution Press.

Johnson, D. D. P., & Bering, J. M. 2006. Hand of God, mind of man: Punishment and cognition in the evolution of cooperation. *Evolutionary Psychology, 4*, 219-233.

Morewedge, C. K. 2007. Negativity bias in attributions of external agency. Manuscript under revision, Princeton University.

Shariff, A. F., & Norenzayan, A. 2007. God is watching you: Supernatural agent concepts increase prosocial behavior in an anonymous economic game. *Psychological Science, 18*, 803-809.

Sosis, R., & Bressler, E. 2003. Cooperation and commune longevity: A test of the costly signaling theory of religion. *Cross-Cultural Research*, *37*, 211-239.
Sosis, R., & Ruffle, B. J. 2003. Religious ritual and cooperation: Testing for a relationship on Israeli religious and secular kibbutzim. *Current Anthropology*, *44*, 713-722.

Religion, Status, and Leadership in Neolithic Avebury

An Example of the Cauvin-Stark Religion Drives Innovation Hypothesis?

Paul K. Wason

The small village of Avebury is located in Wiltshire in Southwest England. It is also located almost entirely within the world's largest stone circle. If you visit you might enjoy the small museum of excavation finds. And a nearby shop offers all the crystals, dowsing rods and creative theories you will ever need to conduct your own explorations.

But except for the occasional crop circle or neo-Pagan ritual, what is most interesting is the magnificent complex of Neolithic monuments (Malone 1989; Pitts 1994; Ucko, Hunter, Clark, & David 1991; Wason 2002; Wason & Baldia 2000). These were built in at least two phases—a causewayed enclosure (Windmill Hill) and the West Kennett Long Barrow somewhere around 3,300–3,000BC, and an extraordinary burst of construction over a portion of the period roughly around 2,800–2,200 BC (Pollard 2005; but the dating is somewhat complicated and uncertain, Pitts & Whittle 1992).

Long barrows, including West Kennett, were not just for burial. West Kennett is a low, solid dirt mound with one section consisting of a roofed stone chamber closed off by another large stone. It was re-opened periodically over a 1,000 year period for ceremonies involving mind-altering substances. Very few people were inside the chamber for these ceremonies, but it is likely that more gathered outside. The people of this time experienced a small degree of social inequality. Ceremonies were conducted by a religious specialist (a leader of sorts). Also, only a small portion of the population was buried there which also indicates a distinction from the rest who weren't.

But things changed. The henge, circle, avenues, and Silbury Hill are probably also religious structures. They suggest a very different religion which engaged ceremonies that were highly visible and that could potentially involve everyone who lived for miles around all at once.

The nature of status relations and leadership also changed dramatically at this time and again over the following centuries. The very fact of these constructions is evidence for some degree of inequality and centralized leadership for which there was no evidence at the time of the barrows.

Colin Renfrew (1973) estimated that digging the ditch and other work on the henge required some 1.5 million hours of labor. Silbury Hill, the largest artificial mound in Europe, required some 18 million hours of labor for its three building phases over perhaps 200 to 300 years. The inference of status and leadership from monumental architecture is a well-rehearsed line of argument (Abrams 1989; Wason 1994). Here I offer a more impressionistic suggestion appropriate to the setting of the conference—how these figures compare with traditional Hawaiian temple building.

Traditional Hawaiian society was very hierarchical. It consisted of several 'layers' of chiefs and sub-chiefs. This very sophisticated society is also well known for the monumental building they undertook. Kolb (1994) has worked out labor calculations for the temples of East and West Maui. The largest temple in all of Hawaii, *Pi'ilanihale*, required some 130,000 labor days. Renfrew's (1973) labor estimate for the Avebury henge translates to at least 150,000 days (figuring 10 hour days) and probably more like 200,000 to 300,000. Either way it is more than the labor needed for the largest temple the powerful leaders of the complex Hawaiian society ever managed to pull off.

Kolb's (1994) calculations for all temples for all phases of the 600-year period he studied was just under 275,000 labor days. Renfrew's calculations for Silbury Hill translate into at least 1,800,000 but probably more like 2.5 million labor days. This is between six and ten times the labor for all building phases for all the temples on East and West Maui together, and likely over a period of between one-third and one-half the time. On average (and we don't know in either case how work was conducted), this means twenty to thirty times as many laborers at any one time.

It becomes hard to imagine that the people of Neolithic Wiltshire would do this without some inspiring leadership. Conversely, it is hard to imagine a leadership system capable of engaging so much effort without leaving any other trace of hierarchy. This probably means that the people themselves had a great heart for the work.

Proposals

I propose that it was a religious change that precipitated the transition from the age of the barrows to the age of the henge, and that this change brought forth new forms of social organization, including both central leadership and status hierarchy. Barrett (1994) suggested what I consider a crucial point: leadership developed as a result of the massive building work. And I believe that religion was the primary causal factor, not an after-the-fact justification for the status quo, as is assumed so often in archaeological models of culture change.

I propose as well that this is significant, both for an understanding of what religion is and does and for our understanding of cultural dynamics. It may even be relevant for how we assess the world around us today.

Proposal 1

There are four basic points that must be demonstrated in order to establish the first proposition:

1. *That these are in fact religious constructions.* To my knowledge the assumption that these works—from the long barrow to the henge, circle, avenues, and Silbury Hill—were created for essentially religious ends has never been seriously questioned. In writing this I realized, with a little irony, that it was hard to defend this point in part because no-one has ever challenged it. But archaeologists have for too long left consideration of what these structures were for to the more eccentric enthusiasts. This is worth another look.

2. *We will need to demonstrate my assumption that both status inequality and centralized leadership were limited prior to the building of the henge and grew stronger afterwards.* I believe this to be well documented, though mainly in a negative sense. These large monuments themselves constitute the only evidence for leadership or hierarchy at this time. There is no evidence from burials, none from residential architecture, artifacts, wealth distribution. There is no other evidence of inequality. Actually, there is not much evidence of settlement of any kind—the people may have been mobile agriculturalists who had not (yet) created permanent settlements. An argument like this risks claiming an absence of evidence as evidence of absence, but there is some corollary positive evidence in that this contrasts dramatically with the following Early Bronze Age, when individual burials in small round mounds show a clear hierarchy and differential wealth.

3. *It is also important to establish that the core change really was religious rather than political, economic, climactic, or something else.* Of course these are not exclusive categories. It seems to me very unlikely that people in the Neolithic would classify some public activities as political, some as economic, some as religious, whatever these might have meant before the advent of modern social science. But point number three is not trivial because there have been counter ideas. Archaeologists have sometimes proposed that the burst of stone-circle building throughout the British Isles was due to migration or even invasion of new people from the continent. This would still mean instantiation of a new religious-ritual complex but through a political cause, not an "internal" change in cosmology or other elements of religion. I do not know that any archaeologist seriously holds these ideas. But we do sometimes abandon ideas as much because some prominent member of the

tribe disparages them as because they were really proved wrong. I worry that there is no more real empirical or logical reason for abandoning diffusionist theories in archaeology than for abandoning group selection in biology. Still, some cultural continuity suggests local development rather than invasion, though of course the idea of building stone circles surely was not first invented in Avebury.

4. *And finally, it must be demonstrated that the correlations I have illustrated represent a causal sequence.* Demonstrating causation in archaeology is not easy. Like most such work I rely heavily on temporal sequence—that is, leadership and hierarchy appear to be very minimal before these construction projects and to have developed during and then further developed after the period of the construction.

Proposal 2

But, so what? My second proposal is that this is significant. First it is significant for scholars trying to work out the dynamics of life in Neolithic Britain, for it would tell us not just what happened when, but also offer a glimpse of motivations and causation. But, more relevant to the present volume, I also believe there are wider implications. If we are to understand religion as fully as possible, we might ask not just how religion changes but what role it plays in wider cultural evolution. What has religion contributed to the course of human history?

We needn't pretend that Avebury was the center of world history. In any case, seriously centralized leadership and social inequality had developed in several other parts of the world well before this time. But Avebury is a significant ceremonial complex in its context, and the possibility that a change in cosmology and ceremony could have greatly influenced the course of culture change here is worth thinking about as a way of refining our views of what religion is or does.

There seems to be a tradition in archaeology of underestimating the social significance of religion, as distinct from its individual personal significance (Wason & Baldia 2000). But there are exceptions. David Sloan Wilson is working to counter the individualistic emphasis, not least by reminding us of the value of Durkheim's definition of religion (Wilson 2002). Rodney Stark (2003) is doing the same with his recent trilogy about the effects of the rise of monotheism—positive and negative. And the late Jacques Cauvin's (2000) argument that religious change led to the origins of agriculture may be most important of all for our purposes.

It seems almost trivial to suggest that religion is important. But we have apparently found it hard to take this seriously when it comes to archaeological theory building. Several scholars have surveyed archaeological theories of culture change and the rise of complex society, and of those I have seen, not one made use of religion as a causal variable (Earle 1997; Hayden & Gargett 1990; Wason & Baldia 2000).

In his 1960 book on Stonehenge, Atkinson (who conducted prominent excavations both at Stonehenge and Silbury Hill) concluded that "the building of Stonehenge is...unlikely to have been the expression of the common will but rather the fulfillment of a purpose imposed from above" (166). This has been a typical view of Avebury as well. But it may be a false dichotomy. It was not basically a power play or a political venture. It took leadership "from above" but the leaders may have primarily mobilized people to build something that was an expression of the common will (and religious in motivation).

Summary

My case for Avebury, along with Cauvin's for the Near East, reinforce the importance of studying religion not just as a phenomenon of the mind but as a social and cultural phenomenon. It is a group or community affair, not just a matter for private individuals.

It also suggests that crusading ideologues who believe they can eliminate religion from our universities, from politics, and from international affairs may wish to revisit their assumption that religious people will be content to pray behind closed curtains and live the rest of their lives as though the most fundamental elements of their view of reality don't matter after all.

Finally, one widespread popular belief about religion is that it is largely explainable as an artifact of a given culture. This old Frazerian theme re-surfaced in a recent conversation with one prominent anthropologist who told me that religion is just the pawn of other elements of culture. Remember, he said, how religions systematically correlate with subsistence systems. By showing that anthropomorphic gods preceded the origins of agriculture, Cauvin in effect suggests that it was this new religious conception and the consequent changes in how humans understood themselves that made agriculture possible. It might be as fair to say that subsistence systems – and patterns of leadership, hierarchy and corporate building activity—follow from religion as to say religions follow from these. They still correlate (as well as they ever did). I propose that we re-think why that is.

References

Abrams, E. M. 1989. Architecture and energy: An evolutionary perspective. In M. B. Schiffer, Ed., *Archaeological method and theory*, Vol. 1, 47-87. Tucson, AZ: University of Arizona Press.

Atkinson, R. J. C. 1960. *Stonehenge*. London, UK: Penguin.

Barrett, J. 1994. *Fragments from antiquity*. Oxford, UK: Blackwell Publishers.

Cauvin, J. 2000. *The birth of the gods and the origins of agriculture* T. Watkins, Trans.. Cambridge, UK: Cambridge University Press. Original work published 1994.
Earle, T. 1997. *How chiefs come to power: The political economy in prehistory.* Stanford, CA: Stanford University Press.
Hayden, B., & Gargett, R. 1990. Big man, big heart?: A Mesoamerican view of the emergence of complex society. *Ancient Mesoamerica, 1,* 3-20.
Kolb, M. J. 1994. Monumentality and the rise of religious authority in precontact Hawai'i. *Current Anthropology, 35,* 521-547.
Malone, C. 1989. *Avebury*. London, UK: English Heritage.
Pitts, M. 1994. *Avebury and Stonehenge*. Avebury, UK: Stones Press.
Pitts, M., & Whittle, A. 1992. The development and date of Avebury. *Proceedings of the Prehistoric Society, 58,* 203-212.
Pollard, J. 2005. Memory, monuments and middens in the Neolithic landscape. In G. Brown, D. Field, & D. McOmish, Eds., *The Avebury landscape: Aspects of the field archaeology of the Marlborough Downs,* 103-114. Oxford, UK: Oxbow Books.
Renfrew, C. 1973. Monuments, mobilization and social organization in Neolithic Wessex. In C. Renfrew, Ed., *The explanation of culture,* 539-558. Pittsburgh, PA: University of Pittsburgh Press.
Stark, R. 2003. *For the glory of God: How Monotheism led to reformations, science, witch-hunts, and the end of slavery*. Princeton, NJ: Princeton University Press.
Ucko, P. J., Hunter, M., Clark, A. J., & David, A. 1991. *Avebury reconsidered.* London, UK: Unwin Hyman.
Wason, P. K. 1994. *The archaeology of rank*. Cambridge, UK: Cambridge University Press.
Wason, P. K. 2002. *Messages from the monuments: How Neolithic monuments communicate about religion and status*. Retrieved February 27, 2007 from <http://www.knowth.com/neolithic~religion~Status. htm>.
Wason, P. K., & Baldia, M. A. 2000. Religion, communication, and the genesis of social complexity in the European Neolithic. In N. N. Kradin, A. V. Korotayev, D. M. Bondarenko, V. de Munck, & P. K. Wason, Eds., *Alternatives of social evolution,* 138-148. Vladivostok, Russia: Russian Academy of Sciences.
Wilson, D. S. 2002. *Darwin's cathedral: Evolution, religion and the nature of society*. Chicago, IL: University of Chicago Press.

Evolution and Spiritual Capital

Barnaby Marsh

A central tenet of evolutionary biology is that actions that have the best fitness consequences are selected for. For this to happen, individuals need to make choices in uncertain environments where fitness consequences are often determined by chance. Evolution has shaped plants and animals to be sensitive to variation and change in the environment, particularly in dimensions that are most closely related to survival.

Making the best "choice" is to some extent dependent on how well cues from the environment are used to make inferences and accurate predictions; this often extends beyond merely reacting to and learning from past experiences. In many cases, extrapolations will be made on the basis of such experiences, but will extend into domain space that is novel. Making the best choice also depends on the strategic deployment of an individual's various resources that can be drawn upon, or "capital".

Kinds of Capital:

"Capital" can take many different forms (see Table 1). In competitive contexts as diverse as playing a ball game, fighting a war, or building a competitive business, a lot more than financial and physical capital is needed to secure competitive advantage. In any of these instances, competitors need know how to use appropriate social relationships (social capital); skills (human capital), and belief/vision (spiritual capital).

Table 1: Kinds of Capital:

Type of Capital	Advantage-granting substance	Sample Reference
Cultural	Customs, ways of doing things	Bourdieu 1986
Human	Education, skills	Becker 1964
Social	Social Connections	Coleman 1988
Financial	Money	Smith 1776
Physical	Buildings, machines, equipment	Marx 1867
Spiritual	Inspiration, motivation, beliefs	Weber 1905

As Adam Smith argued, all capital essentially represents *potential.* There can be no strong claims made for the intrinsic value of *any* form of capital, since value always *depends* on contextual situation and how the specific form of capital is deployed. However, it is generally easy to find examples where the deployment of specific forms of capital lead to competitive advantage. In terms of competitive success, spiritual capital is as important as other forms of capital in building advantage and securing victory; sometimes, it is decisive.

Why is 'spiritual capital" so important?

Spiritual capital is related to how the individual subjectively understands, or "sees" the world. One way of conceptualizing this process is to imagine two worlds that interact with each other—a world that exists as represented in the mind of the agent, and a world outside and independent of the mind of the agent (Figure 1).

Figure 1:

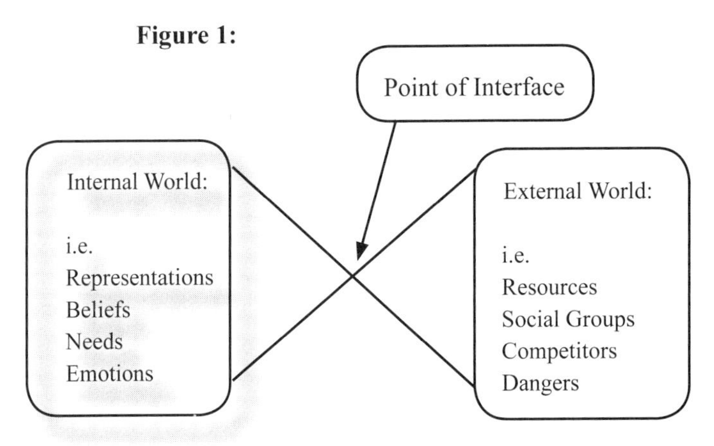

How the world evolves and is represented "inside" the mind of the agent is just as important as the "real" external structure of the environment. It is known that beliefs and outlooks can determine competitive advantage individually and socially across a wide spectrum of competitive activities (for overviews see Covey, Merrill, & Merrill 1994; Waitley 1979; Wind, Crook, & Gunther 2005). Individuals who hold certain beliefs may be more inclined to take risks, to encounter danger and trouble, and accordingly, to gain new information from new or high-opportunity, high risk environments, for instance. Further, individual outlooks and strategies will not necessarily converge as a result of ecological pressures and risk/reward optimization. Since the choices of individuals (and groups) are influenced by experience, future evaluations and choices may be path-dependent. Individuals or groups with different world outlooks or styles of information interpretation may continue to navigate within different perceptual worlds, since the subjective "internal" landscape of possibility, opportunity, and danger (including experience and ability to recover) will differ. Ways of viewing the world thus have real fitness consequences.

The power of one: How belief systems can arise via heroic examples:

At both the group and societal levels, spiritual capital is often closely linked the power of ideas and ideals. These typically originate from sources that are wholly intangible, but which nonetheless may be related to real needs, wants, and desires, both social and material. These wants and desires themselves may be socially constructed, thus rooted in time and place, in culture, and in the construction of new forms of social identity. Ideas and ideals find resonance in the context of hope, desires, and expectations of individuals. Many popular ideas or ideals begin with an example set by an especially passionate, driven individual or individuals. When these individuals succeed, they can serve as an example and inspiration for others.

One of the most commonly cited examples of the importance of appropriate role models can be found in studies of disadvantaged social groups. In this narrative, qualities of the role model become centrally important in terms of the possibilities of personal aspiration and social identity. Returning to the topic of spiritual capital, ideals and related social pressure may result in a focus on individuals who hold attributes that are seen to align with success as it is socially defined, and this can be self-perpetuating. For example, a population where people believe in upward mobility through hard work and persistence may come to have more entrepreneurial dynamism than a population where there are few prospects for upward mobility and where there is a prevailing sentiment of hopelessness and despair. Taking this one step further, to the aggregate societal level, the belief in something as simple as everyone having a fair chance of success can make an essential part of the difference between general depression and prosperity. In this case, believing in the possibility of success itself is a form of spiritual capital.

Aggregated beliefs can transform the nature of reality:

Advanced modern economies function as they do to a large extent because of collectively held outlooks and beliefs. One common example is the widespread belief in the value of fiat currencies. People use currencies because they represent an abstract store of value that is widely recognized and accepted. Currencies have value largely because people believe that they have value. Such beliefs thus create new kinds of reality for as long as people have confidence in them. However, the reality may vanish when the ideal or belief that grants them their validity is undermined. Examples of such breakdowns can be seen through history, especially in the context of perceived strength of government/political power, currency, and economic credit. Examples such as the Dutch tulip mania, the publicly traded shares of experimental "virtual companies" of the late 1990s, or today's art auctions illustrate how individuals can put tremendous trust in the value of a symbolic object simply because a few others share that same trust in current and future value.

Simple ideas or ideals by themselves are powerful enough to create new social, political, and economic realities. One only needs to consider ideologies of political orientation such as democracy, communism, or national socialism to see how an idea or an ideal can transform the structure of society and the behavior of agents within the society. These dynamics are sometimes attributed to the direct pursuit of economic or class interests, but there are plentiful examples of potent and popular ideas, ideals, and outlooks that persist even in the absence of direct economic incentive. One example would be religious beliefs, where examples of robustness and tenacity can be found despite great financial, cultural, and biological costs imposed by carrying these beliefs. Many observers (including the great German sociologist Max Weber) have been interested in why this is so, and whether certain kinds of worldly benefits might be in fact accruing as a result of holding such beliefs.

In the context of religious beliefs, it is important to go back to the model of representation and how related preferences and values influence behavior. For instance, ideas such as a belief in an afterlife with divine judgment *can completely reorder or even invert an individual's utility structures, priorities and values*. Thus, conventional, empirically-derived material notions of individual welfare and return-maximizing may be turned inside out, as the power of an otherworldly idea or an ideal transforms individual outlook. Indeed, many religions and sects specifically revere qualities such as asceticism as a life ideal, as opposed to the implicit goal of maximum resource accrual that is assumed as the ideal endpoint of most competitive situations.

Practiced within a group or on a large scale, such outlooks can change the nature of social reality. Indeed, within a group, ideals such as being generous may be highly costly and lead to competitive disadvantages to individuals in the short term. However, the practice of these same ideals of reliability and generosity may possibly give competitive advantage in the longer term as a result of efficiencies that are gained from higher levels of trustworthiness (including cooperation, fairness, and repayment of social indebtedness), sharing resources in times of need and hardship (over time there can be very significant differences between market value and individual utility; this is commonly overlooked), and less of a need for in-group policing (since believers in an all-knowing deity and ultimate judgment have this as an additional concern).

The result may be the evolution of socially-close-knit groups that effectively bypasses problems of trust and resentment that plague groups not so ordered.

Subjective value and spiritual capital are gained on other dimensions as well, including the satisfaction of fulfilling an *ideal,* such as "doing one's share". Ideals may not seem to be so important at first glace, but people are often willing to make significant sacrifices simply to assert ideals. These sacrifices can be especially high in cases when individual pride or honor is at stake, in cases of standing up for political idealism (as in the case of entering a protest or going to war), in devotion to religious practices, on in standing up for a professional or group norm. While it is common to assume that individuals are motivated and make choices on the basis of proximate cost and benefit, it also seems that individuals find fulfillment in being able to identify with, to strive towards, and to reach towards higher ideals. This action, although sometimes costly in the short term, can arguably lead to an array of downstream social benefits, and is often powered by values and beliefs, or spiritual capital.

Summary

Already, different fields in the social sciences look at individual values, beliefs, and motivations, on one hand, and at constructed norms, incentive structures, and the institutional frameworks that govern these. This interplay is constantly evolving as individuals and groups invest themselves (and sometimes pay necessary costs) in pursuing what they *believe* to be realistic and valuable dreams within the context of formal and informal institutional structures. Spiritual capital influences directly what form investment takes and the intensity of action. Yet, surprisingly, the underlying dependent variable role of beliefs and outlooks are currently largely neglected in economic research and standard economic models, perhaps because of their complex, fickle, and multi-causal nature. Without this key ingredient, standard models might never be able tell the whole story for who is competitively successful, and why.

References

Becker, G. 1964. *Human capital.* New York, NY: Columbia University Press.

Bourdieu, P. 1986. The form of capital. In J. Richardson, Ed., *Handbook of theory and research in education,* 241-258. Westport, CT: Greenwood Press.

Coleman, J. S. 1988. Social capital in the creation of human capital. *American Journal of Sociology, 94,* S95-S120.

Covey, S. R., Merrill, A. R., & Merrill, R. R. 1994. *First things first.* New York, NY: Simon and Schuster.

Marx, K. 1905. *Capital: A critique of political economy.* New York, NY: Modern Library. Original work published 1867.

Smith, A. 1877. *An inquiry into the nature and causes of the wealth of nations.* New York, NY: Putnam's Sons. Original work published 1776.
Waitley, D. 1979. *The psychology of winning.* New York, NY: Berkley Books.
Weber, M. 1958. *The Protestant ethic and the spirit of capitalism.* New York, NY: Scribner's. Original work published 1905.
Wind, Y., Crook, C., & Gunther, R. 2005. *The power of impossible thinking.* Philadelphia, PA: Wharton School Publishing.

Humanism
and the Future Evolution of Religion

Carl Coon

Carter Ide is an old friend who spent many years administering our aid programs in the Indian subcontinent. Back in Washington for consultation, he saw a bunch of young Hari Krishnas demonstrating in the street. They were wrapped in white sheets and were carrying signs and shouting slogans. Just for the hell of it, Carter walked up to one of them and spoke to him in Hindi. The fellow looked at him and said, "What are you, some kind of a nut?"

Well, Carter may have been a bit of a nut to approach the Hari Krishna the way he did, and if so I am certainly some kind of a nut as well, to take on the impossible task of predicting the future course of the established religions, and the future role of humanism. But I do have a sense that the humanist movement is destined to play a much more important role in the future than it does now, and I base this expectation on a bit more than just wishful thinking.

I expect that over the course of this century more and more people will come to regard humanism as more than just an alternative to the old faiths. They will come to understand that it is the evolutionary successor, the logical follow-on, to a mindset that served humanity well in the past but is now eligible for honorable retirement. In the future it will be humanists, following humanist principles, who will lead humanity, not Christians or Muslims or Jews or Hindus or Buddhists.

The old faiths aren't going to roll over and expire. Their adherents may continue to command the loyalties of vast numbers of people, as they do today. Humanism will infiltrate and gradually take over from the top, not the bottom.

One place to watch is the UN Secretariat. Several years ago I was visiting the UN headquarters and had a brief encounter with one of the principle Undersecretaries. He had made some remarks that sounded to me like they were straight out of our Humanist Manifesto (as did Kofi Annan's speech when he accepted the Nobel Peace prize). I told him so, and he smiled and said: "Yes, we are all humanists here." And why not? Do we really want or expect our international civil servants to be true believers in one of the old religions? When they intervene to restore peace in some local or regional conflict, will the antagonists respect their objectivity if they are? Will any of us? I suspect the experience of dealing with problems all over the globe, many with religious overtones, will make a humanist or at least a skeptic out of just about any responsible international civil servant.

In this coming century we will have to work out effective means of coping with global warming. At some point we'll have to bite the bullet and start a process of universal nuclear disarmament, or face the consequences. We'll have to devise more effective measures to control international terrorism, international traffic in narcotics, international refugee movements, and a host of related problems. We'll have to devise a more equitable way of dividing the earth's bounty between the haves and the have-nots. None of these issues can be solved unilaterally, by a single nation, even the USA. All of them require regional cooperation and the most serious ones can only be mastered if the approach is global. So, is there a future for the United Nations? Is there a future for the rapidly growing cadre of international civil servants who are trying to build the institutions and craft the policies the world so urgently needs? Of course, and these individuals will more likely be humanists than not.

And it isn't just the international civil servants. Don't forget the scientists, for example, or the doctors, the diplomats, and the teachers. In Europe and the USA at least, the great majority of these professionals have graduated well beyond simple acceptance of the more superstitious beliefs of the established religions. They may have been born into one of those religions but by now they are either humanists at heart or are moving in that direction.

I see humanism evolving on a global scale rather the way English has evolved in India, as the language of leadership. Only a few Indians spoke English fluently back in the 1950's when I was there, but the ones who did were the leaders. The reason English is still the language of leadership in that huge and important land is that they could not agree on whether Hindi should replace it, and while they were arguing about it the advantages of working in and with a truly international language became apparent. Similarly, I see humanism taking over global leadership, and even though most people may continue to stick with their old religions, they will increasingly view humanism as a kind of second language, a useful bridge to the larger global community.

This brings me to another way in which to view this transition from what you might call hard religion to soft religion and its next door neighbor, humanism. Look at the conditions in which the great world religions were born, and compare those conditions with those of today. People were relatively inexperienced at the business of governance, of ensuring majority cooperation in social groups larger than villages and tribes. Our ancestors hadn't yet worked out the procedures, attitudes, and institutions we take for granted today, memes that grease the skids and lubricate relations between people who may not know each other but still have to interact in a civil way with each other. Religion evolved under the forced draft of extreme need in those days when the Neolithic was morphing into the Iron Age. It was like the practice of reinforcing concrete by putting steel bars inside, producing a structural material that is more versatile and resilient than plain cement. For about a half dozen millennia, religion provided the steel rods that made it possible to govern increasingly expansive territories and populations.

Religion has filled this "steel rod" role rather well in the past because it meets so many human needs and because it has been flexible enough to adapt to new circumstances. One important way religion has helped group solidarity has been the promise of an afterlife. However implausible on rational grounds, this single feature has done yeoman service over the millennia in keeping the faithful in line with the promise of delayed gratification after death. But religion has many other ways of ensuring that its followers share an identity, a common purpose, and common values. Some are quite ingenious, like the Hajj, which brings Muslims from all social levels and all parts of the world together for the annual pilgrimage to Mecca.

The problem with religion is that all the successful ones have been more or less proprietary and competitive. "Thou shalt worship but one God." Back in the early days those gods were pretty rough on the competition, and on any follower who played the field. Check the Bible. Of course, that was the epoch when those steel rods were absolutely essential.

That's an important point, because by now, modern societies have developed a lot of other structural materials and new ways of designing and building things. Reinforced concrete still has its uses and is still important but it isn't as essential as it used to be. Likewise with the ways we manage commerce and politics and a host of other aspects of our lives. In many cases we have some material other than concrete, or some institutions other than religion, that can do the job better.

All of these different facets of the human social condition have been evolving together, in an integrated fashion. Our modern architecture of memes for law and banking and education and diplomacy and so forth has grown to the point where it can stand on its own. Religion has grown too, and has become less proprietary and aggressive, on the average. But there are still widespread populations that retain the old-fashioned attitude of hating and fearing the heathen, trusting only those who share the one and true faith. The people who still think this way are in evolutionary backwaters, only a step or two ahead of the few hunter gatherer societies that still eke out an existence in remote areas. But there are still too many of them for comfort.

Maybe eventually the old religions will die out completely, but my crystal ball doesn't work that far into the future. More probably, they will continue, in progressively less toxic form, for centuries. I hope it won't take nearly that long to tame them to the point that the remaining true believers will be purged of their atavistic urge to send their young men off to die in battle. I also hope they'll stop feeling compelled to send missionaries out to poach on people of other faiths.

Once those changes are in place, who cares if some people cling to their old superstitions? The world will be a much better place, anyway.

A Biocultural Evolutionary Exploration of Supernatural Sanctioning

Christopher Boehm

Introduction

Taboos and morally-involved supernatural sanctioning are perennial anthropological favorites because they provide possible precursors to the rise of religion, yet their systematic evolutionary study is virtually in its infancy. So far, cultural-anthropological attention has gone to just a few particular instances of supernatural retribution, as with incest (e.g., Durham 1991; Ember 1975; Freud 1913/1918) or pollution (Carroll 1982), as opposed to supernatural sanctioning and taboos in general, while from an evolutionary standpoint there are many unanswered fundamental questions (see Johnson & Krüger 2004; Johnson 2005; Sosis & Alcorta 2003). For instance, genetically, is supernatural sanctioning advantaged because it provides social control without incurring risks to group members? Or is personally adaptive for individuals to readily believe in such sanctions? And, more ultimately, when did the supernatural-belief capacity that made such sanctioning possible begin to evolve?

In terms of *cultural* evolution, we may ask whether beliefs in supernatural retribution simply "organize themselves" culturally, or whether people invent and deliberately reinforce them, and whether there are significant differences between moral and nonmoral taboos. We also need to know more about the division of labor between everyday social sanctioning that suppresses moral transgressions, and supernatural sanctions that do the same job.

This paper offers a preliminary evolutionary discussion of some of these issues, first by briefly portraying one tribal system of supernatural belief, and then by looking for suggestive patterns among 18 hunter-gatherer societies.

A Tribal Ethnographic Model

The tribal study site is Upper Morača Tribe in the former Yugoslavia, where I resided for two years. In 1963 this partly literate Serbian tribe of 1,800 is five hours on horseback from the nearest road, and has no electricity, running water, or doctor on duty. Under Tito's regime, religious practice is strictly forbidden, but traditional supernaturally-connected helpers continue to diagnose and treat illness, the name of God (*Bog*) is heard constantly, and vampires and witches are still salient in people's minds.

Specialist curers of dangerous snakebites practice *zavarčivanje*, which involves specialized incantations to reduce the symptoms; the *zduač* is a wizard who manipulates whirlwinds to destroy neighboring tribes instead of his own. *Gatars* treat illness, and in theory these magical herbalists' roles are always benevolent. However, a malevolent personality can use these same powers for sorcery. A *vještica*, or "witch," is a barren woman who out of envy eats the souls of children born to other women in the same clan; an unfortunate "suspect" in my own neighborhood has been totally ostracized by her own family.

The most salient inimical entities, however, are *vampijeri*, or "vampires," also called *vukodlak*, or "wolf's hair." These "ghosts" come back from the dead to have sexual intercourse with close family members, and the only remedy is to open the grave and repeatedly pierce the corpse with a black thorn stake. People believe that a vampire comes into being whenever a cat manages to jump over a corpse, and traditionalists tell me that even in Communist households, when someone dies the house cat is securely trussed to a wooden upright in the stall below the house. As a further precaution, a nocturnal vigil is held to guard the corpse. Oral tradition tells how this wake originated. In the old days, people were always buried with great dispatch until one day a man coming down off the mountain heard strange sounds passing a local graveyard. The fresh grave was opened and the person buried obviously had come out of a coma and desperately clawed at the inside of the coffin. It was then that the all-night vigil was established.

Initially, my only tribal case history of "vampirism" was a woman who claimed her husband had returned as a *vampijer* to make her pregnant, but then my informant scoffed and noted pointedly that it was unseemly for a widow to sleep with anyone during her year of mourning. Eventually, however, I learned that this widow's son had been born in his amniotic sac, and also had "strong eyes" (*jaki oči*)—both supernatural markers. This boy grew up to be the most powerful *gatar* in the valley, and was widely feared as a sorcerer; in people's eyes he was a *vampijer's* progeny.

Vampirism was not brought on by antisocial behavior, for it merely involved a taboo about cats. However, there were other supernatural effects that did relate directly to the moral order. For instance, people believed that *Bog* could punish them in *this* life for moral transgressions, as when He inflicted a heart attack on a woman for weaving on His day of rest. However, even though these Eastern Orthodox Serbs had been taught continuously about a Christian Heaven and Hell for 1,000 years, they seemed virtually unconcerned about afterlife consequences of sinning.

What people did believe in was Saint Vasily as the God of Thunder and Lightning—an obvious holdover from Pre-Christian Slavic animistic beliefs. As a decisive and wrathful punisher of sins, he seemed more prominent in their minds than *Bog*, himself—indeed, when all the adult members of one tribal family were killed in their mountain cabin by summer lightning, people duly noted that only an infant in its cradle survived. *Sveti Vasilije* had spared it "because it was too young to have sinned." Such beliefs obviously involve causal thinking and selective perceptions: if two good men and one bad man are killed by lightning in the same year, tribal attention will focus just on the bad man's getting his just desserts.

Here is a case history which provides an important lead for thinking about how moralistic taboos may evolve culturally. The main "actor" is the largest oak tree in Montenegro and probably in all of Europe. Growing in a tribal graveyard, its diameter is almost *ten meters*. As a Balkan refuge area, Upper Morača had been overpopulated for many centuries (Boehm 1983), and, because firewood and wood for building had to be packed in by horse, a tree's surviving to this age was quite improbable. I was told the tree was "sacred."

The ancient Slavs had a pantheon of gods associated with trees, which included one who dealt in thunder and lightning (Wilkinson 1848). Saint Vasily was obviously a syncretic "reincarnation" in Christian guise, and this was his tree. Again, there was a myth. One day lightning severed one great branch, and a man decided that if Saint Vasily had done this to his own tree, why shouldn't an enterprising tribesman carry away the wood for his fire? Within a year, I was told, this impudent risk-taker was killed by lightning.

The oak's sheer size testifies to how old, and durable, this supernatural-retribution tradition must have been. In addition, the graveyard had not only Christian tombstones with crosses but some older, pre-Christian Slavic *stecci*. These massive oblong stones showed engravings of reclining warriors—but no crosses. If the tree's supernatural protection had begun with a pre-Christian Slavic thunder god, this made it more than 1,000 years old.

This account raises important theoretical questions. For instance, do such beliefs simply arise through the accidental connections that nonliterate people then perceive "causally?" Or, are they deliberately invented to serve social purposes? There is one hint. These Serbs use "bogeymen" to scare their children into obedience, so deliberate social manipulation using the supernatural does take place—even though in this case the manipulative adults are not "believers." Thus, one might *speculate* that when the tribal graveyard was first established, the oak tree provided welcome shade for protracted afternoon socializing after funerals—and that Saint Vasily's protection might have been invoked *deliberately*, to protect this "public good" from selfish woodcutters.

Hunter-Gatherer Sanctioning

In coding 43 ethnographies to cover 18 foraging societies, I found no report of supernatural sanctionings actually being invented, just one case of the supernatural being used to manipulate children, and one case of existing sanctions being appreciated because of their social-control contributions. An Ona informant said that even though real supernatural forces existed, there were also false beliefs which were useful because they contributed to the social order (Gusinde 1937/1961). Although such ethnographic gems are rare, this may well be an artifact of inconsistent ethnographic reporting.

The sample of hunter-gatherer societies in Table I was selected on the basis of suitability for modeling Late-Pleistocene social behavior, the geographical distribution being: *Africa*: Dorobo, Ko, Kung; *Arctic*: Netsilik, Copper Eskimo; *Asia*: Agta, Andaman Islanders; *Australia*: Murngin, Tiwi, Walbiri; *North America*: Chiricahua Apache, Micmac, Ojibwa; *South America*: Aweikoma, Ona, Tubatulabel, Waorani, Yahgan. All these foragers are spatially mobile, economically independent, egalitarian, and oriented to large-game hunting (see Boehm 2002).

One empirical challenge is to discern the division of labor between *natural* sanctioning—deliberate, moralistic social control by aroused human groups—and *supernatural* sanctioning which seems to take place "automatically." Durham's (1991) intensive study of incest proscriptions in 60 mainly-tribal societies shows this to vary: most report a combination of the two, while many have only social sanctioning and just a tiny minority report mainly supernatural sanctions. Does this hold for band-level as well as tribal societies? We know that universally among our foragers (Boehm 2000) murder, incest, cheating, stealing, lying, adultery, and lazy noncooperation are disapproved, and to some degree socially sanctioned through *ordinary* means (see also Brown 1991)—with murder, cheating, theft and lying being especially disapproved in these cooperative hunting societies.

The left side of Table I shows distributions for *supernatural* sanctioning of fifteen behaviors considered locally to be deviant, and several trends are striking. Our main interest is in how supernatural retribution helps to enforce local moral codes, and all 18 societies reported such behavior. Two thirds of the societies make mention of supernatural sanctioning *in general,* as an agency of social control, and 16 mention specific punishable acts, all antisocial. No one act is seen more than half the time, however. The highest frequencies are for incest and murder, while other generally unwanted and naturally-sanctioned behaviors like cheating, laziness, shirking obligations, fighting, theft, and sorcery are reported only sporadically in connection with supernatural retribution. It would appear that there is no antisocial behavior that is supported solely by supernatural sanctioning.

TABLE I: SUPERNATURAL SANCTIONING BY FORAGERS

	MORALLY CONDEMNED BEHAVIORS BEING SANCTIONED															"NONMORAL" TABOOS							
	Devi-ance in General	Incest	Murder	Cheat	Lazy	Shirk	Sorcery	Fight	Steal	Adulery	Canibal	Lie	Disre-spect Elders	Gossip	Jealousy		Food	Ritual	Animal	Sex	Birth	Death	Deity	Object
Agta			●																●					
Andman Islaners	●		●				●	●	●	●		●					●	●	●				●	
Aweikoma								●	●								●	●	●					
Chiricahua Apache	●	●					●										●	●	●	●	●	●	●	●
Copper Eskimo	●		●	●		●											●		●			●	●	
Dorobo	●	●																	●	●	●			
Ko		●	●						●	●			●		●		●	●		●				
Kung	●	●															●		●				●	
Micmac	●	●		●	●	●											●	●	●	●	●	●	●	●
Murngin	●										●						●	●		●				
Netsilik	●	●	●	●	●	●	●				●						●		●	●	●	●		
Ojibwa	●	●	●									●						●	●	●			●	●
Ona	●		●		●									●			●	●	●		●			●
Tiwi		●						●									●	●		●	●	●	●	●
Tubatulabel				●													●	●				●		
Walbiri		●			●												●	●		●	●	●		●
Waorani	●																							
Yahgan	●																							
TOTAL	12	9	7	4	4	3	3	3	3	2	2	2	1	1	1		13	11	11	9	7	7	7	6

With such a small sample of societies, at best I can discuss some other trends that may be useful in thinking about future evolutionary research. For instance, supernatural sanctioning appears rather unpredictably, as a "backup" for the everyday social sanctioning by real people which includes social pressure, ostracism, group shaming, ejection, and capital punishment. With a substantially larger sample, and with the exact means of social control coded for each type of malfeasance, it might be possible to identify specific malfeasances that more strongly invite supernatural sanctioning as a backup mechanism. For instance, murder is extremely disruptive and also is very hard to control in egalitarian bands because they lack strong peacemakers (see Knauft 1991). In Table I, murder is ranked second after incest in frequency of supernatural sanctioning, and a further challenge would be to figure out why incest so often invites supernatural sanctioning compared with other malfeasances, which receive such sanctioning far less frequently.

Another interesting hypothesis to test, based on Johnson's (2005) work, is that the assumed omniscience of supernatural punishers makes their sanctioning especially useful in suppressing readily-concealed crimes such as sorcery, incest, adultery, and cheating. At least in the small sample we are working with, however, unconcealable crimes like murder, fighting and being lazy seem to be equally eligible. It also would be interesting to see if the heinousness of a given crime, as judged locally, might correlate with more frequent use of supernatural sanctioning. I did not code for this variable.

The right side of Table I shows "taboos" which I consider to be "nonmoral," in that the associated behaviors do not involve being predatory on fellow band members. The leading categories are food, animals, sex, and transgressions against ritual rules, followed by taboos concerning birth, death, and deities, and these prohibitions are reported far more often than morally-relevant social prohibitions on the left side of the table. This discrepancy poses yet another interesting question for future analysis.

Discussion

To fully understand the evolution of spiritual belief systems, eventually we will need to examine data from a large number of disciplines, including archaeology, cognitive neuroscience, developmental psychology, religious studies, and others. But as diachronic evolutionary sequences are addressed, the anchor will still be studies of spiritual life using "Pleistocene-appropriate" hunter-gatherer ethnographies, as instruments for both qualitative and quantitative analysis.

For instance, we need to know if individuals who actively promote supernatural sanctioning can create this public good at no personal cost, which would mean that free riders pose no problem for explanation. We also need to explore whether individuals more prone to buy into supernatural belief systems involving retribution gain in personal fitness because in doing so they avoid real-world punishment by their group (see Johnson 2005). It is conceivable that group-selection could be playing a role, either genetically or culturally, so assessing group social functions will also be relevant (e.g., Wilson 2002). In addition, the evolution of self-control ("conscience") through sanctioning selection (see Boehm 1999) will be relevant.

With respect to cultural dynamics, this small-sample preliminary analysis has posed a number of interesting questions for future research, and to these I would add the existence of single, highly potent spiritual entities which are found among a few foragers, and how these relatively powerful figures affect the potency and patterning of supernatural sanctioning. As a source of cultural variation, such case histories could provide major leads in theorizing about the rise of monotheism and the evolution of the kind of moralistic supernatural sanctioning we saw in Upper Morača Tribe.

My final comment is that if we are to move toward a diachronic, Darwinian evolutionary approach to explaining the development of spiritual beliefs, we must focus initially on what I have called "Pleistocene-appropriate" foragers. Unfortunately, the standard samples used in cross-cultural research represent such societies only weakly because more than half the foragers in the world are sedentary or are significantly involved with domestication. Given the inconsistencies of ethnographic reporting, the sample of 18 societies analyzed here needs to be expanded substantially if we are to better understand the evolved spiritual life of Upper Paleolithic humans.

References

Boehm, C. 1983. *Montenegrin social organization and values*. New York, NY: AMS Press.

Boehm, C. 1999. *Hierarchy in the forest: The evolution of egalitarian behavior*. Cambridge, MA: Harvard University Press.

Boehm, C. 2000. Conflict and the evolution of social control. *Journal of Consciousness Studies, 7*, 79-183.

Boehm, C. 2002. Variance reduction and the evolution of social control. Paper presented at Santa Fe Institute, 5th Annual Workshop on the Co-Evolution of Behaviors and Institutions, Santa Fe.

Brown, D. 1991. *Human universals*. New York, NY: McGraw-Hill.

Carroll, M. P. 1982. Totem and taboo, purity and danger...and fads and fashion in the study of pollution rules. *Cross-Cultural Research, 17* (27), 1-287.

Durham, W. H. 1991. *Coevolution: Genes, culture, and human diversity*. Stanford, CA: Stanford University Press.

Ember, M. 1975. On the origin and extension of the incest taboo. *Cross-Cultural Research, 10,* 249-281.
Freud, S. 1918. *Totem and taboo: Resemblances between the psychic lives of savages and neurotics* A. A. Brill, Trans.. New York, NY: Random House. Original work published 1913.
Gusinde, M. 1961. *The Yamana: The life and thought of the water nomads of Cape Horn.* F. Schutze, Trans. New Haven, CT: Human Relations Area Files. Original work published 1937.
Johnson, D. P. P. 2005. God's punishment and public goods: A test of the supernatural punishment hypothesis in 186 world cultures. *Human Nature, 16,* 410-466.
Johnson, D. P. P., & Krüger, O. 2004. The good of wrath: Supernatural punishment and the evolution of cooperation. *Political Theology,* 5, 159-176.
Knauft, B. M. 1991. Violence and sociality in human evolution. *Current Anthropology, 32,* 391-428.
Sosis, R., & Alcorta, C. 2003. Solidarity and the sacred: The evolution of religious behavior. *Evolutionary Anthropology, 12,* 264-274.
Wilkinson, J. G. 1848. *Dalmatia and Montenegro* Volume I. London: John Murray.
Wilson, D. S. 2002. *Darwin's cathedral: Evolution, religion, and the nature of society.* Chicago, IL: University of Chicago Press.

PART IV

Religion and Hard to Fake Signals

Free Love

Religious Solidarity on the Cheap

Joseph Bulbulia

The price of success

Commitment-signaling theory explains religious behavior in terms of religion's average fitness effects over the course of human evolution. It views dispositions to religious behavior as repaid through the goods uniquely returned to individuals living in stable, co-operating groups. We achieve massively more together than we could going the world alone. But notoriously, effective co-operation is easily foiled. Often, one or several agents can benefit from society without contribution. But where many opt out, common goods vanish.

According to signaling theory, non-natural beliefs (henceforth "god-commitments") motivate cooperation by altering perceptions of the payoffs for defection.

> **Without religion (accurate perception):**
> Sometimes [Defection > Fair In-Group Cooperation]
>
> **With religion (inaccurate perception):**
> Almost always [Fair In-Group Cooperation > Defection]

If the gods are watching, and they support social norms, then believing agents have added incentive to cooperate, particularly where natural policing systems are weak. Costly rituals, moreover, reliably identify cooperative motivations because only those possessing strong religious commitments will perceive value in paying for participation. Only the religious will invest in gods. Ritual cost, then, appears to solve a *recognition problem*. It enables religiously motivated co-operators to distinguish each other from frauds.

Commitment-signaling theory conjectures that the rituals associated with religion are adaptations that reliably signal solidarity (Bulbulia 2004a; Irons 1996a, 1996b; Sosis 2003, an idea that nascent empirical studies support (Sosis 2000; Sosis & Bressler 2003; Sosis & Ruffle 2003). Yet commitment-signaling explanations *do not require that religious rituals be costly*. They only require that signals be hard-to-fake. My purpose here is to clarify this aspect.

Religious cost alone does not certify co-operative intention

Cost-based signaling theories are problematic because, in many cultural settings, ritual practice is coerced. Clearly, religious practice cannot effectively screen prior motivations where participation cannot be avoided. Coercion does not respect intention, so it cannot predict intention.

Or so it seems. Anthropologists have long held that rituals weld agents together through emotional experiences (Durkheim 1915/1964; Turner, 1990). These intuitions have been grounded by recent naturalistic approaches. The "sensory pageantry" of rites produces rich episodic memory and emotional effects (McCauley 2001; McCauley & Lawson 2002; Whitehouse 1996, 2000). More directly, religious practices bolster social commitment. Sosis and Alcorta notice that rituals—both public and private —transform us, educating our emotions, intentions, and feelings (Sosis 2003; Sosis & Alcorta 2003). Indeed, the authors observe that both positive and negative affect rituals alter religious commitment—though in distinctive ways (Alcorta & Sosis 2005).

Thus even where rituals do not assess commitments, they may well forge them. Ritual agents may become like Patty Hearst –horrified of the cult before abduction, fanatically committed after. Generalizing, if participation reliably *produces* cooperative commitment, it also reliably *signals* commitment. This remains true even where participation cannot be avoided.

However in these Hearst-like scenarios, "cost" is not necessary for commitment signaling. Cost appears only as a by-product of religious indoctrination. A knowledge of how someone has been encultured forecasts behavior, not the knowledge of what it all costs.

What about cases where participation is costly and freely chosen? Notice that even here, costly displays do not reliably predict cooperation, for agents may harbor diverse reasons for practicing religion, none of which bear on their god-commitments. These reasons may significantly weight their entrance utilities. For example, a priest may endure costly seminary study from a social convention (the eldest child to Jesus!), or from a dread of useful labor, or to secure extra-pair bond copulations with congregates. To perform need not always reflect a desire to commit.

To understand how religious signaling works, we need to return to the basics of commitment-signaling theory. Abstractly, we know that where interests do not perfectly overlap, an evolvable signal must bear an <u>intrinsic</u> relation to the property it identifies. Signals cannot be arbitrary: they must link up with the properties they describe. A signal need not deliver a perfectly indexical relationship. Even if a signal can sometimes be faked, it can nevertheless work (think of a police uniform). Accuracy thresholds are inversely proportional to the costs of error (Military uniforms must be harder to imitate, because the risks of false positives are higher). As the costs of error decrease, tolerance for fallibility rises (Frank 1988; Grafen 1990). Nevertheless, outside pure co-ordination contexts, signals must bear *some* intrinsic relationship to that which they identify. A compass may be leave margin of error and still remain useful, but not if it is soldered fixed.

What do costly displays intrinsically identify? Without further information, we can only say that costly displays indicate *perceived* resource wealth above an entry threshold—with a perceived return falling still higher. But without considering the details of a case, we cannot assume costly religion dependably limns cooperative intent. We can only attribute some strong motive, we know not which. And the worry—for cooperating audiences—is that the motive is sinister.

Symbolic marking

Importantly, some rituals do use cost to effectively assess comment. Agents who receive permanent body markings—scars, tattoos, circumcisions, neck elongations, unusual piercings—strongly pre-commit to a group *by taking this marking* (Boehm 1999). Once branded in tribal regalia, life outside a tribe in conflict will be awkward or impossible. Symbolic marking thus ties an agent's fate to that of her group. This convergence enhances solidarity. Indeed, in a recent study, Sosis and colleagues have demonstrated a close relationship between permanent marking rituals and inter-tribal warfare (Sosis, Kress, & Boster 2007).

Permanent marking is a solidarity pump of enormous power. But it does not intrinsically identify supernatural commitment. Marking does not intrinsically respect an agent's beliefs and desires relative to policing spiritual agents. For symbolic marking to work, all that is required is that 1) a symbolic marker be clear and permanent; that 2) it identify a marked member as belonging to a definite in-group to the exclusion of an out-group; and that 3) both in-group and out-groups recognize the symbolic marker.[1] Within these constraints, norm-motivating god-beliefs may vary widely. Permanent marking cannot support the evolution of supernatural-commitment if it cannot identify *that* commitment.

This matters. Not all co-operation problems involve inter-group conflict. Your neighbor with your tribal tattoo may fight to the death for your group —yet still take your pig. Belief in deities that monitor the exchange relationship motivates fair co-operation (Bering 2005). Thus, religious understandings solve co-operation problems that arise outside contexts of intra-group conflict, of which there are many. Permanent marking is indeed a powerful

1 Secret in-group marking is sufficient to enhance co-ordination but not co-operation where defection is compelling.

solidarity device; but it cannot resolve intra-group conflicts. It cannot solve *those* recognition problems. How, then, does religious signaling work?

Signaling on the cheap

On the version of signaling theory that I endorse, *emotions* both motivate and express pro-social intentions. Religious emotions give religious co-operators the intrinsic signals they need to solve recognition problems, and these signals are reliable without expense.

The economist Robert Frank has long urged that emotions reliably identify pre-commitments (see Frank 1988, 2001) echoing (Darwin 1872/1965). This is so because emotional states are easy to perceive, hard-to-fake, and intrinsically linked (if not infallibly) to motivations that fuel action. Emotions forecast future behavior. This benefits both signalers and audiences, for each party gains through this predictability. Anger deters aggression, even where the costs of deterrence exceed peaceable forfeiture. Knowing that one hot with temper will react no matter what forestalls costly battle, even where the hothead has much to lose. Kissing and other expressions of love give hard-to-fake signals of affection, for it is difficult to tolerate physical encounter with those we loathe. Faking is possible, and emotions are fallible prophets. But we have seen that selection can work with imperfect materials, if their average benefits exceed their average costs.

Now, because most emotional signals track motivational states very directly and clearly, where emotions are turned towards heavenly realities, they empower agents to project and register distinctively religious motivations. This enables audiences to reliably discern whether religious agents possess norm-supporting commitments to the gods. For where there is genuine religious emotion there is likely genuine religious commitment.

Cost alone → NOISY EVIDENCE → religious motivations
BUT,
Emotional signal viz. gods → RELIABLE EVIDENCE → religious motivations

For religious signaling to work, there is no requirement for cost. Emotional expressions themselves are relatively undemanding of resources. They are both cheap and hard to fake. A policing system that co-opts emotional signals will be more efficient than one that relies on costly signals.

Cannot emotions be faked? Defectors, it seems, will evolve the power to simulate un-costly religious emotions, thereby voiding them. But evolving this capacity is not as easy as asserting its possibility. Emotions are processed outside the neocortex and are not easily controlled (Ramachandran 1997).

It remains very hard to suppress raw terror, to fake a violent rage, or to fake laughter at a joke you don't think is funny (Frank 1988; Schloss, this volume).

A small percentage of any human population *is* able to fake emotions easily. We call these people "sociopaths." Indeed, were sociopaths common, then emotional signals would be brittle. Sociopaths are fortunately rare. But they give us insight into the mechanisms that underlie convincing lying, as well as the mechanisms we evolved to assess signal reliably. Effective liars do not believe one claim and project another. They believe their lies (Hirstein 2005). Effective deception of others relies on self-deception (Trivers 2001). And this is so precisely because emotions are reliable indices of motivation and intention. For in noticing her deception, a fraud risks projecting secondary signals that give away the lie.

In understanding this intrinsic connection between belief and behavior, we travel some distance to explaining the reliability of religious emotions. Critically: *to deceive oneself about the gods' reality is indistinguishable from becoming religiously committed*. The only way to reliably display worshipful love towards a norm-supporting god is through self-deception. But if you have thus deceived yourself you have become a religious agent. *Religious self-deception and ordinary religious commitment appear to be functionally indistinguishable*! Religion cannot be reliably faked without religious commitment. Religiosity bears the marks of an exquisitely crafted cooperation device.

Rituals as Amplification Technology

The prospect for emotional expression to godly reality presses the exquisitely functional and ancient emotional signaling system into service to solve recognition problems. As our ancestors built ever-larger cooperative groups, the pairing of emotional expression with moral pre-commitment would have helped to dramatically reduce the burdens of agent tracking and prediction. Notice, this is particularly true where expressions are produced in public settings, for all to see. For it is not feasible to test the religiosity of everyone one by one, and remain efficient. Coordinated expressions of religious emotion dramatically enhance the efficiency of emotional signaling technologies. In certifying how many of those around us feel about the gods, we can better ascertain how they will act—even against immediate gratification and self-interest. Looked at from the vantage point of group selection, these assessment technologies equip groups to combat the critical problem of subversion from within. But this solution also yields massive benefits to individual agents. To belong to a group very efficient at solving cooperation problems is to benefit from a winning team.

The point I wish to emphasize here is that religious rituals need not be intrinsically costly to register co-operation signals. Rather, efficient rituals will act as platforms through which agents prompt, express, and amplify the emotional states that identify god-commitments *at a low fitness cost*. Hence:

Religious commitment motivates → Fair in-group cooperation [>defection temptation]
Religious emotion signals (by reliably identifying) → Religious commitment
Rituals project [Emotional signal → RELIABLE EVIDENCE → religious motivations]

Indeed, efficient religious practices will tend to minimize the wasting of resources to thresholds pragmatically sufficient to amplify emotional expressions that dependably solve co-operation problems. Optimal rituals will evoke and project reliable emotional commitment signals at the lowest cost that does the trick. [There is some early evidence for this relationship in Chen (2003, reviewed in Bulbulia (2004b)].

Conclusion

We have seen that costly display in itself only intrinsically signals perceived resource excess. Yet the recognition problem facing religious cooperators is elegantly solved through signaling practices that induce emotional commitments to norm supporting gods. Rituals work not because they are intrinsically costly, but because they are highly emotional public forums for the display of religious commitment. While it is difficult to date the emergence of ritual life in our lineage's evolutionary past, we know that religious practices capable of eliciting and amplifying signals of supernatural commitment would have greatly enhanced solidarity. And where amplification works, a cost structuring surrounding religious ritual is not necessary to enable religious cooperation. Indeed, efficient cultures will evolve to minimize the fitness costs of these activities.

While commitment-signaling theory does not rely on costly signals of commitment, it is certainly compatible with technologies that exploit cost to certify solidarity emotions (Bulbulia 2004b). I do not deny that many rituals really are costly and risky, and deliberately so (see Atran 2002, for a horrifying catalogue). Moreover, sometimes these costs really do spiral out of control, causing religions to become genuinely maladaptive. Keeping up with how the Jones's express piety may deeply burden us, potentially launching an evolutionary cascade to costlier and costlier expressions (Sterelny, forthcoming). Foot-binding, adult circumcision, life-long celibacy, immolation, and other practices may well be fitness traps—costly-signals of virtue run amok.

Nevertheless, we know that long-lived religious practices cannot be too costly to groups. Social biases and other behavioral strategies may support genuinely costly display. However individual selection will tend to cull any wild and reckless tendency. Moreover cultural selection will work to reduce or eliminate wasteful practices as groups compete with each other over time. Most importantly, the capacity for god-commitment to motivate pro-social behavior enables distinctively religious rituals to supplant costlier secular equivalents. I have shown that a powerful benefit of emotion-based religious signaling is that it enables agents to recognize the co-operative motivations of more distant affiliates reliably, without requiring cost-intensive certificates. Religious agents can signal on the cheap. Indeed, the capacity for religion diminishes the prospects for runaway costly-signaling practices that drown individuals and cultures in deep fitness sinks. Religion gives us an alternative to costly signaling.

References

Alcorta, C., & Sosis, R. 2005. Ritual, emotion, and sacred symbols: The evolution of religion as an adaptive complex. *Human Nature, 16* (4), 323-359.

Atran, S. 2002. *In gods we trust: The evolutionary landscape of religion*. New York, NY: Oxford University Press.

Bering, J. M. 2005. The evolutionary history of an illusion: Religious causal beliefs in children and adults. In B. Ellis & D. F. Bjorklund ,Eds., *Origins of the social mind: Evolutionary psychology and child development,* 411-437. New York, NY: Guilford Press.

Boehm,C.1999.*Hierarchy in the forest*.Cambridge,MA:Harvard University Press.

Bulbulia, J. 2004a. Religious costs as adaptations that signal altruistic intention. *Evolution & Cognition, 10* (1), 19-38.

Bulbulia, J. 2004b. The cognitive and evolutionary psychology of religion. *Biology & Philosophy,18* (5), 655-686.

Chen, D. 2003. Economic distress and religious intensity: Evidence from Islamic resurgence during the Indonesian financial crisis. MIT: Mimeo.

Darwin, C. 1965. *The expression of the emotions in man and animals*. Chicago, IL: University of Chicago Press. Original work published 1872.

Durkheim, E. 1964. *The elementary forms of the religious life*. London, UK: George Allen & Unwin Ltd. Original work published 1915.

Frank, R. 1988. *Passions within reason: The strategic role of the emotions*. New York, NY: Norton and Company.

Frank, R. 2001. Cooperation through emotional commitment. In R. M. Nesse, Ed., *Evolution and the capacity for commitment,* 57-77. New York, NY: Russell Sage Foundation.

Grafen, A. 1990. Biological signals as handicaps. *Journal of Theoretical Biology, 144*, 517-546.
Hirstein, W. 2005. *Brain fiction: Self-deception and the riddle of confabulation.* Cambridge, MA: The MIT Press.
Irons, W. 1996a. In our own self-image: The evolution of morality, deception, and religion. *Skeptic, 4*, 50-61.
Irons, W. 1996b. Morality, religion, and evolution. In W. W. W. M. Richardson, Ed., *Religion and science: History, method, and dialogue*, 375-399. New York, NY: Routledge.
McCauley, R. N. 2001. Ritual, memory, and emotion: Comparing two cognitive hypotheses. In J. Andresen, Ed., *Religion in mind: Cognitive perspectives on religious belief, ritual, and experience*, 115-140. Cambridge, UK: Cambridge University Press.
McCauley, R. N., & Lawson, E. T. 2002. *Bringing ritual to mind.* New York, NY: Cambridge University Press.
Ramachandran, V. 1997. The evolutionary biology of self-deception, laughter, dreaming and depression: Some clues from anosognosia. *Medical Hypotheses, 47*, 347-362.
Sosis, R. 2000. Religion and intragroup cooperation: Preliminary results of a comparative analysis of utopian communities. *Cross-Cultural Research, 34* (1), 77-88.
Sosis, R. 2003. Why aren't we all Hutterites? Costly signaling theory and religious behavior. *Human Nature, 14* (2), 91-127.
Sosis, R., & Alcorta, C. 2003. Signaling, solidarity, and the sacred: The evolution of religious behavior. *Evolutionary Anthropology, 12*, 264-274.
Sosis, R., & Bressler, E. 2003. Co-operation and commune longevity: A test of the costly signaling theory of religion. *Cross-Cultural Research, 372*, 11-39.
Sosis, R., H. Kress, & J. Boster, 2007. Scars for war: Evaluating alternative signaling explanations for cross-cultural variance in ritual costs. *Evolution & Human Behavior, 28*, 234-247.
Sosis, R., & Ruffle, B. 2003. Religious ritual and cooperation: Testing for a relationship on Israeli religious and secular kibbutzim. *Current Anthropology, 44* (5), 713-722.
Sterelny, K. forthcoming. Snafus: An evolutionary perspective. *Biological Theory.*
Trivers, R. 2001. *Self-deception in service of deceit: Natural selection and social theory.* New York, NY: Oxford University Press.
Turner, V. W. 1990. *Drama, fields, and metaphors: Symbolic action in human society.* Ithaca, NY: Cornell University Press.
Whitehouse, H. 1996. Rites of terror: Emotion, metaphor and memory in Melanesian cults. *Journal of the Royal Anthropological Institute, 2*, 703-715.
Whitehouse, H. 2000. *Arguments and icons.* Oxford, UK: Oxford University Press.

Theological Expressions as Costly Signals of Religious Commitment

Andrew Mahoney

This paper examines costly signalling theory as a model for explaining theological discourse. I define theology as the acquisition and expression of knowledge regarding supernatural reality, and a theologian as a person who, through the expression of their theological knowledge, evidences a history of investment in the acquisition of such knowledge.[1] I open by presenting a problem with the common understanding that the content of religious belief consists of minimally counter intuitive noise. Specifically, I explain that the reproductive cost associated with the accidental acquisition of biologically non-strategic information should be selected out in favour of traits that maximise the acquisition of strictly strategic information. I resolve this dilemma by arguing that the cost associated with the acquisition of non-strategic information can be explained in terms of the handicap principle. Essentially, where the acquisition of theological knowledge is costly to acquire, expressing such knowledge reliably signals specific mental capacities and religious commitments of the signaller.

The common approach to understanding theological belief is to investigate why religionists have a preference for certain beliefs over others. Information which conforms entirely to our evolved intuitive expectations, or which maximally violates those expectations, is not memorable. However, minimally counter intuitive (MCI) concepts are easily retained as they conform to many intuitive expectations (Boyer 2001). They represent information that is likely to be recalled as they make a "cognitively profitable exchange". In this respect, such concepts have been said to achieve a "cognitive optimum" (Barrett 2004).

Justin Barrett (2004) has accordingly claimed: "theologians and religious leaders cannot simply teach any ideas they want and expect those ideas to be remembered, spread, and believed; rather, the way human minds operate

1 Note that a lama, shaman, psychic and most other religious experts would be considered a theologian by this definition. I stress that my definition of theology does not refer specifically to the modern academic study of Christian belief that is undertaken within some western tertiary institutions.

gradually selects only those with the best fit to become widespread" (30). I wish to address two assumptions in this statement. The first is that theologians are capable of conceiving of ideas which would normally be forgotten. On this topic Barrett (2004) has commented: "some theological beliefs, more typically held by clergy and theologians than regular folk, do have a large number of counter intuitive features and do not fit the MCI label" (29). Furthermore, Barrett has noted: "If a person believes in an MCI god, through rigorous theological instruction they may be led to accept additional counter intuitive properties of the god" (29). Thus the second assumption I present is the proposition that additional counter intuitive beliefs can be learnt. This raises the question of why a theologian might attempt to teach such beliefs, even though most people cannot acquire moderately to maximally counter intuitive concepts. I return to this question at the conclusion of this paper.

Theological information is often presented in almost incomprehensible language. Try to decipher the following quotation from a Gnostic Christian gospel: "All natures, starting from the revelation of chaos, are in the light that shines without shadow, and in joy that cannot be described, and in unutterable jubilation. They ever delight themselves on account of their unchanging glory and the immeasurable rest, which cannot be described among all the aeons that came to be afterward, and all their powers" (Soph. Jes. Chr. 113.19-114.8, Robinson 1990).

This quotation is typical of the language employed in a scripture called *The Sophia of Jesus Christ*. As this scripture was unearthed in Egypt 62 years ago, having been buried since the fourth century (Robinson 1990), any theological baggage implicit in the discourses of groups that recognised this scripture has been long forgotten. I therefore suggest that no living person could justifiably claim to fully understand all of the theology in this text.

I further propose that a lot of material in the Bible or the Qur'an would be incomprehensible to people who have not been indoctrinated by a Christian or Muslim group. To illustrate, imagine a Tibetan Buddhist, with no knowledge of Christianity, reading the entire Bible. I strongly doubt that this person would acquire any understanding of the papacy or the trinity, unless they also received some form of theological instruction. Nevertheless, Catholics frequently employ the Bible as their primary source in justifying such doctrines.

It seems that the theological information taught by theoloians and religious leaders is confusing at best and meaningless at worst. Contrast theological rhetoric with a more rational statement, such as the fact that there is an axe murderer creeping up behind you. This statement is an example of what I would call biologically strategic information. By this I mean information that can help you survive and ultimately reproduce in the real world.

Given that evolution weeds out any tendency for agents to act against their reproductive interests, let us consider the human being as a biologically rational agent finely adapted toward maximising personal reproductive potential within the ancestral environment.[2] Such an agent should be strictly interested only in the strategic information that could enhance this potential. This information might include: where the cleanest water holes are, what berries are safe to eat, which weapons are best for hunting megamammals, the cooperative reputations of potential exchange partners, the reproductive history of possible mates, etc.

Against this evolutionary backdrop, the acquisition of theological knowledge seems mystifying. One would not expect a biologically rational agent to be interested in: how reincarnation works, how to reconcile the doctrines of *anatta* and rebirth, which mantras invoke which deities, how to understand a long dead language, the nature of the trinity, etc. And here is the rub: No matter how minimally counter intuitive or cognitively optimal these concepts are, agents that are prone to recall and gossip about non-utilitarian information should be selected out in favour of strictly rational agents who are adapted to focussing all time and effort on studying strictly strategic information. Just as our body's immune systems have evolved to resist invasion by dangerous organisms, so too should our minds evolve to resist invasion by memes that may hinder our survival ability.

I now turn to the handicap principle to identify any benefits of theology which may have promoted the selection of theological discourse. This principle states that costly behaviors can be selected for if those behaviors, or the product of those behaviors, reliably signal the quality of an organism (Zahavi & Zahavi 1997). However, to apply the handicap principle to theological discourse is problematic as theological information is predominantly exchanged linguistically; whereas, the study of the biology of animal signalling has traditionally maintained that "verbal language does not contain any component that ensures reliability" (Zahavi & Zahavi 1997, 223). It would seem that the handicap principle should not be able to directly explain theological discourse in itself. At best, all it should be able to explain is the hard to fake emotional signalling that typically accompanies theological expressions.

I suggest however that the key to understanding the adaptive benefit of theological discourse, independent of any accompanied emotional signalling, is the incomprehensibility of theological language. As discussed, theological information possesses the characteristic of being meaningless to out-grou-

2 This is an assumption which some readers may find less plausible than others. However, after millions of years of natural selection, one would expect the members of our species to be incredibly efficient at reproducing. My method is to assess the extent to which theological expressions conform to this prediction so that any discrepancies can be accounted for.

pers. It would almost seem that theologies are finely configured to confuse outsiders in a manner that conditions them to recognise theological information as being useless.

As with any complex knowledge base, I suggest that it is only through a considerable investment of time and deliberate mental application, which entail opportunity costs, that religionists can familiarise themselves with the theology of their group. In this respect, some people will possess a greater degree of theological knowledge than others, and those capable of evidencing an extensive theological familiarity reliably signal the costly investment that they have undertaken to acquire this knowledge. Those only capable of expressing a weak level of theological knowledge indicate their low level of theological investment. So it is not theological information itself that is costly to express; but rather, the acquisition of the knowledge expressed during theological discourse is a self imposed Zahavian handicap.[3] Put succinctly, only those genuinely devoted to the gods will pay the opportunity costs associated with gossiping about them.

This proposition is consistent with the two assumptions that I identified previously. As my theory maintains that theology is a handicap that signals a particular quality of an agent, specifically one's degree of investment into the acquisition of supernatural knowledge, this predicts variation in theological ability. This is consistent with the first assumption that clergy, or religious elites, will possess a larger number of counter intuitive beliefs than non-elites. The second assumption, that a person can be led to accept additional counter intuitive properties of a god through rigorous theological training, conforms to my suggestion that the acquisition of theological information requires considerable investment in a religious group.

As biological handicaps normally signal specific qualities, I hypothesise that theological signalling contextually identifies at least three characteristics of the signaller. The first is moral commitment. Where a person believes that the gods demand certain moral behaviours, as well as familiarity with certain beliefs surrounding the gods, then strong comprehension of correct theology signals dedication to those gods. This, in turn, implies commitment to the moral values of the group.[4]

The second trait identified is intellectual capacity. Acquisition of theological information requires good learning and research abilities. Expressing a theological opinion requires strong analytical and argumentative skills.

---

3 This account does not predict that all religions and religionists will concern themselves with theological speculation. My argument is that within theologically heavy traditions, theology is retained because it is a cultural technology that performs a functional signalling purpose.

4 Whether theological practice is constituted so that only the morally committed will engage cannot be determined a priori, but must be demonstrated on a case-by-case analysis. The same is true for other characteristics of theological signalling.

Geoffrey Miller (2001) has argued that many moral values may have been selected as costly signals of good genes that code for the mental traits necessary to possess such moral values. Accordingly, I suggest that the theologian's ability to extensively acquire and accurately express their supernatural knowledge signals the presence of genes that code for the mental abilities necessary to acquire theological knowledge.

A third function that theology may perform is that of an epistemological adornment. By this I mean that those with the capacity to employ the artful or creative use of theology do so as a means to signal that they possess this capacity. To illustrate, Zahavi and Zahavi (1997) have argued that the extremely long hair possessed by human beings is a handicap that signals our ability to manage long hair. Those who have the resources to waste on personal grooming are able to display a beautiful head of hair, whilst those who struggle to eat on a daily basis will not incur the opportunity costs associated with decorating their heads.

Accordingly, those who opt to waste time and effort on the acquisition of theological knowledge signal that they possess resource surplus above a poverty threshold, whereas those for whom their immediate survival needs are a priority cannot afford this investment. Theological research requires resources that are unnecessary for ritual or emotional signalling, such as education, writing utensils, a means to transport letters, etc. In this respect, theology provides a venue for the display of wealth which the impoverished cannot afford. Take as an example the Hindu class hierarchy in which the theologically savvy brahman priests enjoy a high socio-economic status, whereas the dalits, who are at the lower end of the social hierarchy, tend to lack knowledge of scripture and temple tradition.[5]

Finally, I would like to discuss the implications that theological signalling may have for social prestige.[6] All three functionalities identified above, the signalling of moral commitments, intellectual capacities, and epistemological adornments, can earn prestige for the signaller by demonstrating the signaller's survival and reproductive fitness. As with prestige earned via other means, the presence of theological prestige could signal an individual's reliability and effectiveness as an exchange partner, suitability as a mate choice,[7] and strength as a potential competitor, etc.

5 I am not postulating a causal or proportionate relationship between inclusive fitness and theological wisdom, only that sustained theological acquisition is unlikely to occur within impoverished contexts. For example, theologically knowledgeable Yeshiva students may be economically poorer than their peers, but they are not impoverished.

6 For a detailed examination of the relationship between prestige and signalling behaviour, see Zahavi & Zahavi, 1997.

7 One objection is the proposition that some individuals, possessing much theological knowledge, claim to be celibate. Note that there is little to no evidence of the authenticity of such claims, nor that celibacy is damaging to one's inclusive fitness.

Although prestige is earned via numerous methods, the theoretical possibility of a theological prestige hierarchy exists, with the elite theologians occupying positions at the top of the hierarchy and casual religionists occupying positions near the bottom.[8] This proposition predicts that the individual in a group with the most theological knowledge will occupy the highest position in this hierarchy; I call this individual the alpha theologian. This prediction appears consistent with the structural composition we observe theologically heavy groups to possess, in which a ruling priest or rabbi will regularly address the group. The risk involved in addressing the group in this way functions to maintain the prestige of the alpha theologian. To elaborate, by falsely signalling intention to a large group the theologian risks greater public humiliation than if they were to falsely signal to a small group (Zahavi & Zahavi 1997). This resolves the dilemma of why a theologian might attempt to teach additional counter intuitive beliefs, even though such beliefs are likely to fall on deaf ears. They do so to maintain their prestige.

In conclusion, although theological content often consists of counter intuitive noise, it has not been selected against because it possesses functional purpose. The adaptive value of expressing theological knowledge is the reliable signalling of the substantial investment required to acquire such knowledge. Theological signalling has profound implications. When religious discourse is understood as a necessary commitment device that may have performed a significant role during the history of our species, the annihilation of such belief becomes less desirable. In this respect, we can view religion, not as a spell that needs to be broken, but as an artefact to be preserved.

References

Barret, J. 2004. *Why would anybody believe in God?* Walnut Creek, CA: AltaMira Press.

Boyer, P. 2001. *Religion explained: The evolutionary origins of religious thought.* New York, NY: Basic Books.

Robinson, J., Ed. 1990. *The Nag Hammadi Library*. New York, NY: HarperCollins.

Miller, G. 2001. *The mating mind: How sexual choice shaped the evolution of human nature.* New York, NY: Anchor Books.

Zahavi, A., & Zahavi, A. 1997. *The handicap principle.* New York, NY: Oxford University Press.

---

8 Theology is not the only phenomena around which human beings have constructed knowledge based signalling hierarchies. For example, countless hierarchies of this nature exist within modern academia. I regard such hierarchies to be secular renditions of the theological signalling strategies that exist within the doctrinal mode of religiosity.

Commitment Costs and Cooperation

Evidence from Candomblé, an Afro-Brazilian Religion

Montserrat Soler

Theoretical Background

The role of religion as a cohesive social force has been the focus of extensive theoretical attention but limited empirical work. Durkheim (1915/1965) proposed the notion of collective ritual as a crucial element in the construction and maintenance of social bonds, but the mechanisms by which this occurs have remained for the most part unexplored. Recently, theorists have expanded this notion to suggest that expressions of religious devotion that require significant investments of time, effort or economic resources constitute a powerful mechanism through which members of a community monitor each other's commitment and thus discourage cheaters and promote intra-group cooperation (Iannaccone 1994; Irons 2001; Sosis 2003). In the context of evolutionary theory, the sacrifices that individuals endure to be part of a religious community and which may appear senseless to outsiders may actually serve as "handicaps" (Zahavi 1975) or honest signals of commitment (Frank 1988) that are difficult to fake by virtue of their costliness. Thus, public and costly expressions of religiosity can serve to strengthen and maintain cooperation in a social group. For ritual to be a reliable signal, individuals who display high levels of religious commitment should also behave more cooperatively with members of their own congregation. Previous studies focused on Western religious traditions have provided support for this idea (see Sosis & Bressler 2003; Sosis & Ruffle 2003; Sosis & Ruffle 2004).

As a further test of this hypothesis, I conducted research on a Brazilian population that practices a religion of African origin known as Candomblé. I measured religious commitment through a self-report scale that focused on public expressions of religiosity and used an economic game as a proxy for cooperation. Recent studies have used economic games cross-culturally with interesting outcomes (e.g., Henrich et al. 2004). The research was conducted from August 2005 to October 2006 in Salvador da Bahia, the fifth-largest city of Brazil and widely considered the core of Afro-Brazilian culture. Only a portion of the results will be presented here.

Research Setting

Candomblé arose in the 19th century as a mix of faiths brought to Brazil by enslaved West Africans. Belief is centered on the cult of the *orixás*, deities with distinct personalities and physical representations that interfere directly in human affairs. A positive relationship with the *orixás* ensures the balance of *axé*, the life-energy of the universe. Difficulties are believed to be caused by a lack or misuse of *axé* and rituals are aimed at restoring the delicate balance of *axé* in one's life. In this way, Candomblé is a pragmatic religion primarily concerned with solving the tribulations of everyday life (see Bastide 1958/2001).

The religion centers around houses of worship or *terreiros* which also function as private residences for the leader of the house, family members, and often some followers. Although *terreiros* are self-governing, they share a well-established ritual structure and social organization. The head of a *terreiro* (*ialorixá* in the case of a woman and *babalorixá* in the case of a man) is the undisputed authority in both religious and secular matters and presides over a strict hierarchy. Membership in a *terreiro* varies on a continuum of commitment to the religion and to the house itself: there are fully initiated members, those on the path to initiation, frequent visitors, and occasional clients. *Terreiros* make most of their income from clients that come to the *ialorixá* or *babalorixá* in search of solutions to health problems, money troubles, or unfortunate love affairs.

Communication with the supernatural occurs through various rituals, including elaborate feasts during which the *orixás* possess the faithful in a music-induced trance. Feasts consume a large proportion of the *terriero*'s income and require the coordination and cooperation of all members. In addition to these public occasions, there are frequent internal rituals and periods of cleansing and seclusion that can last up to several months. A devotee of Candomblé must also follow an exacting regime that includes proscriptions on food, dress, and codes of behavior related to *terreiro* hierarchy. The organization of Candomblé provides a natural setting in which differences in religious commitment and cooperation can be studied at both the individual and group level.

Methodology

Participants were members from 13 *terreiros* who responded to a questionnaire, a religious commitment scale and participated in an economic game. All activities were conducted at different *terreiros* on separate dates when most regular members could be present. To maximize variation in factors that could affect religious commitment and cooperation, the chosen *terreiros* were located in various neighborhoods, varied in size from 10 to 300 members (mean = 53.7; s.d.= 93.3) and ranged from 4 to 37 in years since foundation (mean =19.3; s.d.= 10.8). Actual number of participants at each *terreiro* ranged from 11 to 30 (mean = 20.2; s.d.= 6.3).

To measure religious commitment, I created a 14-item 7-point Likert scale (Cronbach's alpha = .87). The following is an example of an item used in the scale:

I have never missed a feast at my terreiro.

1	2	3	4	5	6	7
Completely Disagree						*Completely Agree*

The public-goods economic game was conducted immediately after subjects had responded the questionnaire and the scale. This game is designed so that everyone wins more if more people cooperate, but individuals do better by not cooperating. It provides a measure of cooperation by evaluating each individual's willingness to benefit others at the expense of self gain. Subjects are randomly assigned to *n*-person groups that remain anonymous. An equal amount of money is given to each subject, who then decides how much to keep and how much to donate to his or her *n*-person group. The amounts given by members of individual groups are added up and duplicated by the researcher. The resulting amounts are then divided equally among members of each *n*-group. Participants are allowed to keep the initial quantity they retained as well as whatever they earn from their *n*-person group.

I explained all procedures following a script and mock practices of the economic game were carried out with volunteers from each *terreiro*. Subjects were then randomly assigned to 4-person groups with the other members of the *terreiro* present, but no one other than me was aware of who composed which group. Each person received a closed envelope containing $10 Brazilian Reais in bills of 1's and 2's (the daily minimum wage is equivalent to US $11.60). Subjects were told to go to a separate area and remove from the envelope any amount from 0 to 10 (i.e. 0, 1, 2, 3...10) that they wanted to retain and afterwards to return the envelope enclosing the amount they wished to donate to their anonymous group. After all envelopes had been returned, I did the calculations for each group and participants received their final amount. Two field assistants monitored the room to ensure that decisions regarding the game remained anonymous and subjects could not discuss them with each other before the end of the game.

Results

Two-hundred and forty two subjects participated (133 female; 109 males) but only 196 completed responses to the scale were used in the analysis. Sex had no effect on either the scale (t = 172; df. 195, p = .864) or the game (t = -460, d.f., 239; p = .646). Mean age of subjects was 34.9 (s.d. 13.6) but since women were slightly older, both these variables were included in the regression model. Marital status, coded as a dummy variable, was also included (57.9% of subjects were single, 30.4% married or living with someone, and 11.7% separated, divorced or widowed) as well as race (50.4% of subjects identified themselves as "negro" or black, 20.8% as "moreno" or light brown, 12.1% as "pardo", an older term also meaning light brown, and 7.5% as "other" including "branco" or white). Household income was collapsed into 6 categories dealing with monthly minimum wage (R $350 reais or about US $163.05). More than half the subjects reported earnings of less than 1 minimum wage (16.7% no income, 8.1% up to half a minimum wage, 30.3% half to 1 minimum wage, 29% from 1 to 2 minimum wages, 10.4% from 2 to 3 minimum wages, and only 5.4% more than 3 minimum wages). Multiple answers were not included. Subjects also reported the number of years they had been part of the religion (mean = 15.6; s.d. 12.2) and years frequenting the actual *terreiro* where the questionnaire was being administered (mean = 10. 5; s.d. 9).

Results from the game are quantified as the offer (amount left in the envelope for donation to the 4-person group), while number responses to scale items were added to produce a single score for each individual. The mean offer was 4.8 (s.d. 3.2) with a median of 4 and a mode of 10 (16.9% of players gave the mode; the next most common offer was 2 with 15.3%). Scale responses had a mean of 69.0 (s.d. 19.8). Pearson's correlations reveal that income is the strongest predictor of game offer (r = .223, p = .001, n = 220) and also significantly related to scale, but in the opposite direction (r = -.198, p = .009, n = 175). Thus, when game offer and the sum of the scale are correlated there is no relationship in the expected direction (r = .030, p = .338, n = 196), but it approaches significance when income is controlled (partial correlation, r = .141, p = .064, n = 171).

Table I shows the results of the OLS regression with game offer as the dependent variable and all controls in the model (adjusted R^2 = .139). To test if the scale was consistent with a single underlying element that accounted for religious commitment, I performed a factor analysis with the results from the research sample. This statistical procedure allows the researcher to detect the presence of underlying factors that relate items in a scale to each other.

Table I: OLS Regression Model of the Game Offer (amount left in envelope) Including the Religious Commitment Scale

Model		Unstandardized Coefficients		Standardized Coefficients	T	Sig.
		B	Std. Error	Beta		
1	(Constant)	-1.353	1.746		-.775	.440
	Sex	-.216	.604	-.034	-.358	.721
	Age	.081	.028	.342	2.867	.005***
	Education	.089	.213	.040	.420	.675
	Income	.608	.211	.272	2.882	.005***
	Married or lives with someone	-1.803	.744	-.232	-2.424	.017**
	Separated, divorced or widowed	-.290	1.015	-.029	-.286	.775
	Moreno	-1.065	.681	-.145	-1.564	.121
	Pardo	-.881	.919	-.090	-.959	.340
	Other race	.887	1.048	.078	.847	.399
	Membership in particular terreiro	.005	.090	.006	.060	.953
	Years in Candomblé	-.026	.031	-.104	-.845	.400
	Years in Terreiro	-.024	.036	-.071	-.670	.504
	Religious commitment scale	.031	.017	.181	1.805	.074*

$N = 196$; * $p = .10$; ** $p = .05$; *** $p = .01$ or below

A perfect relationship between an item and a factor is characterized as 1. In this case, results indicated that the existence of two subscales, which I termed the "group commitment sub-scale" (GCS) and the "personal commitment sub-scale" (PCS). GCS items had high loadings on factor 1 (over .5) and low loadings on factor 2 (under .3) and were related to communal activities, such as "I have never missed a feast in my *terreiro*". On the other hand, PCS items had high loadings on factor 2 (over .6) and low loadings on factor 1 (under .3) and dealt with personal commitment, such as "There are certain foods I do not eat because of my *orixá*". The subscales had 6 items each and good reliability scores (Cronbach's alpha = .77; n = 215 for the GCS; Cronbach's alpha = .79, n = 220 for the PCS).

I performed an OLS regression with each of the subscales including the controls shown in Table I. The PCS had no predictive effect on the game offer (β = .087, p = .375) although the model was significant at the .001 level (adjusted R^2 = .117) due to the effects of age (β = .343, p = .003), income (β = .213, p = .019), and being married or living with someone (β = .-221, p = .017). Other variables were not significant. However, as shown in Table II, the GCS did have a significant relationship with game offer (adjusted R^2 = .150):

Table II:
OLS Regression Model of the Game Offer (amount left in envelope) Including Group Commitment Subscale (GCS)

Model		Unstandardized Coefficients		Standardized Coefficients	T	Sig.
		B	Std. Error	Beta		
1	(Constant)	-2.055	1.835		-1.120	.265
	Sex	-.398	.573	-.063	-.694	.489
	Age	.088	.027	.372	3.265	.001**
	Education	.087	.207	.039	.421	.674
	Income	.606	.205	.271	2.962	.004**
	Married or lives with someone	-1.698	.703	-.218	-2.415	.017*
	Separated, divorced or widowed	-.358	.984	-.035	-.364	.716
	Moreno	-1.044	.642	-.144	-1.625	.107
	Pardo	-.986	.880	-.101	-1.120	.265
	Other race	.821	1.035	.070	.793	.430
	Membership in particular terreiro	.021	.083	.022	.250	.803
	Years in Candomblé	-.031	.030	-.124	-1.053	.295
	Years in Terreiro	-.016	.035	-.045	-.449	.654
	GCS	.081	.038	.194	2.139	.035*

N = 196; *p = .05; **p = .01 or below

Discussion

Results show that individuals with higher scores on the religious commitment scale also cooperate more on the economic game. This supports the notion that ritual functions as a reliable signal of individuals' willingness to cooperate with members of their own group. Factor analysis revealed a data-grounded division of the results of the scale into two subscales that deal with different aspects of religiosity. While the subscale that captures elements of personal religiosity (PCS) did not have a predictive effect on results of the game, scores for the community-oriented subscale (GCS) were positively related to individual offers in the game. This further supports the idea that it is public aspects of ritual that are important to promote cooperation because they are more open to inspection and easily monitored. It may be that expressions of religiosity that are personal in nature and thus more open to cheating are associated with more sinister aspects of religion, such as deception and manipulation (see Trivers 2000). These instances are undeniably part of the repertoire of religious behavior and there has been theoretical work from an evolutionary perspective that suggests that religion-as-a-signal does not necessarily imply positive sociality (Cronk 1994).

Further research should attempt to separate aspects of ritual in more discrete categories that identify the diverse functions of ritual and the different processes by which it has become a universal referent of human societies. Religion consists of multi-layered categories of behavior, cognition and emotion and in the context of evolutionary theory this presents an obstacle to conceptualizing it as an adaptation. It is important to point out that evidence presented here tells us something about the adaptive value of religion, but not necessarily about its characterization as an evolved adaptation.

Author's Note

This project was made possible by a National Science Foundation Dissertation Improvement Grant and a Wenner-Gren Foundation Dissertation Research Grant. I am grateful to Lee Cronk for advice during the research and his comments for this paper. I would like to thank Almir Dos Santos Moreira for his help throughout the fieldwork and especially the people of Candomblé for their generosity and hospitality.

References

Bastide, R. 2001. *O Candomblé da Bahia*. São Paulo, Brazil: Companhia das Letras. Original work published 1958.

Cronk, L. 1994. Evolutionary theories of morality and the manipulative use of signals. *Zygon: Journal of Religion & Science*, 291, 32-58.

Durkheim, E. 1965. *The elementary forms of religious life*. New York, NY: Free Press. Original work published 1915.

Frank, R. H. 1988. *Passions within reason*. New York, NY: Norton.

Henrich, J., Boyd, R., Bowles, S., Camerer, C., Fehr, E. & Gintis, H. Eds.. 2004. *Foundations of human sociality*. Oxford, UK: Oxford University Press.

Iannaccone, L. R. 1994. Why strict churches are strong. *American Journal of Sociology, 99* 5, 1180-1211.

Irons, W. 2001. Religion as a hard-to-fake sign of commitment. In R. Neese, Ed.. *Evolution and the capacity for commitment*, 292-309. New York, NY: Russell Sage Foundation.

Sosis, R. 2003. Why aren't we all Hutterites? Costly signaling theory and religious behavior. *Human Nature, 14* (2), 91-127.

Sosis, R., & Bressler, E. 2003. Cooperation and commune longevity: A test of the costly signaling theory of religion. *Cross-Cultural Research, 37*2, 211-239.

Sosis, R., & Ruffle, B. J. 2003. Religious ritual and cooperation: Testing for a relationship on Israeli religious and secular kibbutzim. *Current Anthropology, 44* (5), 713-722.

Sosis, R., & Ruffle, B. J. 2004. Ideology, religion and the evolution of cooperation: Field tests on Israel kibbutzim. *Research in Economic Anthropology, 23*, 89-117.

Trivers, R. 2000. The elements of a scientific theory of self-deception. *Annals of the New York Academy of Sciences, 907* (1), 114-131.

Zahavi, A. 1975. Mate selection – A selection for a handicap. *Journal of Theoretical Biology*, 53 (1), 205-214.

Ritual, Agency, and Sexual Selection

Ilkka Pyysiäinen

Introduction

I present the hypothesis that religious beliefs and practices are widespread in human cultures partly because sexual selection has at some point seized ritualized behavior related to supernatural agents. I say "partly" because other factors, such as natural selection, must also have contributed to the evolution of religion. In sexual selection, some trait in sexually reproducing organisms becomes a sign of either good overall condition (good genes) or of the fact that the individual is likely to be capable and willing to invest resources in the care of the offspring. A peacock's tail, for example, is costly to grow in terms of energy, difficult to carry, and an obvious handicap when trying to avoid predators. Therefore, it is a reliable sign of good condition of its carrier for the peahen.

When a genetic mutation at some point in evolution made a given peahen develop a liking for a long tail in the male, her offspring inherited both the liking (females) and the long tail (males). Therefore, when in the following generations the average length of the tail gradually grew, an arms race of sorts developed. Peacocks with the longest tails produced more offspring than others, and thus the average tail length kept growing. Despite the sexual selection pressure, not all peacocks could grow a long tail because it requires a good overall condition which, in turn, is determined by many different genes (see Kokko, Brooks, & Jennions 2003; Kokko, Jennions, & Brooks 2006; Kotiaho, Simmons, & Tomkins 2001; Miller 2000a, b; Tomkins, Radwan, Kotiaho, & Tregenza 2004). Psychologist Geoffrey Miller provides theoretical arguments to the effect also that cultural phenomena such as music, morality, and religion might be due to sexual selection (Miller 2000a, b; Miller 2007; Dennett 2006, 87-89). Haselton and Miller (2006) have also shown that women near peak fertility (midcycle) prefer inherited creativity over wealth in short-term mating. As creativity is a sign of good genes, women prefer creative males as mating partners.

Ritual

Boyer and Liénard (2006) argue that a *hazard precaution system*, geared to the detection of and reaction to inferred threats to fitness, can lead to ritualization of behavior in individuals. Such threats create a specific adaptive problem because (1) they are quite diverse; (2) there is no straightforward feedback demonstrating that a threat has been removed, since it is in the nature of such threats that they are not directly observable; (3) appropriate measures cannot be mapped one-to-one to physically different classes of threats, since each type of threat may require very different precautions, depending on the situation. Ritualized action is then typified by stereotypy, rigidity, repetitiveness, and partition of behavior into subactions which do not seem to have any immediate instrumental goals. Such ritualization of action is found not only in cultural ceremonies but equally in children's rituals and the obsessive compulsive disorder (see also Liénard & Boyer 2006).

The hazard precaution system activates a safety motivation system, leading to arousal and a feeling that *something must* be done. Certain actions seem intuitively to be called for, although one does not have any explanation for why this is so. In the aroused state, attention is focused on low-level properties of action which thus is "parsed" in smaller units than normally. Such upper-level categories as "walking" are replaced by such lower-level categories as "walking-in-this-or-that-specific-manner." To this is connected a "just right" syndrome: everything must be done very carefully, and yet one can never be sure that a goal has been reached. As the relationship of the low-level actions with the more general goal of the ritual is close to a mystery, repetition of action follows. The types of actions concerned relate to a few salient themes such as pollution and purification, danger and protection, as well as intrusion of others and the construction of an ordered environment. (Boyer & Liénard 2006; Liénard & Boyer 2006).

Agency

I suggest that an inferred threat is most readily interpreted with reference to some invisible agent (see Boyer 1996; Guthrie 1993). By agents I mean organisms whose behavior can be successfully predicted by other organisms by postulating conscious beliefs and desires (Dennett 1987, 15-17). We are hypersensitive for cues about human-like agency because in the environment of evolutionary adaptedness, the most important threat to humans has been other human agents (see Alexander 1979, 222-224). We have what psychologist Justin Barrett (2000) calls a "hyperactive agent detection device." Even minimal cues can trigger the postulation of agency to account for ambiguous perceptions and feelings of presence. Also the inference from apparent order in reality to an intelligent designer and creator springs from the same psychological root (Kelemen 2004; Pyysiäinen 2005; see Bering 2003). The false positives that an overreacting detector produces are not biologically maladaptive as long as their costs are lower than their benefits (Atran 2006).

We do not merely scan the environment to find agents, however; we also try to predict the intentions of agents (see German & Hehman 2006; Leslie, German, & Polizzi 2005; Wellman & Miller 2006). We are eager to know what others think, feel, and are up to. This is apparent in such phenomena as gossiping (Boyer 2001), divination methods such as telling fortune from tea leaves (Dennett 2006, 132-135), or projective tests that are supposed to reveal the subject's personality on the basis of what one sees in random inkblots, for example (Wood, Nezworski, & Garb 2003).

Sexual selection

Miller (2000a, 345) points out that ritualization means evolutionary modification of movements and structures to improve their function as signals. Ritualization results from the sexual selection of signals and displays to excite optimally the perceptual systems of receivers. Courtship, for example, is typified by ritual action. I now suggest that Miller's and Boyer and Liénard's views of ritualization might be combined. I hypothesize that sexual selection has seized the ritualization of individual behavior that is then used as a behavioral modality in cultural ceremonies in which supernatural agents appear as agents or patients of action (see Lawson & McCauley 1990). Men who could dance longer than others, who sacrificed more than their competitors, or who could memorize longer and more elaborate narratives, excited the interest of females, which meant a better reproductive success for these males (see Miller 2000b, 349-353). Women may have preferred such "religious" males as mating partners, because dancing indicates good motor skills and therefore good overall condition; sacrifice signals that one has a surplus of resources and thus could be a good provider; reciting narratives and secret knowledge, for its part, is an indication of good cognitive skills and, possibly, empathy, which means that the male is in good overall condition and is competent in taking care of the offspring. When females prefer such males over others, the genetic traits expressed in male behavior will become ever more elaborate and (up to a point) widespread (see Kokko et al. 2003, 2006; Kotiaho et al. 2001).

Although this is so far only a speculative hypothesis, it is testable in principle (see Miller 2007). It is possible to explore, for example, if men display their "religiosity" as part of courtship, whether they also try to downplay the "religiosity" of their sexual competitors, whether females really prefer "religious" males, and whether females at peak fertility prefer "religious" indications of good genes over wealth. Moreover, it could also be studied whether "non-religiosity" correlates with bad genes (due to inbreeding, for example); if it does, that could mean that "religiosity," indeed, is a reliable sign of good genes. Perhaps the biggest challenge is to develop an application of a mathematical model that allows us to evaluate the *relative* contribution of sexual selection, compared to natural selection and other factors such as migration, genetic drift, and co-evolution (see Richerson & Boyd 2005).

I use the word "religious" in quotes because I am actually not talking about the very heterogeneous domain of religion but rather about some and only some such traits that are currently grouped under the umbrella term "religion" (see also Kirkpatrick 2006). "Religion" thus is here only a placeholder for certain traits, such as ritual dancing, sacrifice, and beliefs about supernatural agents. It is a folk-psychological way of talking about those things that ultimately realize "religion." "Religion" thus can be "multiply realized" by many different sorts of things (see Lewis 1972).

It is even possible in principle that the object of selection has been some trait that underlies "religion," among other things, without which "religion" itself would be fitness-enhancing (see Boyer 1994; Kirkpatrick 2006). It is possible that what is generally known as "religion" is even a maladaptive low-fitness extreme of some variable mental trait that evolved through mutual mate choice. Where certain alleles increase the extent to which high-fitness family members develop impressive courtship abilities, they also increase the maladaptive behavior in low-fitness family members (see Shaner, Miller, & Mintz 2004). "Religion" would thus be a degenerate form of some fitness-enhancing trait(s), a runaway process in the cognitive evolution of our species (cf. Dennett 2006, 74-93).

However, my own hypothesis is that "religion" is an arena for elaborate courtship behaviors, whereas schizophrenia might be the low-fitness extreme of the same mental traits (Shaner et al. 2004). If the hypothesis is true, it will go a long way towards explaining why individual ritualized action has in certain cases grown into elaborate ceremonies with much sensory pageantry as well as why information about supernatural agents and their mysterious will is often held in such high esteem (cf. McCauley & Lawson 2002; Pyysiäinen 2001, 84-97). The following are among the things that might speak for sexual selection of "religious" beliefs and practices: "religion" is adopted in puberty (rites of initiation) and is male-dominated (women mostly as "audience"), it is costly in terms of time and resources, it is species-specific like all sexually selected traits, there are heritable differences in "religious" attitudes and behavior (see Koenig & Bouchard 2006), and "religion" has a multimodular basis in mind (see Boyer 2001).

Author's Note

I want to thank Hanna Kokko and Pierre Liénard for helpful comments.

References

Alexander, R. D. 1979. *Darwinism and human affairs*. Seattle, WA: University of Washington Press.

Atran, S. 2006. The cognitive and evolutionary roots of religion. In P. McNamara, Ed., *Where God and science meet: How brain and evolutionary studies alter our understanding of religion*, Vol. 1, 181-207. Westport, CT: Praeger Perspectives.

Barrett, J. L. 2000. Exploring the natural foundations of religion. *Trends in Cognitive Sciences, 4*, 29-34.

Bering, J. M. 2003. Towards a cognitive theory of existential meaning. *New Ideas in Psychology, 21*, 101-120.

Boyer, P. 1994. *The naturalness of religious ideas: A cognitive theory of religion*. Berkeley, CA: University of California Press.

Boyer, P. 1996. What makes anthropomorphism natural: Intuitive ontology and cultural representations. *The Journal of the Royal Anthropological Institute*, 2 (1), 83-97.

Boyer, P. 2001. *Religion explained: The evolutionary origins of religious thought*. New York, NY: Basic Books.

Boyer, P., & Liénard, P. 2006. Why ritualized behavior? Precaution systems and action-parsing in developmental, pathological and cultural rituals. *Behavioral & Brain Sciences, 29* (6), 595-650.

Dennett, D. C. 1987. *The intentional stance*. Cambridge, MA: The MIT Press.

Dennett, D. C. 2006. *Breaking the spell: Religion as a natural phenomenon*. New York, NY: Viking.

German, T. P., & Hehman, J. A. 2006. Representational and executive selection resources in 'theory of mind': Evidence from compromised belief-desire reasoning in old age. *Cognition, 191*, 129-152.

Guthrie, S. E. 1993. *Faces in the clouds*. New York, NY: Oxford University Press.

Haselton, M. G., & Miller, G. F. 2006. Women's fertility across the cycle increases the short-term attractiveness of creative intelligence. *Human Nature*, 17 (1), 50-73.

Kelemen, D. 2004. Are children "intuitive theists"? Reasoning about purpose and design in nature. *Psychological Science, 15* (5), 295-301.

Kirkpatrick, L. A. 2006. Religion is not an adaptation. In P. McNamara, Ed., *Where God and science meet: How brain and evolutionary studies alter our understanding of religion*, Vol. 1, 159-179. Westport, CT and London: Praeger Perspectives.

Koenig, L. B., & Bouchard, T. J., Jr. 2006. Genetic and environmental influences on the traditional moral values triad – authoritarianism, conservatism, and religiousness – as assessed by quantitative behavior genetic methods. In P. McNamara, Ed., *Where God and science meet: How brain and evolutionary studies alter our understanding of religion*, Vol. 1, 31-60. Westport, CT and London: Praeger Perspectives.

Kokko, H., Brooks, R., & Jennions, M. D. 2003. The evolution of mate choice and mating biases. *Proceedings of the Royal Society of London, Series B, 270*, 653-664.

Kokko, H., Jennions, M. D., & Brooks, R. 2006. Unifying and testing models of sexual selection. *Annual Review of Ecology, Evolution, & Systematics, 37*, 43-66.

Kotiaho, J. S., Simmons, L. W., & Tomkins, J. 2001. Towards a resolution of the lek paradox. *Nature, 410*, 684-686.

Lawson, E. T., & McCauley, R. N. 1990. *Rethinking religion: Connecting cognition and culture*. Cambridge, UK: Cambridge University Press.

Leslie, A. M., German, T. P., & Polizzi, P. 2005. Belief-desire reasoning as a process of selection. *Cognitive Psychology, 50*, 45-85.

Lewis, D. 1972. Psychophysical and theoretical identifications. *Australasian Journal of Philosophy, 50* (3), 249-258.

Liénard, P., & Boyer, P. 2006. Whence collective rituals? A cultural selection model of ritualized behavior. *American Anthropologist*, 108 (4), 814-827.

McCauley, R. N., & Lawson, E. T. 2002. *Bringing ritual to mind: Psychological foundations of cultural forms*. Cambridge, UK: Cambridge University Press.

Miller, G. 2000a. Evolution of human music through sexual selection. In N. L.Wallin, B. Merker, & S. Brown, Eds., *The origins of music*, 329-360. Cambridge, MA: MIT Press.

Miller, G. 2000b. *The mating mind*. New York, NY: Anchor Books.

Miller, G. 2007. Sexual selection for moral virtues. *Quarterly Review of Biology*.

Pyysiäinen, I. 2001. *How religion works: Towards a new cognitive science of religion*. Leiden, Netherlands: Brill Academic Publishers.

Pyysiäinen, I. 2005. God: A brief history with a cognitive explanation of the concept *Temenos*, 41(1), 77-128.

Richerson, P., & Boyd, R. 2005. *Not by genes alone: How culture transformed human evolution*. Chicago, IL: University of Chicago Press.

Shaner, A., Miller G., & Mintz, J. 2004. Schizophrenia as one extreme of a sexually selected fitness indicator. *Schizophrenia Research, 70*, 101-109.

Tomkins, J. L., Radwan, J., Kotiaho, J. S., Tregenza, T. 2004. Genic capture and resolving the lek paradox. *Trends in Ecology & Evolution*, 19 (6), 323-328.

Wellman, H. M., & Miller, J. G. (2006). Developing conceptions of responsive intentional agents. *Journal of Cognition& Culture*, 6 (1-2), 27-55.

Wood, J. M., Nezworski, M. T., & Garb, H. N. (2003). *What's wrong with the Rorschach?* San Francisco, CA: Jossey-Bass.

The Attraction of Religion

A Sexual Selectionist Account

D. Jason Slone

Why is Religion Attractive?

Nearly 2 billion of the world's people belong to an institution that regularly serves its members a small meal of baked dough and fruit juice. The members are told that the meal is the flesh and blood of a dead-but-living fatherless god-man who has the super-powers to grant utopian immortality to those who eat him.

Nearly 1.5 billion of the world's people belong to a different institution that requires that five times a day members wash parts of their bodies with water, get down on their knees, bend over, and put their heads on the ground while repeating prescribed words. Members of this institution are also required to starve and parch themselves all day every day for a full lunar month. Some believe that taking even a sip of water during this time can result in eternal hellish punishment after death.

In every culture we know—large and small, simple and complex, past and present—people engage in these strange types of behaviors called "religion." Religions are strange because they require people to engage in activities that seem, from a biological point of view, to be *costly* and apparently *useless*. Therefore the widespread existence of religion is puzzling because according to the theory of evolution by natural and sexual selection, nature is supposed to weed out (i.e., select against) organisms that engage in behaviors that don't lead directly or indirectly to survival or reproduction. Thus an evolutionary approach to explaining religion asks, "What benefits, if any, do individuals gain by committing to institutions that require costly and useless behaviors based on mythical stories about counterfactual worlds?"

Fortunately, such an answer may be available, because it turns out that humans are not the only species that engages in costly and useless behaviors. Therefore we may be able to employ theories that evolutionary biologists have put forth to explain costly and useless behaviors in other species to explain religion.

Costly Signaling Theory of Religion

Consider the bowerbird (Family: *Ptilonorhynchidae*) of Australia/New Guinea. Male bowerbirds build elaborate nest-like constructions called "bowers" in cleared patches of earth and then spend hours meticulously decorating them with striking accessories like leaves, berries, feathers, shells, etc. Bower building is serious business, too. Each bower is unique, and males compete with other males for the most beautiful design (even going so far as to steal materials from other bowers.) Why spend so much costly time and effort on useless decorations?

Bower building seems to make no evolutionary sense, until you see the behavior of *female* bowerbirds. During mating season, females travel from one bower to the next, judging them according to some (as yet unclear to ornithologists) criteria. Once the female identifies the finest bower, she proceeds to reward its architect by mating with him. So engaging in bower building is not useless after all; it is a *mating strategy*.

This bowerbird model employs a framework known as "costly signaling theory." In short, costly signaling theory argues that costly and useless behaviors (or traits, like the peacock's tail) communicate strategic information about oneself to others in the environment, like parents, predators, allies, and potential mates (see Maynard Smith & Harper 1995). Obviously, depending on the species, context, etc., different species engage in different types of costly signaling. In mate attraction, however, the sex with the lower parental investment costs typically produces more elaborate signals to the sex with the higher parental investment costs, because the latter tends to be more reproductively choosy given her/his asymmetrically higher parental investment costs.[1] Thus females tend to be choosier than males and so males "show off" as a means of signaling that they possess desirable mate characteristics. In our species, however, males also tend to invest heavily in offspring—albeit typically not as heavily as females—and therefore sex-based differences in human mate preferences are relatively minor compared to other species (Buss 2003).

Nonetheless, what is it that women and men want, and therefore men and women claim to have? Through numerous studies involving more than ten-thousand participants in several dozen countries, D. Buss and colleagues found that women and men everywhere tend to desire the following characteristics (among others) in a mate: considerate, honest, dependable, kind, understanding, fond of children, and good family background (Buss 2003). Why these preferences? The logic is seemingly straightforward for females.

1 Parental investment costs include any expenditure (time, energy etc.) that benefits an offspring at a cost to a parent's ability to invest in other components of fitness (Trivers 1972).

Given their high reproductive costs, women seek men with strong "family values"[2] to help with rearing offspring.

How can a woman know that a man has such values? One way to find out would be, of course, to ask him. However, that strategy is far from foolproof. As most women know, men will lie. Therefore a more reliable strategy for mate evaluation may be to track what a man does rather than what he says. Behaviors are more honest and reliable indicators of character than words because behaviors are typically more costly and therefore hard-to-fake. In this sense, we may amend the old cliché from "actions speak louder than words" to "actions *signal* louder than words."

As such, an effective strategy for a male to increase his attractiveness is to engage in "good" behaviors as signals of having a desirable character. It should be obvious, then, why religion may be attractive. By being committed to a religious system (as evidenced by being willing to engage in its costly and apparently useless behaviors) and its ethical demands, which typically includes prohibitions against selfish, anti-social behavior, a man signals that he possesses the types of characteristics that a woman would find desirable. Indeed, it is striking to compare the types of characteristics women find desirable in men (again: considerate, honest, dependable, kind, understanding, fond of children, and good family background) with the types of behaviors that the ethical systems of world religions encourage. In this view, it is not a coincidence that all of the major world religions (i.e., Judaism, Christianity, Islam, Hinduism, and Buddhism) preach some version of the "golden rule" to treat others the way you wish to be treated.

However, if this claim is accurate, why don't we find the world's churches and temples filled exclusively with men? Why should women also bother with all the costliness and uselessness of religion if it's only men who have to signal? The key word in that question is, of course, "only." Obviously, men engage in mate choice, also. As such, women compete with other women to increase their attractiveness to men, just as men compete with other men to increase their attractiveness to women.

So what do men want? Typically, men want beauty (signals of gene quality) and youth (signals of reproductive capacity). However, when considering *long-term* mates, with whom they will produce and rear offspring, men prefer women who show signs of chastity (signals of paternity reliability) and fidelity (signals of parental investment). Thus, we should expect to find—and we do—that religions encourage women to cultivate these characteristics.

---

2 It seems to me *not* a coincidence that religions seem to obsess over instilling "family values" in their adherents, as well as eliminating perceived threats to such values, as in the case of the resurgence of "fundamentalism" in all the world's religions in the modern period.

Indeed, women are often *forced* to adhere to such rules via threats (typically, but not always, from male leaders) of severe punishment for rule-violations.

The Usefulness of (Otherwise) Useless God Concepts

If religion is merely an arena for mate evaluation, why does religion involve stories about gods, goddesses, ghosts, demons, etc.? Couldn't groups create secular rules and laws that would work just as well without all the unnecessary mythology? In principle, the answer is yes. However, in practice, the use of supernatural agents as gods, goddesses, ghosts, etc., is a "good trick" (Dennett 2006).

Why is the use of supernatural agents a good trick? There may be several reasons. One reason may be what I call the "Santa Claus effect." Teaching people that supernatural agents exist that can see your every move (and know your every thought, which may lead to moves) and may punish you for transgressions may help to deter people from "sin." If people are convinced that someone is always watching them, they may be less likely to engage in selfish behavior (Johnson 2005).

An alternative to (though compatible with) the Santa Claus hypothesis is that requiring people to profess belief in a non-empirically verifiable deity is an effective way to ensure quality control over membership. Requiring potential members of a religious organization to commit to a god that has no verifiable existence—which is to say, require them to make a costly and useless commitment—is a good trick for discovering who is and who isn't thoroughly committed to the group and its principles. Simply put, other members will be able to tell if you are committed to the group by whether or not you are willing to engage in the costly and useless rituals they require. In this sense, it is precisely the costliness and uselessness of such commitment requirements that make them useful as honest signals of group commitment.[3] Such requirements may deter "free-riders" who could be merely posing as committed to the group (Sosis, 2004). So why is religion attractive? Simply put, it may be an effective way to find a good mate (Irons 2001).

The Reproductive Logic of Religious War

If accurate, this theory may also explain why religion is commonly involved in war. One evolutionary theory of war is that war involves attempts to mate poach, and in defense, to mate guard (see Buss 2002). Mate poaching is accomplished by either gaining direct access to mates or by gaining

3 Indeed, this is a common strategy used in other types of organizations that require engaging in costly and useless rituals (e.g., dress, language, group-specific activities, etc.) as a sign of one's commitment to the group, like militaries, fraternities and sororities, political parties, and corporations.

access to reproduction-enhancing resources. Cosmides and Toody write, "[c]oalitional aggression evolved because it allowed participants in such coalitions to promote their fitness by gaining access to disputed reproduction enhancing resources that would otherwise be denied to them" (Tooby & Cosmides 1988, i). Importantly, wars are typically fought by men in their peek reproductive years of life when peer competition is most intense, roughly ages 17-35, and over three issues of vital concern to their reproductive success: perceived threats to status and/or reputation, control over territory, and access to resources (Goldstein 2003). Wars may erupt because reproductively competitive men produce and/or perceive threats regarding their status and/or reputation, their ability to control a territory, and/or their access to resources—because any/all of these occurrences may lead to "mate poaching" by competitors and/or "mate defection" by females.

A costly signaling theory of religious violence argues that since one of religion's functions is to weed out men who are not truly committed to a group (as judged by willingness to engage in costly and useless behaviors), religion could be useful in times of war. Religion may provide an effective way to decipher which men and women can (and cannot) be trusted in conflict zones. Thus we ought to expect religious commitment and commitment requirements to increase during times of war, as well as occurrences and severity of punishment of defectors (Boyer 2001, Ch. 8). Also, if religion is used as a means of ensuring that women remain chaste and loyal, then in war contexts we ought to see the use of religion to restrict women's ability to interact with the potential mate poachers. This can be accomplished by concealing women from public sight and/or restricting their movements.[4]

Is there empirical support for the reproductive logic of religious war? Although limited, there are some supportive data. For instance, R. Pape (2005) has shown that all suicide terrorist acts (N=315) from 1980-2003 were committed by weak, non-state actors in defense of homelands occupied by democratic nations with significant religious differences. And, J. Goldstein (2003) has shown that mate poaching, including rape, and defection are common in conflict zones during times of war. Thus one "logical" response to the risks of inter-group mating in war zones is to use religion to promote in-group trust among soldiers and to "guard" females (and possibly opportunistic males) from defecting.

Conclusion

Ultimately, the costly signaling theory of religion claims made above—that religion is a costly signal of desirable mate qualities, and that "religious wars" are ultimately *not* religious in nature but are rather about mating

4 For example, life for women in Afghanistan under rule of the Taliban (Rashid 2001).

opportunities—must be tested empirically and experimentally to be taken seriously. Indeed, R. Sosis and colleagues have recently obtained empirical data which suggests a positive correlation between warfare and the costliness of male initiation rites (Sosis, Kress, & Boster, in press). Thus it seems plausible that signals of religious commitment, like engaging in costly rituals, serves multiple functions—promoting group solidarity in one situation and advertising fitness in another. The plausibility of the hypothesis, combined with the successes of costly signaling theory in accounting for costly and useless behaviors in other species, leaves me to believe that there is no obvious reason why this hypothesis would be falsified by studies of human populations. If not falsified, then this evolutionary approach to religion may explain religion's ultimate functions.

References

Boyer, P. 2001. *Religion explained: The evolutionary origins of religious thought.* New York, NY: Basic Books.

Buss, D. 2002. Human mate guarding. *Neuroendocrinology Letters, 23* Suppl. 4, 23-29.

Buss, D. 2003. *The evolution of desire: Strategies of human mating,* Reprint ed. New York, NY: Basic Books.

Dennett, D. 2006. *Breaking the spell: Religion as a natural phenomenon.* New York, NY: Viking Adult Books.

Goldstein, J. 2003. *War and gender: How gender shapes the war system and vice-versa,* New ed. Cambridge, UK: Cambridge University Press.

Irons, W. 2001. Religion as a hard-to-fake sign of commitment. In R. Nesse, Ed., *Evolution and the capacity for commitment,* 292-309. New York, NY: Russell Sage Foundation.

Johnson, D. D. P. 2005. God's punishment and public goods: A test of the supernatural punishment hypothesis in 186 world cultures. *Human Nature, 16* (4), 410-446.

Maynard Smith, J., & Harper, D. 1995. Animal signals: Models and terminology *Journal of Theoretical Biology, 177,* 305-311.

Pape, R. 2005. *Dying to win: The strategic logic of suicide terrorism.* New York, NY: Random House.

Rashid, A. 2001. *Taliban: Militant Islam, oil, and fundamentalism in Central Asia.* New Haven, CT: Yale University Press.

Sosis, R. 2004. The adaptive value of religious ritual. *American Scientist, 92,* 166-172.

Sosis, R., H. Kress, , & J. Boster, 2007. Scars for war: Evaluating alternative signaling explanations for cross-cultural variance in ritual costs. *Evolution & Human Behavior, 28,* 234-247.

Tooby, J., & Cosmides, L. 1988. The evolution of war and its cognitive foundations. *Institute for Evolutionary Studies Technical Report No. 88-1*. Presented at the Evolution and Human Behavior Meetings, Ann Arbor, Michigan, April 1988.
Trivers, R. 1972. Parental investment and sexual selection. In B. Campbell, Ed., *Sexual selection and the descent of man*, 136-179. Chicago, IL: Aldine Press.

Firewalking and the Brain

The Physiology of High-Arousal Rituals

Dimitris Xygalatas

In the village of Agia Eleni in Greece, firewalking rituals are performed by a community called the Anastenaria. Its members are Orthodox Christians. In addition to the Church rituals, however, they observe a separate annual ritual cycle, focused on the worship of saints Constantine and Helen. The most important event in this cycle is the festival of the two saints, which lasts for three days and includes various processions around the village, an animal sacrifice, music, and ecstatic dancing. The most dramatic moment of the festival is the firewalking ritual itself, where the participants, carrying the icons of the saints, dance over the burning-red coals.

The *Anastenaria* claim to be guided by saints Constantine and Helen, especially the former, who often appears in their dreams and gives them advice or orders, and draw their inspiration from the icons of the saints. Their tradition started by Greek populations at the Black Sea coast of Eastern Thrace, an area that was then part of the Ottoman Empire and today belongs to Bulgaria. After the Balkan wars, the Anastenarides came to Greek Macedonia, bringing with them their icons and their rituals. Already from the time of their performance in Eastern Thrace, the clergy had persecuted the Anastenaria, accusing them of idolatry, threatening and beating the firewalkers, and throwing their icons into the fire. When they arrived at Greece, they had to perform their rituals in secret. When the Church found out, they confiscated their icons; priests and theologians wrote against them; they were often ridiculed, and in some cases they were excommunicated. Even today, the Church is very hostile towards them, and even in their villages they often face contempt. Despite this troubled history, the tradition of firewalking is alive and well, and keeps drawing new participants.

Why are the Anastenaria so keen on performing such a costly ritual? High-arousal rituals often appear to be stressful, unpleasant, or even dangerous. Sometimes participation is coerced by a social group, as happens with many initiation rituals. Firewalking, however, is performed voluntarily, and actually *against* social pressure. Why then are many individuals willing to participate in ritual activities that would normally intimidate or seem appalling to most people?[1]

High-arousal rituals and Commitment

It has been suggested that costly rituals function as proof of commitment to the group (Sosis, 2003). Human coalitional behaviour entails considerable risks, and sometimes defection is more beneficial to the individual. It might therefore be costly to participate in a coalition when others defect. Certain violent rituals such as initiations can function as a means of warranting commitment, by challenging potential members to pay a costly price *in advance*, before joining the group. People's willingness to go through costly ordeals in order to join a group is evidence of their seriousness about their participation.

This hypothesis seems to provide a plausible explanation for people's participation in costly rituals. Firewalking could be a way of signaling commitment to the community, thus e.g., gaining social status in exchange. And this might very well have been true about the Anastenaria until recently. However, the composition of the group has radically changed during the past decades, due to specific socio-economic factors. While for some hundreds of years firewalking was performed exclusively by the people of Eastern Thrace, and later their descendents who lived in the villages of Greek Macedonia, today the firewalkers come from all over Greece, and meet in Agia Eleni twice a year to take part in the festival. Thus, for most of the participants, the performance of firewalking appears to be a goal in itself rather than a means of participating in the group. The Anastenaria get together in order to perform the ritual; this is the purpose for the group's existence.

The cost of participation is significant on various levels. First of all, firewalking is an extremely stressful or even painful activity, and so is the preparation for it. Attendance also implies financial costs, as the participants have to be away from their work as well as to cover their expenses for the duration of the festival. On the other hand, those who have prestigious jobs risk loosing credibility and status in their field by signalling themselves as Anastenarides. The opposition of the Greek Church to this tradition makes matters worse for the Anastenarides, as they are seen by many as pagan, heretics, or superstitious.

---

1 Firewalking rituals are performed in many cultures the world over, and people usually do not get burned, because of the low conductivity of coals. However, the extraordinary thing about this ritual is not that people are able to firewalk unharmed but rather that they are willing to try it in the first place. I stress this point and thank Daniel Dennett for pointing out that this might not always be as self-evident as I might have thought.

It thus seems that some rituals, including firewalking, can continue to draw new participants, even when the original conditions of their performance have been completely altered. What is it then that makes those activities so appealing to people, despite their high cost?

Ritualistic and obsessive behaviour

Pascal Boyer (2005) has spoken of a possible relation between ritual behaviour and certain neuropsychological conditions like Obsessive Compulsive Disorder (OCD). Those suffering from OCD feel a strong compulsion to perform certain actions that have no technical purpose in a very specific way—in other words, rituals—without being able to justify their behaviour. Indeed, they often recognise that this urge is irrational, but they feel that they have to behave in a certain way *in order to* avoid some vague but serious danger. In the same way, people who perform rituals will often admit a sense of urgency, an intuition that if these rituals are not performed in a very precise way something terrible might happen.

All the Anastenarides I interviewed claimed that every single element (using the icons, the incense, music, candles, dancing, or performing the animal sacrifice) is necessary for the performance of the ritual. They also claimed that it would not be possible to perform the ritual if any of those elements were missing. However, when asked about the purpose of those actions, they were not able to answer, although everyone was convinced that there *must* be a meaning; they just didn't know what it was. Furthermore, people were strongly convinced that no alterations could be made in the way the ritual is performed. "This is how we have found those things, and this is how we must keep them," as they often say. In reality, however, as we shall see, the ritual changes all the time, adapting to practical and environmental conditions, but in the eyes of the participants it appears unchanged.

Boyer links ritualistic behaviour to the human contamination-avoidance systems. The consideration of those systems, according to Boyer, can explain the compulsion of performance, the obsession with accuracy and the anxiety at incorrect or missed performance involved in high-arousal rituals. Also, it can explain the conceptual vagueness and the lack of a "standard" meaning attributed to the ritual elements. "Whatever meaning people find in ritual actions consists in interpretations of these actions rather than content transmitted by these actions" (Boyer 2005, 14).

Indeed, there does not seem to be a standard explicit reason for the performance of the ritual. The most common answer people provide is that they do it "for the Saint". But when pressed to elaborate on what this means, many of my subjects admitted to me they didn't know why the ritual is performed, and some even said that "nobody knows". Others gave me some justification for its performance, which however changed from person to person. What is more interesting is that there was a big discrepancy between the accounts of novice and experienced participants. It seems that many of them perform firewalking without any specific reason, but later come up with an explanation for it, in a process of cognitive dissonance (Xygalatas, in press).

Endogenous substances and motivation

High-arousal rituals can stimulate the production of endogenous substances in the human body. Motor hyperactivity, emotional hyper-arousal, stress, pain, dehydration, sleep deprivation and exposure to extreme temperatures, are all elements that can lead to increased release of endorphins (Henry 1982; Prince 1982). Endorphins can affect emotion and motivation, and even produce analgesic effects, anxiety reduction, and feelings of ecstasy, euphoria or tranquillity, which follow a state of stress or terror in certain rituals without any apparent reason. Subjects often attribute this sudden relief to supernatural intervention and speak of miraculous healing (Frecska & Kulcsar 1989).

Endorphins can also increase the release of another neurotransmitter, dopamine, into the synapses. Both types of substances can elevate attention and emotion (Damasio 2000, 60). According to the "motivational salience hypothesis" (Deeley 2004; Kapur 2003), dopamine mediates the representation of an external stimulus as an attractive or aversive reality, assigning salience and motivational importance to an experience. In this way, sensory-emotional hyper-arousal can influence cognitive elements such as perception, attention and memory. Extreme levels of dopamine are typically produced in schizophrenic patients and further increase before and during psychotic episodes. These patients then experience delusions and hallucinations, to which they attribute the utmost significance. Antipsychotic medication is aimed to block dopamine receptors in the brain, thus lessening this sense of salience.

The Anastenarides often report having hallucinations during the performance of the ritual: "as I was dancing, I raised my eyes, and the ceiling was gone. There was nothing! I saw the sky above me, clear and blue. I saw the angels in white clothes, dancing and singing the Great Doxology". Other Anastenarides report having seen Saint Constantine talking to them or dancing with them, while a woman told me that she saw (and felt!) Saint Helen pouring water in front of her feet while she was firewalking.

Psychotic patients report experiences of increased consciousness, such as: "I developed a greater awareness... my senses were sharpened. I became fascinated by the little insignificant things around me"; "I noticed things I had never noticed before"; "I felt there was some overwhelming significance in this"; "I felt like I was putting a piece of the puzzle together" (Kapur 2003, 15).

Similarly, firewalkers have told me, reflecting on their experience: "This experience has changed the way I see the world, the way I deal with things"; "It has opened my eyes"; "It has made me notice small details that I thought were insignificant before".

In this process, delusions appear as a top-down cognitive explanation of these experiences of extreme salience and significance. Psychotics invest explanations on these experiences in an attempt to rationalize an otherwise confusing sensation. And since delusions are constructed by the individual, they are shaped on the basis of the patient's relevant cultural context (Kapur 2003, 15). Thus, a patient in Texas might speak of a conspiracy to overthrow the government organized by communists or Saddam Hussein, while a villager in Cameroon might speak of spirits or witches. This process is so powerful that it can often lead to apocalyptic or conversion experiences.

One patient I interviewed was undergoing treatment for psychotic behavior, caused by drug abuse. I had talked to him various times while his condition was developing, and he expressed various theories about people—including me—machines, or even aliens conspiring against him. Although his treatment still continues, he now shows no symptoms of psychotic behavior and can realize what happened to him. This is how he described one of his experiences: "I was hearing voices in my head and I was trying to make sense of them. I said: 'They must be coming from some god; and if I am the only one who is hearing them, then I must be a very special person.' I was convinced that I was some kind of prophet [laughing]". This patient is an atheist.

The same kind of convictions can be observed in firewalkers after their first performance. Characteristically, some of them said: "I came to realize that the whole universe was conspiring to bring me here to perform the ritual", "I was called by Saint Constantine to perform the ritual", or "I realised that it was my destiny to become a firewalker". Once a patient arrives at such an explanation, it serves as an overall framework of further action and thought, driving him or her to find further confirmatory evidence (Kapur 2003). In this way, they develop a grand theory of their entire existence, using a kind of post hoc reasoning to justify previous actions.

> Throughout my life... things were happening to me. Things that were not accidental. There was a whole set of seeming coincidences, which I *later* [after firewalking] realised that were simply part of my life's nexus (15, emphasis mine).

In this way, the meaning and significance of high-arousal rituals can be constructed by the participant after its actual performance. Participation might be a random event, caused by personal impulse or curiosity. However, the sensory and emotional extravagance involved in such rituals begs interpretation. Endorphins can produce subjective rewards on a brain level, and dopamine can invest them with a feeling of significance and utter reality, offering a powerful schema into which all sorts of new events can be incorporated. This in turn provides participants with sufficient motivation to maintain and transmit the ritual, further reinforcing its consequences and dynamics. Thus, the ritual acquires an independent dynamics as an attractor of susceptible individuals, independent of any reasons that might have been responsible for its original collective performance.

Of course, direct measures of endorphin and dopamine levels during the performance of the ritual remain very difficult to obtain, as this would require very intrusive methods (although there are indirect indications). However, there is solid data from experimental studies conducted in the laboratory on the effects of neurotransmitters (e.g., see Harris & McNamara, this volume). After all, there is nothing special about firewalking, and the same physiological processes can be involved in other rituals, as well as other high-arousal situations, e.g. a rave party, or even be induced by drugs (Greenfield, 2000). It is therefore possible that more research on the functions of neurotransmitters could broaden our understanding of religious behaviour, and particularly high-arousal rituals.

Author's Note

I would like to thank Jesse Bering and Joseph Bulbulia for commenting on the manuscript of this paper and for providing valuable comments.

References

Boyer, P. 2005. A reductionistic model of distinct modes of religious transmission. In H. Whitehouse & R. McCauley, Eds., *Mind and religion: Psychological and cognitive foundations of religion*, 3-29. Walnut Creek, CA: AltaMira Press.

Damasio, A. 2000. *The feeling of what happens: Body, emotion and the making of consciousness*. London, UK: Vintage.

Deeley, P. Q. 2004. The religious brain: Turning ideas into convictions. *Anthropology & Medicine*, 113, 245-267.

Frecska, E., & Kulcsar, Z. 1989. Social bonding in the modulation of the physiology of ritual trance. *Ethos*, 171, 70-87.

Greenfield, S. 2000. The private life of the brain. London, UK: Penguin.

Henry, J. L. 1982. Possible involvement of endorphins in altered states of consciousness. *Ethos*, 104, 394-408.

Kapur, S. 2003. Psychosis as a state of aberrant salience: A framework linking biology, phenomenology, and pharmacology in schizophrenia. *American Journal of Psychology*, 160, 13-23.

Prince, R. 1982. Shamans and endorphins: Hypothesis for a synthesis. *Ethos,* 104, 409-423.
Sosis, R. 2003. Why aren't we all Hutterites? Costly signaling theory and religious behavior. *Human Nature,* 142, 91-127.
Xygalatas, D. in press. Firewalking in the Balkans: High arousal rituals and memory. In I. Czachesz, Ed., *Changing minds: Religion and cognition through the ages.* Leuven: Peeters.

He Who Laughs Best:
Involuntary Religious Affect as a Solution to Recursive Cooperative Defection

Jeffrey P. Schloss

"Deception stretches unconditionally as far as the truth, falsity unconditionally as far as honesty; there is no unconditional criterion of truth or of honesty and integrity. So it is also with love; hypocrisy, artifice, wiliness, and seduction stretch unconditionally as far as love does, and they can imitate true love so strikingly that there is no absolute criterion, because in every expression of truth or of true love there exists the possibility of deception which corresponds to it exactly,,."

(Kierkegaard, Works of Love 1962, 215).

Explanatory Landscape

After 150 years of debating manifold religious understandings of evolutionary theory, the tables have turned during the last decade or so, with an eruption of discussion over evolutionary understandings of religious belief itself. Of course naturalistic accounts of religion are by no means new (Freud 1927/1964; Hume 1776; James 1902). What is new is the entry of evolutionary biology into this endeavor, with ambitions of providing an account that is not just natural but universal, i.e., explaining the origin and character of religion in the context of general Darwinian processes that apply to physical and behavioral characteristics of all organisms.

At this point the very theoretical advances that have made possible this discussion are also the source of considerable debate. Although various taxonomies have been proposed for evolutionary accounts of religion (Atran & Norenzayan 2004; Dennett 2006; Wilson 2005), current theories tend to segregate into three approaches (Table 1).

Cognitive spandrel accounts do not view religion as an evolutionary adaptation at all, but as a by-product of other cognitive capacities that do have selective value. Various aspects of religion have been proposed to pleiotropically ensue from anthropomorphic projection (Guthrie, 1993), from extension of otherwise adaptive capacities and needs for attachment (Kirkpatrick, 2004), from reification of repetitive or obsessive harm avoidance behaviors (McCauley & Lawson, 2002), and most prominently, from hypertrophy or positive attribution bias of innate mechanisms for agency detection (Atran

2002; Barrett 2004; Bloom 2005; Boye, 2001; Hyperactive Agency Detection Device = HADD).

Table 1. Evolutionary Accounts of Religion

Mal- or Non-adaptation	Biological Adaptation	Cultural Innovation
Vestigal Trait	Sexual Selection	Memetic Pathogen
Runaway Armament	Individual Selection	Biocultural Co-adaptation
Cognitive Spandrel	Group Selection	Biological/Cultural Neutrality

On the other hand, biologically adaptationist accounts view religion as a genetically-endowed characteristic (or suite of characteristics) with net reproductive benefit. Proposals include the sexually-selected enhancement of mate recruitment (Sloan, this volume), reduction of stress or of self-subversive behaviors, and the facilitation of cooperation that is dramatically more extensive and intensive than that observed in other social mammals (Alexander, 1987; Roes & Raymond 2003; Schloss 2004, 2005; Wilson 2002). This latter hypothesis has generated the greatest number and variety of both theoretical and empirical studies, which emphasize variations on two themes, each amenable to operating at two levels of scale. Religion may serve as an adaptation for detecting and controlling cooperative defection (Bulbulia 2004; Irons 2001; Johnson & Bering 2006; Johnson & Krüger 2004), and/or it may function to coordinate cooperative strategies and goals (Atran & Norenzayan 2004; Roes & Raymond 2003; Wilson 2002). Cheater control and interactive coordination are the two challenges that must be met for any cooperative system, from genomes to multi-cellular organisms, to social groups and formal economic systems. In principle, there may be individual and group level adaptations to these challenges of cooperation. They are established, respectively, by selective regimes that confer reproductive advantage to individuals having a trait relative to those lacking it within a group, or by situations in which there may be a within-group decrement in fitness that is offset by inter-group benefit. Religious adaptations have been proposed to accrue from both individual (Johnson & Bering 2006) and group (Wilson 2002) selection. As we shall see, this has implications for both the degree of cooperative investment and the mode by which it is maintained in religious groups.

Finally, memetic (or more broadly, cultural evolutionary) accounts view religion primarily as neither genetic by-product nor genetic adaptation, but as non-genetic information, differentially transmitted by (distinctively human) processes of cultural evolution. By far the most prominent, if not dominant, approach posits religion to be a pathogenic but highly infectious memetic virus that is transmitted to human hosts at the expense of biological and cultural flourishing (Dawkins 2007; Dennett 2006). However, as with all co-evolutionary processes, there are multiple options for the relationship between memetic and genetic information, or cultural innovation and biological and group function (Durham 1992). Religious memes could function as beneficent symbionts rather than parasites, enhancing (and propagating via) biological reproduction or cultural success. Or they could be adaptively neutral in terms of organismic or cultural impacts.

Although these major explanatory approaches are widely recognized as alternative hypotheses amenable to empirical testing (Atran & Norenzayan 2004; Wilson 2005), there has not been widespread comparative assessment or even interaction between constituencies—a deficiency which this volume seminally addresses. Nevertheless, viewing them as "alternative" approaches is not altogether appropriate for several reasons.

First, even if the approaches employed a common definition of religion (and they do not), they often focus on different *aspects of* religion (Alcorta & Sosis 2005). Religion entails cognitive, affective, experiential, behavioral, and institutional components, each of which involves both capacities and content in need of explanation. Second, the various approaches not only may focus on different aspects of religion, but also explain them at different and non-exclusive levels of causation—cognitive function, genetic selection, and cultural transmission. Third, the debate over religious adaptation does not involve a simple dichotomy. Some aspects of religion, or different forms of a given aspect, may be adaptive; others not. Or—like sickle cell—the same characteristic may be adaptive in one context but not in another. And finally, natural selection is voraciously entrepreneurial, and a spandrel or viral meme may end up not only having reproductive benefit, but driving selection for genetic enhancement of the benefit. Thus, in addition to lacking empirical tests of alternative hypotheses, we also lack theoretical proposals for integrating hypotheses. What follows is a provisional account along these lines, positing a role for cognitive, affective, and behavioral aspects of religion in stabilizing cooperation.

Religion, Cooperation, and Defection Regress

All cooperation is vulnerable to cheaters who exploit its benefits but defect on its costs. This is especially true in human social interactions, which a) involve dyadic cooperation within groups too large to guarantee histories of exchange between participants, and b) rely on collective action that is especially vulnerable to "tragedies of the commons." It has been shown theoretically that punishment is an effective mechanism of social control (Boyd & Richerson, 1992), and experimental work has demonstrated not only that punishment promotes cooperation and reduces defection, but also that humans are willing to punish at net cost to themselves (Fehr & Gächter 2002).

Table 2. Recursive Defection in Cooperation

Order	Defection	Solution
1^0	Cooperation Free-Riders	Social Control: Punishment
2^0	Punishment Free-Riders	Belief in Cosmic Sanctions
3^0	Unbelievers	Costly Signals of Commitment
4^0	Hypocrites	Hard-to-fake Autonomic Displays of Commitment
5^0	Self-Deceived Sentimentalists	Internalized Costs & Benefits of Belief

However, this "raises a second order social dilemma…acknowledged to be a major puzzle in the evolution of cooperation" (Hauert, Traulsen, Brandt, Nowak, & Sigmund 2007, 1905). Because punishment of those who defect on the costs of cooperation is itself costly, there can be 2^0 defectors who renege on punishing (Table 2). Of course these defections also could be punished, but this would seem to usher in an "infinite regress" (Colman 2006, 745). A number of solutions to the establishment of punishment have been proposed and debated (Boyd, Gintis, Bowles, & Richerson 2003; Fowler 2005; Henrich & Boyd 2001; Panchanathan & Boyd 2004), but even if stable, any system of punishment is ultimately constrained both by its costs and by the ability of punishers to detect cheaters. Belief in the existence of all-knowing moral agents who punish defection, or other kinds of internalized supernatural sanctions, has been proposed as a solution to both of these challenges (Johnson & Krüger 2004; Roes & Raymond, 2003; Wilson 2002). Ideally (though not in practice), there are no net costs to punishment, no defectors on meeting out punishment, and no (believed) chances of escaping detection. However, for someone genuinely to internalize the idea of an omniscient being capable sanctioning defections that human peers either might not detect or might not invariably punish—i.e., for someone to avoid defections they could likely get away with—is itself a form of intra-group altruism that would require group selection to establish. A more modest —individually selected - version of this involves the internalization of moral norms only insofar as they constrain defections likely to be detected (Alexander 1987), and belief in supernatural sanctions merely reinforces the fitness-enhancing, constraining power of conscience (Bering & Johnson 2005; Johnson & Bering 2006). These alternatives generate different expectations for the cooperative impacts of religiously internalized moral sanctions, which are empirically distinguishable.

In either case, cooperation is nevertheless vulnerable to a tertiary level of defection: those who refuse to believe in supernatural sanctions shared by and constraining the behavior of the group (in today's parlance, "brights"!). Virtually all religious communities have historically marginalized non-believers, and the very term "infidel," while used synonymously with unbeliever, actually derives from the Latin *infidelis*: unfaithful or disloyal. Of course the problem is not so much honest infidels, who are easily identified and excluded, but dishonest religious posers—those who profess commitments they do not have. One solution to this is an entrance fee into the believing community or a cost of profession. Religious communities are notable for their costly practices involving economic sacrifice, bodily mortification or mutilation, celibacy, time and energy intensive rituals, etc. A substantial theoretical literature exists on costly signaling in biology in general (Gintis, Smith, & Bowles 2001; Grafen 1990) and religion in particular (Bulbulia 2004; Irons 2001). And an emerging empirical body of work impressively demonstrates the efficacy of such costly demands within religious communities (Sosis 2000, 2003; Sosis & Alcorta 2003). Costly signaling theory helps makes sense of a distinctive aspect of religious belief that neither spandrel nor memetic accounts alone address (Atran & Norenzayan 2004): not why people believe, but why their beliefs motivate such substantial investments.

Nevertheless, costly signals themselves are open to a quaternary level of defection. To the very extent such costs can be construed as investments, payoff can be calculated. Thus, costly signals can be undertaken as means of personal gain, independent of honest belief in or commitment to what they are intended to signal. *Costly* signals therefore, are not intrinsically *reliable* signals (Bulbulia, this volume). This has long been recognized within religious traditions as the problem of hypocrisy, or the prominent but disingenuous display of reified public behaviors. Since such displays of belief can be feigned, the solution to this form of cheating involves signals of interior disposition that—costly or not—are involuntary or hard to fake. Emotions are probably the most readily interpreted, difficult to conceal or conjure, tightly volitionally linked, and therefore reliable signals of motivational disposition (Frank 1988, 2001). There are several proposals for the role of religious emotions in communicating cooperative commitment (Alcorta & Sosis 2005; Bulbulia 2004).

Notwithstanding this, many of the afore-mentioned evolutionary accounts of religion have emphasized supernatural cognition, religious behaviors, or social organization with little consideration of emotion. Interestingly, participant accounts and historical studies—particularly of religious revivals - indicate that the employment of both everyday emotions (fear, remorse, gratitude, cherishing) and specifically if not strictly religious emotions (reverence, sacred awe, "conviction") plays a crucial role in the maintenance and expansion of many religious communities. Alcorta and Sosis (2005) link emotions with other aspects of religion in an evolutionary account that posits the synergistic interaction of emotion and costly, symbolic ritual contributes to the twin tasks of free-rider policing and motivational coordination.

When it comes to religious signaling however, equally if not more important than emotions themselves, is the way they are provoked and conveyed. Ritual is one way, though it is widely recognized to be easily routinized and subject to the very 3^0 inauthenticity that emotions are posited to solve. Another way—sometimes attending ritual but often contrasted with it—is the widespread, varied, and in many respects distinctive existence of highly visible, involuntary, dramatic manifestations of religious experience: Glossalalia ("speaking in tongues"), convulsive weeping ("veil of tears"), contagious laughing or singing ("holy laughter" or "singing in the spirit"), fainting ("slain in the spirit"), trembling/shaking ("under the power"), religious trances, spontaneous bleeding, etc.

The existence of these ecstatic human behaviors, especially in the religious context, warrants both proximal (neurophysiological) and ultimate (evolutionary) explanation. Unlike involuntary displays such as blushing or piloerection, which merely signal emotional arousal, or vasomotor fainting/epileptic seizures, which are not associated with particular cognitions—these autonomic manifestations are taken to reflect the experience of a very specific (and sublime) reality. Duchenne laughter, as a hard-to-fake signal of seeing or experiencing the humor in something, may be the most comparable non-religious analogue of these displays. Like the above, Duchenne laughter is difficult to conjure, highly contagious, and is experienced as betokening both the perception of and yielding to an ineffable reality. It has been interpreted both as a trust-building signal of interior disposition (Owren & Bachorowski 2001, 2003) and as a coordinator of group solidarity (Gervais & Wilson 2005; Provine 1992).

There is considerable though circumstantial empirical evidence that involuntary manifestations of religious experience function very powerfully in just these ways. In the religious history of the west, the most dramatic renewals of religious commitment and non-coercive expansions of religious community across boundaries of national, ethnic, and class identity have been attended by these manifestations. As with all signals, the benefit of cooperation with those whose commitments are trusted, is paid for by the exclusion of those whose commitment is doubted: all of the above affects have functioned as emblems of authenticity, which were interpreted by those experiencing them as signs of not only commitment, but of salvation, and criticized by non-participants as destructive excess (Edwards 1746/1982). More recently, the Pentecostal movement, which started with a small, racially-integrated group of several hundred people in 1906, has spread to every country on earth, is estimated to number 500 million, and has become the most rapidly growing religious tradition—the fastest spreading religious meme—in history. Preliminary analysis of data from the largest cross-cultural comparative study of global Pentecostalism and other religious and non-religious communities, indicates that various measures of trust within Pentecostal communities is significantly higher than neighborhoods or other religious communities (Pew 2006).

Of course none of this means that people who join such communities and trust in religious signals are not suckers. It is possible that these highly contagious religious displays are not adaptations for human flourishing at all, but are viral memes parasitizing reward systems that have been selected for other purposes or distorted by various deprivations. Although I have been arguing that this is not the case and that religious affections along with their distinctive manifestations play an important role in promoting cooperative commitment, still, they are notoriously vulnerable to a final, quinternary level of cheating: self-deception. Unlike intentional hypocrisy or consciously manipulative employment of costly signals (Cronk 1994), the best way to fake a hard-to-fake signal is to be sincerely, though inauthentically persuaded of ones own commitment. Religious (or any) belief is thought of as being potentially "self-deceived" in two ways. One involves convincing oneself that the object of belief is true, working around or denying evidence to the contrary. But the other way involves convincing oneself not so much that the object of belief is true, but that one *believes* it to be true—in the absence of genuine conviction or existential commitment. Oscar Wilde's famous description of a sentimentalist as "one who desires to have the luxury of an emotion without paying for it" applies also, perhaps especially, to the sentimentalism of religious self-deception. Daniel Dennett's (2006) "belief in belief" comes to mind, and far more energy may be spent professing the proposition than either examining or living by it. It is this persistent gap between actual cooperative commitment and profession—even profession attended by costly and hard-to-fake signals—that requires bridging.

Not surprising from either an evolutionary or a theological point of view, religious communities emphatically attempt to identify and confront self-deception, a fourth order defection that may constitute the most subtle and disruptive threat to cooperation. In western monotheism, for example, the gap between commitment and profession has been challenged by virtually all the major reform movements—from ancient Hebraic prophetic traditions, to Franciscan and Ignatian monastic orders, to Calvinist and Anabaptist reform, to 1st and 2nd "Great Awakenings" and abolitionism. This has involved an articulation of authenticity that couples each of the above aspects of religion—belief, practice, and affect - in an ethic of love and care, especially for those unable to care for themselves or to return care (Stark 1996, 84). [For extensive theological discussions of the relationship beween displays and commitment, that I am commenting on here, see for example, Edwards 1741/2007, 1746/1982; Wesley 1766/2006; Wilberforce 1797/1997.]

Since exhortations against self-deception are themselves vulnerable to intentional or self-deception and an infinite regress is possible in principle, it is amenable to two types of constraints. First, once the moral connection between affective display and normative cooperative action has been overtly identified—"genuine religion cares for widows and orphans in their affliction" —significant instances of self-bias can be empirically identified. Second, and very speculatively, a terminal evolutionary solution could entail not just internalized belief in sanctioning agents, but internalized consequences of cooperative commitment—i.e., organically instantiated penalties for inauthentic and benefits for authentic commitment (Bulbulia 2004). Indeed, there is a substantial though uneven literature on the benefits of religious commitment for health and well-being (Paloutzian & Kirkpatrick 1995), and a more modest but rigorous literature on the benefits of altruistic other regard (Post 2007). What is equally interesting, is the elucidation of internalized *dis*benefits to religious inauthenticity (Pargament, Koenig, Tarakeshwar, & Hahn 2001). Even if the capacity for religious belief is an adaptation, it is not an inevitable advantage. Like Pope's (1711/2006) learning, it may be that "shallow draughts intoxicate the brain, And drinking largely sobers us again" (24).

References

Alcorta, C., & Sosis, R. 2005. Ritual, emotion and sacred symbols: The evolution of religion as an adaptive complex. *Human Nature*, 16 (4), 323-359.

Alexander, R. 1987. *The biology of moral systems*. New York, NY: Aldine de Gruyter.

Atran, S. 2002. *In gods we trust: The evolutionary landscape of religion*. New York, NY: Oxford University Press.

Atran, S., & Norenzayan, A. 2004. Religion's evolutionary landscape: Counterintuition, commitment, compassion, communion. *Behavioral & Brain Sciences*, 27 (6), 730-70.

Barrett, J. 2004. *Why would anyone believe in God?* Walnut Creek, CA: AltaMira Press.
Bering, J. M., & Johnson, D. D. P. 2005. 'Oh Lord, you hear my thoughts from afar': Recursiveness in the cognitive evolution of supernatural agency. *Journal of Cognition & Culture, 5,* 188-142.
Bloom, P. 2005. Is god an accident? *Atlantic Monthly, 296I* (5), 105-112.
Boyd, R., Gintis, H., Bowles, S., & Richerson, P. J. 2003. The evolution of altruistic punishment. *Proceedings of the National Academy of Sciences, USA,* 100 (6), 3531-3535.
Boyd, R., & Richerson, P. J. 1992. Punishment allows the evolution of cooperation or anything else) in sizable groups. *Ethology & Sociobiology, 13,* 171-195.
Boyer, P. 2001. *Religion explained.* New York, NY: Basic Books.
Bulbulia, J. 2004. Religious costs as adaptations that signal altruistic intention. *Evolution & Cognition, 10* (1), 19-38.
Colman, A. 2006. The puzzle of cooperation. *Nature, 44,* 744-745.
Cronk, L. 1994. Evolutionary theories of morality and the manipulative use of signals. *Zygon, 4,* 117-135.
Dawkins, R. 2007. *The God delusion.* New York, NY: Houghton Mifflin.
Dennett, D. 2006. *Breaking the spell: Religion as a natural phenomenon.* New York, NY: Viking.
Durham, W. 1992. *Coevolution: Genes, culture, and human diversity.* Palo Alto, CA: Stanford University Press.
Edwards, J. 2007. *The distinguishing marks of a work of the spirit of God, applied to that uncommon operation that has lately appeared on the minds of the people of New England: With a particular consideration of the extraordinary circumstances with which this work is attended.* Cornwall, UK: Diggory Press. Original work published 1741.
Edwards, J. 1982. *A treatise concerning religious affections.* Grand Rapids, MI: Baker Books. Original work published 1746.
Fehr, E., & Gächter, S. 2002. Altruistic punishment in humans. *Nature, 415,* 137-140.
Fowler, J. 2005. Human cooperation: Second-order free-riding problem solved? *Nature, 437,* E8.
Frank, R. 1988. *Passions within reason: The strategic role of the emotions.* New York, NY: Norton and Company.
Frank, R. 2001. Cooperation through emotional commitment. In R. Nesse, Ed., *Evolution and the capacity for commitment,* 57-77. New York, NY: Russell Sage Foundation.
Freud, S. 1964. *The future of an illusion.* In J. Strachey ed. and trans. New York, NY: W. W. Norton & Company. Original work published 1927.
Gervais, M., & Wilson, D. S. 2005. The evolution and functions of laughter and humor: A synthetic approach. *The Quarterly Review of Biology, 80* (4), 395-428.

Gintis, H., Smith, E. & Bowles, S. 2001. Costly signaling and cooperation. *Journal of Theoretical Biology, 213,* 103-119.

Grafen, A. 1990. Biological signals as handicaps. *Journal of Theoretical Biology, 144,* 517-546.

Guthrie, S. 1993. *Faces in the clouds.* New York, NY: Oxford University Press.

Hauert, C., Traulsen, A., Brandt, H., Nowak, M. A., & Sigmund, K. 2007. Via freedom to coercion: The emergence of costly punishment. *Science, 316* (5833), 1905-1907.

Henrich, J., & Boyd, R. 2001. Why people punish defectors: Weak conformist transmission can stabilize costly enforcement of norms in cooperative dilemmas. *Journal of Theoretical Biology, 208* (1), 79-89.

Hume, D. 1776. *Dialogues concerning natural religion.* London, UK: Penguin Classics.

Irons, W. 2001. Religion as a hard-to-fake sign of commitment. In R. Nesse, Ed., *Evolution and the capacity for commitment,* 292-309. New York, NY: Russell Sage Foundation.

James, W. 1902. *The varieties of religious experience.* London, UK: Longmans, Green.

Johnson, D. D. P., & Bering, J. 2006. Hand of God, mind of man: Punishment and cognition in the evolution of cooperation. *Evolutionary Psychology, 4,* 219-233.

Johnson, D. D. P., & Krüger, O. 2004. The good of wrath: Supernatural punishment and the evolution of cooperation. *Political Theology, 52,* 159-176.

Kierkegaard, S. 1962. *Works of love.* New York, NY: Torchbook. Original work published 1847.

Kirkpatrick, L. 2004. *Attachment, evolution, and the psychology of religion.* New York, NY: Guilford Press.

McCauley, R. N., & Lawson, E. T. 2002. *Bringing ritual to mind.* New York, NY: Cambridge University Press.

Owren, M. J., & Bachorowski, J. A. 2001. The evolution of emotional expression: A "selfish gene" account of smiling and laugher in early hominids and humans. In T.J. Mayne & G. A. Bonanno, Eds., *Emotions: Current issues and future directions,* 152-191. New York, NY: Guilford Press.

Owren, M. J., & Bachorowski, J. A. 2003. Reconsidering the evolution of nonlinguistic communication: The case of laughter. *Journal of Nonverbal Behavior, 27,* 183-200.

Paloutzian, R. F., & Kirkpatrick, L. A., Eds. 1995. Religious influences on personal and societal well-being. *Journal of Social Issues, 512.*

Panchanathan, K., & Boyd, R. 2004. Indirect reciprocity can stabilize cooperation without the second-order free rider problem. *Nature, 432,* 499-502.

Pargament, K.I., Koenig, H. G., Tarakeshwar, N., & Hahn, J. 2001. Religious struggle as a predictor of mortality among medically ill elderly patients. *Archives of Internal Medicine, 161* (10), 1881-1884.

Pew. 2006. *Spirit and power: A 10-country survey of Pentecostals.* The Pew Forum on Religion and Public Life.

Pope, A. 2006. An essay on criticism. In P. Rogers Ed., *Alexander Pope: The major works,* 17-40. New York, NY: Oxford University Press.

Post, S. 2007. *Altruism and health: Perspectives from empirical research.* New York, NY: Oxford University Press.

Provine, R. R. 1992. Contagious laughter: Laughter is a sufficient stimulus for laughs and smiles. *Bulletin of the Psychonomic Society, 30,* 1-4.

Roes, F. L., & Raymond, M. 2003. Belief in moralizing gods. *Evolution & Human Behavior, 24,* 126-135.

Schloss, J. P. 2004. Evolutionary ethics and Christian morality: Surveying the issues. In P. Clayton & J. Schloss, Eds., *Evolution and ethics: Human morality in biological and religious perspective,* 1-24. Grand Rapids, MI: Eerdmans.

Schloss, J. P. 2005. Hath Darwin suffered a prophet's scorn? Evolutionary theory and the scandal of unconditional love. In C. Harper, Ed., *Spiritual information,* 291-299. Philadelphia, PA: Templeton Press.

Sosis, R. 2000. Religion and intragroup cooperation: Preliminary results of a comparative analysis of Utopian communities. *Cross-Cultural Research, 34* (1), 77-88.

Sosis, R. 2003. Why aren't we all Hutterites? *Human Nature, 14* (2), 91-127.

Sosis, R., & Alcorta, C. 2003. Signaling, solidarity, and the sacred: The evolution of religious behavior. *Evolutionary Anthropology, 12,* 264-274.

Stark, R. 1996. *The rise of Christianity.* Princeton, NJ: Princeton University Press.

Wesley, J. 2006. *Plain account of Christian perfection.* Peabody, MA: Hendrickson Publishers. Original work published 1766.

Wilberforce, W. 1997. *Real Christianity: Discerning true faith from false beliefs.* Minneapolis, MN: Bethany House Publishers. Original work published 1797.

Wilson, D. S. 2002. *Darwin's cathedral: Evolution, religion, and the nature of society.* Chicago, IL: University of Chicago Press.

Wilson, D. S. 2005. Testing major evolutionary hypotheses about religion with a random sample. *Human Nature, 16* (4), 419-446.

PART V

GODS IN MINDS

"Religious Experience" and the Brain

Ann Taves

Two Models

There have been two major approaches to the study of "religious experience" in religious studies and the psychology of religion, which I will refer to as the *sui generis* model and the attribution model. The two models disagree about whether there are uniquely religious (or mystical or spiritual or sacred) experiences, emotions, acts, or objects. The *sui generis* model assumes implicitly or explicitly that there are. The attribution model claims that religious or mystical or spiritual or sacred "things" are created when religious significance is assigned to them. In the attributive model, subjects have experiences that they or others consciously or unconsciously deem religious. One of the ways that ambiguity is maintained with respect to the two models is by referring to "religious experience," as if it were a distinctive thing, rather using the more awkward, but clearly attributive formulation, "experiences deemed religious."

Since the formulation "experiences deemed religious" specifies neither who does the "deeming" nor what they mean by "religious," I will argue in what follows that switching from a *sui generis* to an attributive formulation is a necessary but not sufficient basis for constructing a scientifically useful object of study. As scholars of religion are well aware, any specification of "religious" (or "spiritual" or "mystical" or "sacred"), whether by scholars or subjects, excludes some things that some people sometimes deem religious and includes other things that most would not consider religious. While this fact has long presented difficulties for scholars intent on specifying a uniquely religious set of phenomena, it can be put to good use by those interested in pursuing a comparative, biologically grounded approach to the sorts of experiences traditionally deemed religious. For those interested in the latter course, a focus on experiences that subjects associate (directly or indirectly) with superhuman agents provides a good starting point. This specification not only includes a broad swath of what people commonly consider religious experiences but also encompasses experiences often deemed pathological and/or imaginary. Because I do not think that this is the only way that experiences deemed religious might be specified, I will continue to use the term religious as a way to refer to the broader set of possible specifications.

Methodological Issues

There are major methodological issues at stake in this seemingly small shift from the *sui generis* to the attributive model that need to be clarified before we can have any rigorous exploration of "religious experience" or, more precisely, "experiences deemed religious" and the brain (see Table 1). The chief difference between the two models lies in the way that comparisons are set up and the purposes for which they are utilized. In the *sui generis* model "religious experiences" are compared in order to identify their alleged common core; in the attribution model "experiences deemed religious" are compared with experiences that share common features, whether viewed as religious or not, in order to understand the workings of the human mind and culture as well as the processes whereby some experiences come to be viewed as religious.

Table 1. Methodological Differences between the *Sui Generis* and Attribution Models

	Sui Generis Model	**Attribution Model**
1	Assumes that some experiences are inherently religious or mystical.	Assumes that experiences are not inherently religious or not-religious but must be constituted as such by persons.
2	Assumes that there is one underlying experience that can or should be understood as (authentically) religious or mystical.	Assumes (based on historical evidence) that diverse things can be deemed religious, that "mysticism" is a modern category, and that there are diverse views regarding what should "count" as religious, mystical, or spiritual.
3	Compares religious experiences in order to identify their common core. The common core is often granted evidential force relative to religious claims.	Seeks to compare experiences that have some similar feature(s) whether they are viewed as religious or not.
4	Commonalities are primarily of religious or theological interest.	Similarities and differences are of interest in relation to understanding the workings of the human mind and culture as are the processes whereby "things" come to be viewed as religious.
5	Religious experience is set apart from other experiences that seem to share common features and tacitly protected from comparison with them.	Experiences deemed religious are viewed in relation to other experiences and subject to comparison with them.

Arguments against the Attribution Model

Some religious studies scholars have argued that the attribution model, by assuming that people constitute experiences as religious, overrides the views of religious subjects who understand their experiences as inherently religious and do not view themselves as having attributed religious significance to their experiences (Barnard 1992). This is a reasonable criticism of classical attribution theory in so far as it suggests that attributions are consciously ascribed to ambiguous events after the fact. The literature on attribution, however, does not assume that processes of attribution always occur consciously (Försterling 2001).

Explanations of experiences deemed religious must be able to account for experiences that individuals experience as inherently religious or mystical. To account for the subjective feeling that some experiences are *sui generis*, a scientific model needs to show how religious attributions can be built into experiences through pre-conscious mental processes and not just attributed consciously to experiences after the fact. Here I use attribution to refer to both types of processes, those that occur unconsciously as well as consciously.

Problems with the Sui Generis Model

By inhibiting empirical observation and comparison, the *sui generis* model creates insurmountable problems for those who want to explain experiences that actual people have deemed religious. Due to the restrictions imposed by the tacit theological claims embedded in the *sui generis* model, it holds little promise for linking the study of religion and brain research, while the attribution model opens up a series of interesting research questions.

Linking religious studies, psychology, and cognitive neuroscience

There are two broad kinds of research relating religion and the brain, neither of which focuses directly on experiences deemed religious. The first, research in religion and cognitive science rooted in evolutionary psychology focuses on *religion*, typically defined in terms of superhuman beings understood as "counter-intuitive agents" (Boyer 2001). This body of research has embraced the attribution model, identifying the attribution of agency to counterintuitive entities as a distinctive feature of religious phenomena, and located the emergence of these attributive tendencies in evolutionary psychology. Apart from Pyysiäinen (2003), little of this research has focused directly on experience per se or tried to explain how subjects or observers differentiate between experiences of counter-intuitive superhuman agents variously understood as pathological, fictional, or real.

The second body of research—on brain states underlying the transformative processes associated with contemplative and healing practices —typically focuses on *experiences*, rather than on "religion" per se. These experiences include, for example, the pure consciousness experiences that Robert Forman refers to as mystical (Forman 1998), experiences of *samatha* or mental quiescence associated with Buddhist contemplative practices (Wallace 2007), the experience of *kensho* or the loss of sense of subject-object dualism associated with Zen practice (Austin 2000), and the absorption of the self into something larger that d'Aquili and Newberg (1999) associate with religious experience in general. This type of research has focused on experiences without rigorously embracing the attribution model. While the experiences in question are frequently deemed religious, it is not clear in many cases who is doing the "deeming," whether scholars or subjects, and on what grounds.

Both lines of research can contribute to the study of experiences deemed religious if (1) we construct an experience-related object of study that does not presuppose that the experiences in question are inherently religious and (2) the experiences in question are specified in such a way that they can be examined across disciplines, e.g. cultural studies, psychology, and neuroscience. Since what we are seeking to explain is subjective experience, the object of study must be constructed at the level of subjective experience from first-person accounts. To compare experiences across disciplinary and conceptual boundaries, we must find a way to specify what the experiences we want to study have in common without obscuring the differences between them. To accomplish this, we need to abandon the attempt to specify a uniquely religious set of phenomena and focus instead on identifying an "exact, stipulated point of analogy" between the things we want to compare (Paden 2005, 1880).

Stipulating a focus on experiences that subjects attribute directly or indirectly to superhuman agents provides one possible way of specifying the sorts of experiences we want to examine in a way that will capture much of what people typically mean when they refer to religion. This specification not only includes a broad swath of what people commonly consider religious experience but also encompasses experiences often deemed pathological and/or imaginary, which have been largely neglected by cognitive scientists of religion. Moreover, if we expand the idea of attribution to include indirect attribution of experiences to superhuman beings, this focus also provides a basis for including some of the experiences associated with healing and contemplative practices under this general rubric. Setting up our object of study in this way allows us to compare situations in which superhuman agents are variously understood as pathological, fictional, or real, on the one hand, and situations in which experiences are and are not attributed to superhuman agents, on the other.

Given a specific object of study, we can link religious and cultural studies, psychology, and cognitive neuroscience by linking two kinds of research: (1) research on processes of attribution in which some sort of subjective experience is implicated and (2) psychological and neuroscience research on experiences to which people sometimes attach religious attributions.

Two types of attribution

The first task—research on processes of attribution in which some sort subjective experience is implicated—is one that can be taken up by conventionally trained scholars of religion utilizing empirical and historical methods. Here the task is to analyze how and under what conditions various kinds of experiences are deemed religious and, thus, caught up in processes of "making religion." This, I am suggesting, can be done either directly or indirectly. In direct deeming, subjects explicitly deem an experience as religious in their description of the experience itself. In indirect deeming, subjects implicitly deem an experience as religious by associating it with something else they deem religious. Thus, if we are specifying religious in terms of superhuman agents, some experiences that do not themselves involve such agents, but are indirectly linked to them by virtue of their association with beliefs and practices that are, would fall within our stipulated comparative universe. So, for example, experiences that are indirectly deemed religious may be highly valued as evidence of the truth of teachings associated with superhuman agents or as signs of progress or the lack thereof in relation to a goal such as enlightenment or salvation that is associated with superhuman agents.

Experiences sometimes deemed religious

While focusing on experiences attributed directly or indirectly to superhuman agents ensures that many experiences commonly deemed religious will be caught up in our comparative net, we must specify what we mean by experience more precisely in order to link a broadly specified object of study, such as experiences attributed to superhuman agents, with psychological and neuroscience research. Because any experience <u>can</u> be deemed religious or attributed to superhuman agents, there are innumerable ways to do this. Nonetheless, unusual experiences that support the counter-intuitive claims of religious innovators stand out historically and have proved particularly fascinating to scholars and practitioners. Thus, claims of divine revelation are often based on seeing visions or hearing voices (e.g., God speaking to Moses, the transfiguration of Jesus, or the inspiration of prophets) while experiences of mental quiescence or non dualism both generate and reflect teachings about the nature of reality in Eastern religious traditions.

These unusual experiences have also figured prominently in the history of psychiatry and in the construction of psychiatric illnesses. Until recently, researchers often compared religious and psychiatric phenomena at the level of the syndrome. Shamanistic, mediumistic, and mystical experiences have been compared to and sometimes equated with psychiatric disorders, such as schizophrenia, multiple personality, and epilepsy. In a move parallel to what I am advocating with respect to religious experience, medical researchers interested in the neurological substrates of psychiatric illness are focusing on symptoms (subjective manifestations reported by the individual) rather than syndromes (a constellations of symptoms and externally observable signs) (Bentall 2000). The decoupling of syndromes and symptoms by psychiatric researchers allows us to identify a set of subjective features reported by individuals that variously appear in experiences deemed religious, non-religious, pathological or normal. Looking at just the more unusual subjective experiences, it is clear that some involve either the apparent appearance of an external agent or the overt alteration or loss of the subjective sense of agency, while others do not (see Table 2).

Table 2. Agency in Relation to Various Unusual Subjective Experiences

Agency-Related Experiences	**Non-Agency Related Experiences**
(1) Hallucinations suggestive of the presence of another agent, e.g. hearing voices, seeing visions, or a felt sense of another agent.	(1) Heightened emotional states, e.g., peace, love, joy, or compassion.
(2) Dissociative experiences suggestive of the presence of another agent in the body, e.g. multiple personality, spirit mediumship, demonic possession, shamanism.	(2) Heightened attentional states, e.g. samatha.
(3) Involuntary motor symptoms suggestive of control by another agent, e.g. glossolalia, falling as if dead.	(3) Alterations in the relationship between self/subject and environment/object, e.g. experiences of unity or oneness, pure consciousness experiences, non-dual experiences.
	(4) Alternations in the relationship between self and body, e.g. out-of-body experiences.

Linking Experience and Religion Directly and Indirectly

While agency-related experiences have the potential to be directly attributed to superhuman agents, non-agency related experiences are more likely to be linked to superhuman agents indirectly. I will briefly discuss one example of each type—the indirect attribution of agency in experiences of *kensho* or no-self and the direct attribution of agency in hearing voices.

The experience of kensho

James Austin describes kensho as an experience in which the ordinary sense of self dissolves and is replaced by a sense of timelessness, peace, and a sense of seeing 'things as they really are' (Austin 2000 228). The experience, while involving the loss of the ordinary sense of self and, thus, presumably the ordinary sense of oneself as an agent, does not involve agents, superhuman or otherwise. We do know, however, that kensho is a technical term in Zen Buddhism and that the Zen tradition promotes practices intended to cultivate such experiences. We also know that the concept of "no-self" is one component of the traditional Buddhist understanding of reality as taught by the Buddha, that kensho experiences must be validated by a teacher to be deemed authentic, and that authority to teach is transmitted through lineages that are traced back to the Buddha. So while the experience of kensho in and of itself does not involve superhuman agents, the significance of the experience—specifically the claim that this experiences provides a glimpse of "reality," of "things as they really are"—is linked through Zen teaching and practice to the teaching and experience of the Buddha. As long as the Buddha "counts" as a superhuman agent, the experience of kensho would fall into a set of experiences whose authenticity is established by means of links to superhuman agents even though the agent is not directly involved in the experience itself.

The experience of hearing voices

In terms of mechanism, there is widespread consensus in the literature that "auditory hallucinations occur when the individual misattributes ordinary inner speech to a source that is external or alien to the self" (Bentall 2000, 100). Current research would suggest that the process of attribution involves a complex mix of cognition and culture arising from the perceptual ambiguity of hallucinatory experiences. Increasingly complex and dynamic models of culture developed by cognitive psychologists are providing more sophisticated ways of understanding how attributions of agency are made. If, as Hong, Morris, Chiu, and Benet-Martinez (2000) theorize, most individuals are aware of various competing cultural theories of agency, then factors outside the individual such as institutions, discourses, and relationships are likely to play an important role in keeping particular theories in the forefront of people's minds. We can hypothesize that individuals who are culturally primed with religious theories of agency are more likely to deem experiences religious than those who are not.

Conclusion

The examples discussed here were based on a stipulated focus on experiences that subjects attribute directly or indirectly to superhuman agents. In cases involving direct attribution, the significance and reality of the experience rests on whether or not the experience is directly attributed to an agent that is understood as imaginary or real but unseen. In cases of indirect attribution, the experience acquires significance through an indirect link to a superhuman agent. In both instances, certain kinds of experiences acquire significance for subjects and some observers through their association with superhuman agents. A focus on experiences that subjects associate directly or indirectly with superhuman agents allows us to compare experiences variously deemed religious, pathological, and/or imaginary. If we want to know why—evolutionarily speaking—humans postulate and engage with superhuman agents, we need to look at a much wider range of phenomena, including psychopathology, experiences induced by drugs or computer simulations or fiction and art, and experiences associated with creative inspiration.

References

Austin, J. H. 2000. Consciousness evolves when self dissolves. In J. Andresen and R. Foreman, Eds., *Cognitive models and spiritual maps*, 209-230. Bowling Green, OH: Imprint Academic.

Barnard, G. W. 1992. Explaining the unexplainable: Wayne Proudfoot's *Religious Experience. Journal of the American Academy of Religion, 602*, 231-256.

Bentall, R. P. 2000. Hallucinatory experiences. In E. Cardena, S. Lynn, & S. Kripner, Eds., *Varieties of anomalous experience*, 85-120. Washington, D.C.: American Psychological Association.

Boyer, P. 2001. *Religion explained*. New York, NY: Basic Books.

d'Aquili, E., & Newberg, A. 1999. *The mystical mind*. Minneapolis, MN: Fortress Press.

Försterling, F. 2001. *Attribution*. Philadelphia, PA: Taylor & Francis.

Forman, R. Ed. 1998. *The innate capacity*. New York, NY: Oxford University Press.

Hong, Y., Morris, M., Chiu, C., & Benet-Martinez, V. 2000. Multicultural minds: A dynamic constructivist approach to culture and cognition. *American Psychologist, 557*, 709-720.

Paden, W. E. 2005. Comparative Religion. In L. Jones, Ed., *Encyclopedia of religion*, 2nd ed., Vol. 3, 1877-1881. New York, NY: Macmillan.

Pyysiäinen, I. 2003. *How religion works*. Leiden, Netherlands: Brill Academic Publishers.

Wallace, A. 2007. *Contemplative science*. New York, NY: Columbia University Press.

Are We All "Believers"?

Jonathan A. Lanman

The Question

There are a multitude of complex and difficult questions to ask about religion, such as how and when "religion" first appeared in human societies, whether or not religion is "good" for us in some sense, and even what "religion" as a term actually means. The question I ask in the title of this chapter, however, does not seem to be one of these complex and difficult questions. In fact, it seems quite simple. Of course we are not all religious "believers." One only has to compare the views of Jerry Falwell and Richard Dawkins to settle the question quickly and emphatically.

Yet, science seems to have a knack for complicating what appears to be simple. For example, the chair I am sitting in as I type seems quite solid to me; I even say that I "believe" the chair is solid. Yet, I also "believe," being somewhat of a scientific realist, that the chair is almost wholly composed of empty space. The cognitive sciences have documented numerous such cases where two different types of "beliefs" seem to exist alongside one another in human minds, one type of belief being explicit, conscious, and reflective, and the other type being implicit, unconscious, and reflexive. Specifically in the realm of belief in the supernatural, British psychologist Eugene Subbotsky documents that however ardently people may explicitly deny believing in magic, their behavior in situations where the reality of magic might do them physical harm reveals an implicit belief in its reality (Subbotsky & Quinteros 2002).

So, when I ask whether or not we are all "believers," I am not concerned with the explicit beliefs upon which we all reflect, but rather the implicit beliefs that guide much of our intuitive reasoning and some of our behavior. I am asking, then, whether or not our cognitive systems are constructed in such a fashion that we implicitly believe in the existence of supernatural agents, regardless of our explicit reasoning to the contrary. And, indeed, there is a small but growing body of evidence pointing in this direction.

The Evidence

In two separate studies, experimental psychologists find that "priming" someone with the idea of a supernatural agent can discourage cheating and can also encourage higher levels of generosity, regardless, apparently, of whether or not that person explicitly believes in the supernatural. The postulated explanation of this effect is that people unconsciously believe in the existence of supernatural agents, believe that these agents might be observing their behavior, and, caring about their reputations, adjust their behavior in socially desirable ways.

Jesse Bering and his colleagues investigated the possibility that telling people about a ghost in the immediate environment stops people from cheating when they are left alone to complete a competitive task ($50 prize) (Bering, McLeod, & Shackelford 2005). While the experimenters gave all participants the same task and cheating opportunity, they divided the participants into three experimental groups and gave each group a different prime before having them complete the task.

Participants in the control group received no prime, heading immediately to the task. Participants in what the experimenters called the "In Memoriam" condition read a brief statement dedicating the task to Paul J. Kellogg, a graduate student who helped design the task and who had died recently. Participants in the "Ghost Story" condition, after reading the same statement, were told by the experimenter that he or she (and others) had recently seen Paul Kellogg's ghost in the testing room.

Bering and his colleges found that those who received the Ghost Story prime were much less inclined to cheat on the competitive task than those who did not receive the prime. The experimenters' explanation for this change in behavior was that the people who heard about the ghost of Paul Kellogg unconsciously believed in the ghost's existence and therefore no longer felt like they were alone in the testing room. Thus, they thought that they might be being observed and stopped themselves from behaving in a way they would not want others observing.

While this effect held for all participants in the study, suggesting that personal factors such as socio-economic background, gender, and belief in the supernatural were not involved, the experimenters did not specifically ask participants whether or not they believed in ghosts. This is a significant weakness for a study claiming to show that people have an implicit belief in ghosts, as the possibility is present that all of the participants happened to explicitly believe in ghosts and that this explicit belief explains why they refrained from cheating when told that a ghost had been sighted nearby.

This weakness was not present, however, in a recent study by Azim Shariff and Ara Norenzayan, who not only tested whether or not priming people with supernatural ideas caused them to behave more generously, but also had participants complete a questionnaire in order to find out whether or not they were explicit "believers" in the supernatural (Shariff & Norenzayan, in press). Ascertaining the explicit beliefs of their participants allowed Shariff and Norenzayan to establish whether or not the supernatural primes resulted in increased generosity in people who denied believing in the supernatural.

Shariff and Norenzayan had participants play a dictator game (a common game from experimental economics in which one participant is given a sum of money by the researchers and is able to freely choose how much of it to keep and how much of it to give to another person who is ignorant of the participant's identity). Some of the participants received a supernatural prime prior to the game; others did not. The supernatural prime was a sentence unscrambling task with 50% of the word sets containing notably religious words (e.g., divine, spirit, sacred, prophet, God). After the dictator game, participants completed a series of personality and religiosity questionnaires that included direct questions about their explicit religious beliefs. The experimenters documented that those people who received the supernatural prime gave significantly more money to the other person than those people who did not receive the prime. This effect held for both self-proclaimed atheists and theists. Shariff and Norenzayan offer several possible explanations for their data but agree with Bering and his collaborators that participants most likely felt that they were being watched by supernatural agents.

Both of the studies above document people being exposed to ideas of supernatural agents and then adjusting their behavior. Hearing about a ghost in the room stops one from cheating, while merely seeing the word "God" or "prophet" is enough to significantly raise one's level of generosity, regardless of whether or not one actually believes in supernatural agents.

Given that only two studies have been done on this topic, there are still many questions and caveats regarding the claim that we are all believers. Shariff and Norenzayan note that we have not yet distinguished the explanation that people change their behavior because they believe they are being watched from the explanation that people change their behavior because of the semantic associations between supernatural agents and morality (similarly to people being more likely to interrupt conversations after seeing the word "rude"). Shariff and Norenzayan also note that, in one follow-up study, adult atheists did not change their behavior when primed with the religious words, leaving open the possibility of a developmental shift in our unconscious beliefs; we might not all be believers, just immature students. This difference might be explained, however, by the fact that Shariff & Norenzayan used an implicit rather than an explicit supernatural prime; they did not directly tell participants that a supernatural agent was in the vicinity, as Bering and his collaborators did. It is possible that the stronger, explicit prime is required for the behavioral effect in adults. Only further research will answer this question.

There is also the issue of what type of supernatural prime is necessary; are we only "believers" when it comes to culturally familiar supernatural agents? Would an American atheist who has never heard of the *sega* forest spirits of a group in Papua New Guinea respond the same way to stories or words associated with them as he/she would to stories or words about Jesus or Allah?

One of the biggest remaining questions is whether or not this implicit belief is the product of a direct process of adaptation or merely a by-product of other cognitive adaptations. For Bering and his camp, implicit belief in the existence of supernatural agency is an evolved feature of the human mind. The rationale is that, with the dawn of language and, therefore, gossip in human societies, information about a person's misdeeds would spread rapidly through a population and would result in that person having lower prestige and mating prospects, at best, and being ostracized or killed at worst. Either way, that person's net genetic fitness would be substantially lowered. Therefore, any cognitive traits that keep one from engaging in reputation-damaging behavior, even when one does not see anyone around, enjoy a fitness advantage. For Bering and his colleagues, implicit belief in supernatural agency is an example of such an adaptation. Those who think a supernatural agent is watching their behavior are less likely to engage in reputation-damaging behavior when they think they are alone and, therefore, likely to retain their fitness prospects in situations in which their belief that they are alone is mistaken. For Bering, atheism in the implicit, unconscious sense was rooted out of our minds over the course of evolution so that now, when presented with an idea of a supernatural agent, our unconscious reasoning and resulting behavior is guided by an implicit belief in the existence of such an agent.

For Shariff and Norenzayan, as well as other scholars such as Pascal Boyer and Justin Barrett, the implicit belief in supernatural agents revealed by the experiments described above is not indicative of an adaptation of belief in supernatural agency but is merely an accidental by-product of a variety of routine cognitive mechanisms. Ideas about supernatural agents are compelling to human minds because they trigger a variety of cognitive mechanisms in just the right ways. Ideas about supernatural agents are "counter-intuitive," which raises their chances of being noticed and remembered; they trigger a variety of relevant inferences about agents and their mental states, which results in their being pondered unconsciously and affecting our behavior.

Only further experimental research will be able to answer whether or not our apparent implicit belief in supernatural agency is an adaptation or a by-product. Regardless of how that question is answered, however, the possibility remains that evolution, through either a direct adaptation or a by-product, has left human beings a legacy of implicit belief in supernatural agency.

The Implications

This legacy of implicit belief would not be without consequence. The world is saturated with discourse about supernatural agents, from one-on-one interactions between parents and children to religious leaders reaching an audience of millions via televised speeches and internet blogs. In many of these cases, it appears that Machiavellian-inclined individuals are intentionally mentioning supernatural agents, and their abilities to observe, reward, and punish, in order to influence the behavior of others. Many parents tell their children that they better be good because God (or Santa Claus, depending on the time of year) is watching them in order to reward and punish their behavior. Many missionaries tell indigenous peoples that God sees their ways as sinful and will punish them accordingly. Some environmental activists insist that supernatural agents are tied to certain landscapes and these agents will be angered if the landscape is harmed.

Given the experimental evidence outlined above, such discourse has some effect on our thoughts and behaviors, even if we do not explicitly believe in the supernatural. Once we leave the psychology laboratory and enter these "real-world" settings, however, the situation gets more complex and questions arise. Do ideas of supernatural agents only cause us to refrain from certain general categories of behavior such as cheating and selfishness, or can they also cause us to follow more specific, culturally-sanctioned conventions, such as not drinking alcohol? Do all supernatural agent concepts cause us to more closely follow our own accepted codes of conduct or can foreign supernatural agent concepts make us behave more in line with other sets of conventions? For example, does hearing that Allah is monitoring our behavior make non-Muslims, temporarily and at some level, think and behave more in line with what they see as Islamic interests?

These are interesting and relevant questions in today's multi-cultural and multi-religious societies, which contain a variety of religious interests hoping to affect our thoughts and behaviors. Yet, it is clear already that while we may all become more generous or refrain from cheating in a psychology laboratory when primed with the idea of supernatural agency, we all obviously do not change all of our habits and lifestyle choices to fall in line with an explicit moral code every time we hear a televangelist. Some behaviors and environments seem to allow more easily for supernatural ideas to have their influence. Figuring out which ones and why will be an interesting avenue of research as we try to ascertain the consequences of our possible status as implicit "believers."

References

Bering, J. M., McLeod, K. A., & Shackelford, T. K. 2005. Reasoning about dead agents reveals possible adaptive trends. *Human Nature, 16*, 360-381.

Shariff, A. F., & Norenzayan, A. (in press). God is watching you: Supernatural agent concepts increase prosocial behavior in an anonymous economic game. *Psychological Science.*

Subbotsky, E., & Quinteros, G. 2005. Do cultural factors affect causal beliefs? Rational and magical thinking in Britain and Mexico. *British Journal of Psychology, 93*, 519-543.

Memory Systems and Religious Representation

Michael Teitelbaum

In the past year, I made a concerted effort to find out what we know about representations of god-like agents and human memory. I wanted to know what kinds of data humans store about such agents. Where do they store it, and how do they access it? What I discovered during the course of my literature search is that we don't know all that much. We do, however, know quite a lot about how humans store information about human-like agents. We know, for instance, that at least two of the five human memory systems that have been identified thus far actively shape our representations of human-like agents. During the course of this paper, I'm going to spend some time discussing why and how we use our memory systems to represent natural agents. I will then show how these same systems help generate god-like agents. In keeping with the spirit of this conference on the importance of experimental evidence in the study of religion, I will conclude my paper with a discussion of an experiment that I plan to run in the next year to test some of the hypotheses that I will present here.

Before we narrow our discussion to the two memory systems that are most closely related to agent representation, let me first list all of the memory systems that have been identified to date. Given the disparity in the literature, I shall focus on only one account of these systems—that found in Klein, Cosmides, Tooby and Chance (2002)—a paper that I will rely on for much of my discussion of memory and natural representations. These memory systems are: (1) procedural memory, dedicated to conditioning and skill acquisition; (2) perceptual-representational memory, used for object recognition; (3) primary or working memory, which acts as a temporary input data-store for certain language and inference processing modules; (4) semantic memory, used to store general facts and impressions about individuals and objects that can be accessed quickly, but without historical context; and (5) episodic memory, used to store detailed personal and third person histories that can be recalled accurately but slowly.

I mention these different memory systems just to give you a sense of the kinds of memory systems that are available to us. Here I focus my concern on those systems that inform our cognitive structures related to representations of human-like and god-like agents. That is, the semantic and episodic memory systems.

Episodic memory is perhaps the easiest of these two memory systems to understand. It is an inceptive memory system, meaning that it is populated with information that is laid down as it is learned or experienced. If you've been engaged in this conference, you've stored a vast number of entries about the arguments that you've heard in the last few days. Each entry is labeled with the location of where you heard it, when you heard it, and who you heard it from (even if you only remember that he had a beard, or that she didn't). Episodic memory, then, stores detailed information about the episodes that have happened in your life and in the lives of others. It is a memory system that is accurate, but slow. Semantic memory, on the other hand, is a memory system dedicated to speed. It is a derived memory system, meaning that it is populated with information that is not directly laid down when it is learned or experienced, but is instead derived from memories stored in other systems. In cases where memories are facts about the world, such as capital cities for instance, they are initially stored in episodic memory with all the information about where and when that information was first encountered. It is then encoded into semantic memory without the time, location, and source markers, making these memories informationally lean and quickly accessible.

As we've seen, episodic and semantic memories work together to create our own personal histories, but how do they contribute to our knowledge of others? A growing body of evidence shows that agents build personality summaries or impressions about others in semantic memory by summarizing the data entries stored in episodic memory (Klein, Sherman & Loftus, 1996). This is the same pattern that humans follow when moving common facts from episodic to semantic memory. It isn't clear, though, how many entries need to exist in episodic memory to generate these personality summaries in semantic memory, nor is it clear how quickly these memories are generated once the necessary threshold is reached. It is clear, though, that personality summaries are generated very much like the way that I just described.

Now that we have some understanding of the kinds of data that are held in episodic and semantic memories, it is time to look at how these memory systems might work together to create an overall system that is both fast (semantic memory) and accurate (episodic memory). Klein et al. (2000) argue that these memory systems must interface with at least two other cognitive layers if these systems are to work well together. The first layer consists of decision rules that decide which memories are required to satisfy the input requirements of the inference engines that they are associated with. Once the data retrieval strategy has been formulated, a second layer, called a search engine, then retrieves the necessary data and delivers it back to the inference engine in need of that information.

Klein et al. postulated the existence of decision rules because coordinating search strategies between multiple memory systems without them would be almost impossible. Individual memory systems would have no way of knowing which memories to access without some kind of outside instruction, and individual instructions could be counterproductive in some cases unless they were coordinated with the instructions for other memory systems. For example, Klein et al. realized that although representations based on semantic memories can be accessed quickly, they don't give us any information about those rare situations where an impression about someone is incorrect, even though we may have information about that violation stored in episodic memory. Everyone here, for example, probably knows someone who they would label as "nice", but if you were to forget their birthday, they would not act in accordance with the label you have stored in semantic memory. They would not, in other words, be very nice for some time. Klein et al. argue that such strategic information would have been too important for natural selection not to incorporate it into our data retrieval strategies. We should expect then, that agents retrieve trait related information from semantic memory when they need to access the personality traits of well-known others, but they also retrieve information from episodic memory that contradicts their target personality-summary to set limits on the generally vague information stored in semantic memory.

To test this hypothesis, Klein et al. conducted the following experiment. They tested subjects to see which memories are primed after thinking about their mother's personality traits, which would tell them what systems subjects accessed. Subjects were given a list of trait adjectives and were then asked to do one of three things with these words: (1) decide if the word applied to their mother; (2) recall an episode where that trait was exhibited by their mother; (3) define the word. The subjects were then given a new list of either the same words or antonyms of those words (traits opposite from the previous list, such as happy - sad) and were assigned to one of the other two conditions not yet completed. For example, if a subject is assigned to condition 1 in the first trial, they would be assigned to either condition 2 or 3 in the second trial where they might get the same word again, or its antonym.

Klein et al. predicted that subjects who were asked if the trait applied to their mother in the first trial and then asked to recall an episode where their mother had exhibited an opposite trait in the second trial would be able to recall the exhibited trait faster than the other groups due to priming. This was found. Subjects appear to have accessed the relevant trait summary in semantic memory and trait inconsistent episodes of those traits in episodic memory. It was also predicted that none of the other conditions would show priming affects. This was also found. Trait inconsistent episodes were only accessed when subjects were asked to perform a trait judgment, and trait consistent episodes were never accessed.

To recap, humans access one and sometimes two memory systems when storing and retrieving information about others. They may access only one memory system when retrieving information from semantic memory about long known facts about the world, or they may only access information from episodic memory when retrieving information about a recent event in their life. They may combine information from both memory systems as well, such as when they are retrieving personality-related information about a well-known conspecific. Finally, decision rules and search engines allow humans to access multiple memory systems simultaneously while keeping irrelevant information from slowing down human cognitive processes.

My interest in memory's role in supernatural representation began when I read Justin Barrett's and Frank Keil's (1996) paper on anthropomorphism and supernatural representation. In their paper, Barrett and Keil (1996) wonder if humans are capable of representing god-like agents, specifically the God of western religions, given the unnaturalness of God's many abilities. God can, according to most theologies, be in multiple places while performing multiple activities in the past and the future, all simultaneously. Plainly, God is not just a petty miracle worker, but do we have the cognitive machinery to adequately represent such an agent? Barrett and Keil ran a series of experiments to find out.

In their first experiment, Barrett and Keil had subjects listen to a series of tapes that told a story where God was a main character in that story. One story, much shortened here, sounded something like this:

> While God was helping an angel with a crossword puzzle, a woman in South America became lost in the jungle. She was very afraid and prayed to God for help. God heard her prayer and led her out of the jungle. God helped the angel finish his crossword puzzle (244).

Subjects were then asked to answer questions about the story. Some of the questions were designed to measure how well subjects remembered the story, while other questions were designed to measure how subjects represented God while processing narrative information about Him. One of the representation-related questions sounded like this: God stopped helping the angel work on a crossword puzzle to help the woman. Subjects were instructed to put yes or no by each of these questions. If you are using your theological knowledge right now to answer this question, your answer should be 'no' since God is capable of performing multiple actions simultaneously and nothing in the story mentions that God stopped helping with the crossword puzzle. Subjects, though, tended to answer 'yes' to such questions even though they usually answered the memory related questions correctly. Subjects were then given a questionnaire asking them to answer questions about God's abilities. The vast majority of subjects demonstrated at least some theological knowledge by agreeing with statements such as 'God can do multiple things simultaneously' or 'God can be in multiple locations simultaneously'. Clearly, most subjects 'knew' that God could do multiple things simultaneously even as they unconsciously limited God to one action at a time when processing narratives about Him.

Let's walk through Barrett and Keil's experimental results again, but this time, let's use Klein et al.'s theoretical approach and terminology. In the first part of Barrett and Keil's experimental protocol, subjects were asked to listen to and recall a narrative where God was a character in that story. Since a narrative is merely a description of an episode or series of episodes, and since the most efficient memory retrieval strategy to retrieve episodic information is to only access episodic memory, it is probable that subjects in this condition only accessed episodic memory to complete this task. Episodic memory, of course, is designed to store historical information about others, not information about another's traits, so it is not surprising that subjects did not have access to God's supernatural traits during this task. In the second part of the experiment, subjects were asked to fill out a questionnaire about God's supernatural traits. This task is functionally identical to the trait-recall task found in Klein et al.'s experimental design. We know from Klein et al.'s experiments that humans access semantic memory in order to retrieve the personality traits of others. It seems probable, then, that the subjects in Barrett and Keil's supernatural trait-recall task retrieved God's supernatural traits from semantic memory, as well. Based on this reasoning, it is my hypothesis that supernatural traits for god-like agents are stored in semantic memory, and that these traits are not accessible when humans are engaged in narrative tasks unless these traits had been recently primed prior to the narrative task.

In the coming year, I intend to test this hypothesis by running a series of experiments based on Klein et al.'s experimental design, albeit with two changes. First, I plan to remove the condition 'word definition' used by Klein et al. and replace it with a narrative condition. In this new condition, subjects will be asked to read a narrative and answer a question about it in the first stage of the experiment, and then they will be assigned to either the 'decide' or 'recall' conditions in the second stage. The goal of this change is to see if recalling information from a narrative primes either episodic or semantic memory. As you might have guessed, I predict that retrieving narrative-related information will only prime episodic memory. For my second change, I will use God to replace "mother" in trait-recall tasks. I predict that God will show the same priming affect as natural agents, except that subjects will not attempt to retrieve counter-examples of God's personality traits from episodic memory. This prediction is a direct result of predictions made by commitment signaling theory, which predicts that humans will have cognitive mechanisms designed to shield believers from doubt (Bulbulia, 2004). The existence of different decision rules for natural and god-like agents would be just the kind of protective mechanisms that costly signaling predicts.

As we have seen, memory is a critical component of religious representation, yet we still know very little about how it affects these representations. I hope that by bringing together the work by Klein at al. with the work done by Barrett and Keil, I have at least shed some light on the role that memory plays in religious cognition. There is, though, much left to study. Uncovering how memories related to religious representations are formatted within different memory systems needs to be worked out. Such information could help us understand whether religious information differs from other kinds of data in a meaningful way, or if, as many argue here, religious information is just information stored for its own sake. Like anything in science, we won't know until we look.

References

Barrett, J., & Keil, F. 1996. Conceptualizing a non-natural entity: Anthropomorphism in God concepts. *Cognitive Psychology, 31*, 219-247.

Bulbulia, J. 2004. Religious costs as adaptations that signal altruistic intentions. *Evolution & Cognition, 10* (1), 19-42.

Klein, S., Cosmides, L., Tooby, J., & Chance, S. 2002. Decisions and the evolution of memory: Multiple systems, multiple functions. *Psychological Review, 109*, 306-329.

Klein, S., Sherman, J., Loftus, J., & Chance, S. 1996. The role of episodic and semantic memory in the development of trait self-knowledge. *Social Cognition, 14*, 277-291.

The Cognitive and Evolutionary Roots of Paradise Representations

Jani Närhi

Imaginary Real Worlds

Until at least the 16th century, there was a widespread belief in Europe that The Garden of Eden really existed on Earth. Inspired by the description of the Genesis, several expeditions were organized to find this mythical garden. Not surprisingly, the efforts were all but successful although some people, Christopher Columbus, for example, actually believed they had found Eden on their expeditions (Partin 2005).

Whether Eden or any of its counterparts exists or not, the idea of a blooming sanctuary with plenty of sensual pleasures is widespread. That place is believed to be reached either after individual death, in the end of time, or it represents the primordial happy era of humankind. Variations of this idea are found in most religious traditions. For example, the Celts believed that the afterworld, Síd, was either a festive hall or a distant island that possessed a never-failing supply of the choicest food and drink. Life in that world was described as a continuous feast in eternal peace without toil and strife. Death and diseases were unknown and even the colours were brighter than in this world (see Carey 1982; O'Rahilly 1946).

Similar representations are found across the world. Tlalocan, the afterworld of Aztecs, was believed to be a fortunate land with lakes, rivers, cacao trees, and eternal summer. Life in there was a pleasant existence surrounded by flowers and trees. Abundance of fruit, corns, and beans was notable (see Hultkrantz, 1967/1980). For the Aboriginals of Australia, the afterworld was a fertile land with abundant resources of water and easily hunted game. Life there was believed to be comparable to this life, except for the fact that all the difficulties were absent (Charlesworth, Morphy, Bell, & Maddock 1984, 222-226).

Even many new religious movements have their own ideas about an afterworld, or the new era, which closely resemble their old counterparts. Today's themes are basically the same as the old ones: Ease and happiness of life, abundance of resources, lack of diseases and death, with the problems of the real world solved (see e.g., Grünschloß 2004; Steinbauer 1971/1979 for Cargo cults; Wojcik 2003 for UFO cults). Thus, it is obvious that these narratives and imagery, which I will call "paradise representations" from now on, are too similar to be explained away as coincidence.

My aim here is to explain this invariance by utilizing the results of cognitive science and studies of environmental preferences. I try to show that the evolved architecture of mind is likely to be the best explanation of the prevalence of these representations.

In addition to the term "paradise representations", I will use the terms "real world" and "imaginary world" to refer to the two classes of representations. "Real world" refers to the world about which we can make empirical observations. "Imaginary world" refers to the worlds that cannot be directly observed, but of which we can hold beliefs and mental representations similar to those of the real world.

Paradises and Environmental Preferences

In order to understand the role of innate cognitive processes behind the paradise representations, we need to examine the challenges the struggle for survival sets. I will first concentrate on the environmental preferences that shape our emotional responses to different type of environments.

In nature, all living organisms from the simplest bacteria to humans need to know what happens around them and what possible effect the course of events can have to them. Without information about the state of the environment, no organism can act effectively and its fate depends on the luck of the draw.

This capacity of valuing the world based on acquired information is primarily unconscious and it helps organisms act rapidly without slow conscious decision-making in situations where immediate responses are essential. Due to this, according to several authors (e.g., Kaplan 1987; 1992; Orians & Heerwagen 1992; Silverman & Choi 2005), unconscious environmental preferences are a result of natural selection, an adaptation for increasing the probability of survival.Indeed, human responses to environments of various kinds are highly affective and with little or no conscious processing involved (Korpela, Klemettilä, & Hietanen 2002; Ulrich1983; Zajonc 1980), and the preference pattern seems to be cross-cultural (Herzog, Herbert, Kaplan, & Crooks 2000), thus indicating a genetically derived predisposition as a function of survival (Kaplan & Kaplan 1989, 40-42, see also Balling & Falk 1982) rather than culturally acquired information about what one should prefer.

From an evolutionary perspective, these results indicate that humans have a reason to favor environments of a certain kind at the cost of others. Appleton (1975) suggests that humans generally prefer environments that offer visibility to open spaces and shelter from others' eyes. Being sheltered from predators but being able to observe them and all potential resources at the same time is a vital advantage in the struggle for life.

Since preferences are a result of an automatic processing, they cannot be consciously controlled. By favoring certain kind of information, our brain sets constraints to what will be processed after the initial handling of a stimulus. Some information is always put to the recycle bin. As a consequence, the content that can be consciously processed is dependent on the "low-level" pruning (cf. Sperber 1996, 88-89). In the case of environments, this means that what could consciously be considered as ideal, or undesirable, probably borrows most of its elements from the filtered information instead of inventing completely new ideas or designs. Imaginary ideas with no references to the observable world probably have no relevance and thus no value in the context they are supposed to fit in.

Considering this, a comparison between the general elements of paradise representations and those present in preferred environments shows an interesting correlation between certain elements. The presence of water and shelter, the abundance of resources and lack of threats repeatedly occur from paradise to paradise. Moreover, the elements correspond to generally preferred real world elements that provide either nutrition or shelter.

These observations are explained by the notice that the basic needs are universal although there are always differences in the exact ways they are fulfilled. Flora, fauna, and geography differ in different parts of the world. Therefore, nomads living in the desert may develop a very different kind of concept of the ideal world than, say, Aztecs. Still, I argue, any occurring difference is primarily illusory. Instead of comparing the actual content of paradise representations we should compare *the functional value of the content*. By this I mean that we should examine if an element of paradise provides some advantage or disadvantage if it was present in the real world. By analyzing paradise representations this way we see that their content is very uniform from paradise to another regardless of their geographical or even temporal origin.

Thus, environmental preferences and our mental representations about imaginary worlds are closely connected to our basic needs. Environments that can provide us with the resources we need and that are safe at the same time also please us most. Paradises seem to do so in an extraordinary manner. Moreover, paradises lack the typical uncertainties of the real world. In paradise, there are no threats of any kind and this is valid for agent interactions as well: conflicts such as wars are absent and humans live their lives together without competition, violence, or betrayal.

However, while paradise representations seem to inherit their basic properties from actual environments and from the same preference mechanisms, there is a need for an explanation for their durability and dispersion capacity. In other words, we must understand the way our mind processes and creates representations in general and representations about supernatural environments in particular, and how these representations endure in minds.

Paradises and the Architecture of the Mind

Humans tend to remember better things that can be connected to some relevant context. Our mind is equipped with several innate, context-sensitive mechanisms that are specialized to process certain kind of information. For example, language acquisition, basic emotions, and predator-prey interactions are innate and based on our brain structures (see e.g., Barrett 2005; Damasio, 1999; Pinker & Bloom 1990).

While useful in specific problem-solving situations, these mechanisms are, on the other hand, limiting, as they tend to prefer a certain kind of information at the cost of another. Especially information that promotes chances for survival (Tooby & Cosmides 1992) or has relevance from the receiver's point of view (Sperber 1985, 1996; Sperber & Wilson 1986) is likely to be successful, as it is often vital and thus intuitively considered as relevant. In this game, irrelevant information has little chance to win, as cognition tends to be geared to the maximization of relevance (cf. Sperber & Wilson 1986, 260-266).

The other effect is the limitations of our intuitive thinking. It is very difficult for the human mind to even produce extremely odd concepts or representations (Ward 1994). From that follows that even our imaginary representations are likely to resemble those that we have about the real world. Again, in evolutionary context, this is perfectly understandable, for constructing purely abstract ideas would be a waste of time.

Indeed, religiously relevant representations in general seem to "suffer" from these phenomena. Several studies (for review, see Boyer 2003) have shown that humans have difficulties in recalling theological ideas about gods or other supernatural agents. Instead, they are replaced by more intuitive representations that are cognitively less complicated. For example, gods are best understood as anthropomorphic agents with properties comparable to those of humans. The idea of an omnipotent invisible being is much harder to recall without time-consuming conscious processing (Barrett & Keil 1996).

Respectively, it looks that the mind sets boundaries for the paradise beliefs. Although it is fully possible to develop complicated abstractions about invisible souls gathered to the sweet emptiness, it is much easier to adhere to familiarity. While the properties of supernatural agents are also typical of humans, the properties of paradises are typical of natural environments.

However, as paradise representations are not accurate representations of the real world, they must be constructed in the mind somehow. This requires an ability to rearrange acquired information in a way that makes representations about imaginary worlds possible. As the hyperactive agent detection device (HADD) hypothesis suggests (see Barrett 2000; Guthrie 1993), this is not only a possible but also typical trait of our species. While HADD is activated in case of potential agent interactions only, there is a much broader use for a similar mechanism, as agent interactions are not the only ones we constantly encounter. We have to be aware of possible interactions with inanimate and non-agent entities as well.

Still, the purpose is the same. The ability to foresee and imagine potential scenarios is vital for us in a broader context and it plays a role in paradise building. An essential component in the paradise building is therefore, in addition to innate preferences and relevance filters, the associating device that works too hard and begins to build representations that cannot have a counterpart in this world. Therefore, paradise representations are built with tools evolved to respond to the real world problems, but their hyperactivity makes it possible to imagine realms that can never be observed directly.

Conclusion

The available historical data indicates that it is justified to say that belief in paradises is based on cognitive mechanisms and is rooted to our evolutionary history. Paradises are thus best understood as decorated symbols of evolutionarily-driven universal desires.

Therefore, the emergence and durability of paradise representations are primarily based on the desire to survive. This desire overdrives the associating device of the mind to create imaginary realms that fulfill all our evolutionary needs. This is why paradises across the world are similar. The needs are the same and the architecture of the mind is the same. The diversity among paradise representations is mostly illusory and is best explained in terms of local variation of circumstances. Therefore, paradises should not be seen so much as worlds beyond this reality but rather as idealized reflections of the ordinary world in which we live.

References

Appleton, J. 1975. *The experience of landscape*. London, UK: John Wiley & Sons.

Balling, J. D., & Falk, J. H. 1982. Development of visual preference for natural environments. *Environment & Behavior, 14*, 5-28.

Barrett, H. C. 2005. Adaptations to predators and prey. In D. M. Buss, Ed., *The handbook of evolutionary psychology*, 200-223. New York, NY: Wiley.

Barrett, J. L. 2000. Exploring the natural foundations of religion. *Trends in Cognitive Sciences, 4*, 29-34.

Barrett, J. L., & Keil, F. C. 1996. Conceptualizing a non-natural entity: Anthropomorphism in god concepts. *Cognitive Psychology, 31,* 219-247.

Boyer, P. 2003. Religious thought and behaviour as by-products of brain function. *Trends in Cognitive Sciences, 7,* 119-124.

Carey, J. 1982. The location of the otherworld in Irish tradition. *Éigse, XIXI,* 37-43.

Charlesworth, M., Morphy, H., Bell, D, & Maddock, K. Eds. 1984. *Religion in aboriginal Australia: An anthology.* St. Lucia, Queensland: University of Queensland Press.

Damasio, A. R. 1999. *The feeling of what happens: Body and emotion in the making of consciousness.* New York, NY: Harcourt Brace.

Grünschloß, A. 2004. Waiting for the "Big Beam". In J. R. Lewis, Ed., *The Oxford handbook of new religious movements,* 419-444. New York, NY: Oxford University Press.

Guthrie, S. E. 1993. *Faces in the clouds.* New York, NY: Oxford University Press.

Herzog, T. R., Herbert, E. J., Kaplan, R., Crooks, C. L. 2000. Cultural and developmental comparisons of landscape perceptions and preferences. *Environment & Behavior,* 32, 323-346.

Hultkrantz, Å. 1980. *The religions of the American Indians* M. Setterwall, Trans. Berkeley, CA: University of California Press. Original work published 1967.

Kaplan, R., & Kaplan, S. 1989. *The experience of nature: A psychological perspective.* New York, NY: Cambridge University Press.

Kaplan, S. 1987. Aesthetics, affect and cognition: Environmental preference from an evolutionary perspective. *Environment & Behavior,* 19, 3-32.

Kaplan, S. 1992. Environmental preference in a knowledge-seeking, knowledge-using organism. In J. H. Barkow, L. Cosmides & J. Tooby, Eds., *The adapted mind:Evolutionary psychology and the generation of culture,* 581-598. New York, NY: Oxford University Press.

Korpela, K. M., Klemettilä, T., Hietanen, J. K. 2002. Evidence for rapid affective evaluation of environmental scenes. *Environment & Behavior, 34,* 634-650.

O'Rahilly, T. F. 1946. *Early Irish history and mythology.* Dublin, Ireland: Dublin Institute of Advanced Studies.

Orians, G. H., & Heerwagen, J. H. 1992. Evolved responses to landscapes. In J. H. Barkow,L. Cosmides, & J. Tooby Eds., *The adapted mind: Evolutionary psychology and the generation of culture,* 555-579. New York, NY: Oxford University Press.

Partin, H. B. 2005. Paradise. In L. Jones Ed., *Encyclopedia of religion* 2nd ed., 6981-6986. Detroit, MI: Macmillan.

Pinker, S., & Bloom, P. 1990. Natural language and natural selection. *Behavioral & Brain Sciences, 13,* 707-727.

Silverman, I., & Choi, J. 2005. Locating places. In D. M. Buss, Ed., *The handbook of evolutionary psychology*, 177-199. Hoboken, NJ: John Wiley & Sons.
Sperber, D. 1985. Anthropology and psychology: Towards an epidemiology of representations. *Man, 20*, 73-89.
Sperber, D. 1996. *Explaining culture. A naturalistic approach*. Cambridge, MA: Blackwell Publishers.
Sperber, D., & Wilson, D. 1986. *Relevance: Communication and cognition*. Oxford, UK: Basil Blackwell.
Steinbauer, F. 1979. *Melanesian Cargo cults: New salvation movements in the SouthPacific* M. Wohlwill, Trans. London, UK: George Prior. Original work published 1971.
Tooby, J., & Cosmides, L. 1992. The psychological foundations of culture. In J. H. Barkow, L. Cosmides, & J. Tooby, Eds., *The adapted mind: Evolutionary psychology and the generation of culturel*, 19-136. New York, NY: Oxford University Press.
Ulrich, R. S. 1983. Aesthetic and affective response to natural environment. In I. Altman & J. F. Wohlwill, Eds., *Behavior and the natural environment* pp. 85-125. New York, NY: Plenum Press.
Ward, T. B. 1994. Structured imagination: The role of category structure in exemplar generation. *Cognitive Psychology, 27*, 1-40.
Wojcik, D. 2003. Apocalyptic and millenarian aspects of American UFOism. In C. Partridge, Ed., *UFO religions* 274-300. London, UK: Routledge.
Zajonc, R. B. 1980. Feeling and thinking: Preferences need no inferences. *American Psychologist, 35*, 151-175.

Spiritual Beings

A Darwinian, Cognitive Account

Stewart Guthrie

Introduction: Something old and something new.

Belief in spiritual beings, termed animism by E. B. Tylor, appears culturally universal. Nowadays, animism in the sense of "spirits everywhere" often is associated with people in small-scale societies, such as hunter-gatherers. Jean Piaget defined animism somewhat differently: as the attribution of agency to the biologically lifeless. Piaget associated this, as many still do, with children.

However, both associations are too narrow, since animism is common in industrial societies and adults. Moreover, according to Darwin, higher mammals may be animists as well. We all are fundamentally similar, he wrote, and all may see inanimate objects as inhabited by agents, as when his dog, seeing a parasol moved by wind, barked and growled fiercely.

Animism still puzzles us. Where does it come from? How does it relate to religion? *Was* Darwin's dog an animist? New work on cognition is relevant. My theory of religion is buttressed by this work and, in turn, provides a context for applying it to religion.

A Cognitive Theory.

My argument first appeared as "A Cognitive Theory of Religion" (Guthrie 1980). Three of that paper's propositions—detecting intentional agents is of special concern, our sensitivities to them are correspondingly well developed, and we inevitably over-detect—have been adopted in cognitive approaches to religion. Still, the theory struck some as leaving an important question unanswered: If, as it holds, gods, ghosts and other humanlike agents, including their traces and messages, are anthropomorphisms, why are they frequently represented as invisible and/or immaterial, when actual humans are not? And if invisible, why are they plausible?

The 1980 paper (and Guthrie 1993) deals with this in two ways. First, it notes that not all gods are invisible and intangible. To hide, for example, Homer's gods must produce cloud or smoke. Second, invisibility and immateriality are not unique to gods. Many animals in their habitats, and humans in camouflage, are invisible until they move. Like gods, such agents are revealed more by their actions than their shapes. Further, some life forms simulate intangibility, as by schooling or flocking, which make individuals hard to see, or by small size, as in bacteria and viruses.

Thus, neither invisibility nor intangibility may distinguish gods. As Burkert notes in *Origins of the Sacred,* dealing with unseen gods differs little from dealing with unseen distant merchants. Nonetheless, some have urged that gods such as Abrahamic ones may be absolutely invisible and that this is different, so I've continued to mull the question.

Guthrie (1980) made three general assertions. First, religious thought and action resemble and are continuous with secular thought and action, and spring from the same cognitive processes. This now is widely conceded (although it seems to contradict another current claim, that religions are counterintuitive).

Second, anthropomorphism—attributing human characteristics to nonhuman things and events—pervades thought and action, mostly unconsciously. It occurs in ordinary perception, as when we hear a wind-slammed door as an intruder, see AIDS as punishment, or find design in nature. Acknowledgements of this pervasiveness keep arriving.

In cognitive psychology, for example, Wegner (2005, 22) notes our "compelling inclination to perceive even . . . geometric figures" as agents. Mar and Macrae (2006, 110) write, "we routinely view quite abstract nonliving representations as if they were intentional agents." In archeology, Lahelma (in press) writes that "some of the earliest . . . paleoart feature[s] anthropomorphism" (16) and that a jasperite pebble carried into a South African cave by a hominid two to three million years ago evidently was chosen because it had natural "eyes" and a "mouth." Similar anthropomorphism infuses the history of art and appears even in science (Guthrie 1993).

My third general proposition was that religion is a systematized form of anthropomorphism: that is, over-detection of humanlike agency. Feuerbach, Hume, Spinoza and others also called religion anthropomorphism, but lacked a convincing explanation of anthropomorphism itself. Such an explanation is the heart of the 1980 paper and my ongoing work. Simply put, anthropomorphism, and hence religion (systematized thought and action concerning humanlike beings such as gods, ghosts and demons), results from a strategy of interpretation. The argument is as follows:

In trying to grasp the world, we must guess how to construe phenomena. That is, perception is interpretation. It is interpretation because phenomena are chronically ambiguous, since every stimulus has more than one potential cause (a tickle on the skin may be a loose thread or a spider, a thump in the night may be a door closed by wind or a burglar.) Ambiguity starts with the simplest percepts—for example, lines and edges—and continues up to our most comprehensive pictures of the world, typically those we call religious.

As Ernst Gombrich puts it, perception is betting (Guthrie 1993, 42). In my terms, it's betting about what phenomena represent: about what—or who—causes them. In this betting, we choose the most significant possibilities we know: the spider, not the thread; the burglar, not the wind.

The most significant possibilities usually are organisms, especially humans. Practically, humans are most significant because their organization makes them most powerful and able to generate the widest range of effects. Intellectually, as models for understanding the world, they also are most significant, generating endless inferences, for the same reasons.

Their presence, however, may be hard to detect because, like most animals, they exacerbate the uncertainty of perception by camouflage and other deceit. Indeed, their behavior is so protean that almost nothing, from catching smallpox to global warming, can be excluded as an effect of human or humanlike action. Thus we bet high, involuntarily and unconsciously, on humans—or other intentional agents—even though we're often mistaken.

This strategy has evolved, based on a good principle: Better safe than sorry. Walking in the woods, it's better to mistake a stick for a snake, or a boulder for a bear, than the reverse. If we're right, we gain much, and if wrong, we lose little.

Because intentional agents, especially humans, are our hair-trigger default models for an uncertain world, we necessarily interpret that world as more humanlike than it is. The results are broad: Plagues appear as punishments, earthquakes as messages, and the universe as designed.

I then raised a key question: What is "humanlike" in a model? What do we think we see in the world, that we (mis)identify as gods, or as their traces or messages? I argued in 1980, and continue to, that we search primarily for minds and behaviors. Wegner (2005, 22) agrees, noting our "readiness to perceive minds behind events" and that our "faculty for mind perception is a strong guiding force in perception more generally." Central to human mind and behavior, in turn, are language and other symbolism. Because we are deeply linguistic and symbolic, all events—taps on the window, comets, illnesses—seem to signify.

A related question was, and is: What is *not* humanlike, in gods, spirits, and demons? No clear distinction exists. Rather, they, we, and other animals are on a continuum or, better, on various continua. Gods have various human qualities: they may be born, eat, drink, grow old, get sick, and die.

Yet gods also frequently are invisible and intangible. So the question is, do humans share these features, or are they distinctive? Since both spiritual beings and humans are intentional agents, to answer this is to say how we conceive agents. Here, work on cognition gives new answers.

Recent Cognitive Science on Agency

Folk-psychological, or intuitive, agency resembles spiritual beings in five ways. First, it is informed by intuitive mind-body dualism, as scholars in several disciplines note (including Koch, this volume). Anthropologists, for example, report dualism, with material body and immaterial mind (or near equivalents, often plural), around the world. Absent evidence of worldwide transmission, this distribution suggests that dualism itself is intuitive or innate. In psychology, Bering (e.g., 2002) shows that although young children understand physical death, they intuitively expect that a mind survives it, in part because they consider mind separate; and Paul Bloom argues extensively that dualism is not merely intuitive but is innate, appearing even in infancy.

How do mind and body rank in our conception of agents? This brings us to the second aspect of agency: Mind (widely conceived as the immaterial or ethereal basis of identity, sentience and volition) has priority over, and independence of, body. Although morphology (e.g., eyes, a mouth, bilateral symmetry) provides cues for detecting agency, behavior (motions compatible with mind) is more important.

Again, several disciplines indicate mind's priority and independence. In anthropology, Gell (*Art and Agency*) notes "distributed agency": we act not only through our body but also through our artifacts, at a distance and over time. For example, a soldier, by laying mines, can go on killing even after he is dead. Maurice Bloch (in press) writes that by symbolic interaction, we produce similar states in each other's minds, making the location of ideas, thoughts, and agency indeterminate. In philosophy, Leder (*The Absent Body*) draws on medicine to argue that we think of ourselves as minds because we're unaware of our bodies except when they bother us, as in sickness or disability. Similarly, Lakoff and Johnson (*Philosophy in the Flesh*) say humans consider their essential selves immaterial (and therefore immortal).

In psychology, studies of infant and adult perception (Csibra, Gergely, Bíró, Koós & Brockbank 1999; Scholl & Tremoulet 2000) also show that no animal-like body, or even a bounded body, is necessary for agency, since we perceive even a collection of dots moving together as an agent (Bloom & Veres 1999). Kelemen (2004) notes that children, by about three or four, represent immaterial agents; and Kuhlmeier, Bloom and Wynn (2004) argue that five-month-old infants do not see humans as material objects, since they are not surprised at discontinuous motion by humans, unlike material objects. Lillard and Skibbe (2005 281) doubt that theory of mind is domain specific, noting for instance that people say of the sky, "It wants to rain." Last, a computer scientist, Turchin (1998, 1) writes that "an *agent* is a representation of an action. We do not see agents, we see only what they are doing."

A third aspect of agency is that teleology is central to it. But teleology also appears independently, as when our prior sense that the world shows design leads us to infer a designer. Csibra et al. (1999, 265) show that infants attribute goals even to a non-self-propelled moving object, without prior ontological commitment as to type of object. This contradicts proposals that purposeful objects first must be seen as agents. Thus teleology is not domain specific, and infants have the teleological stance as a "primary interpretational system." Kelemen (and Kelemen & DiYanni, 2005) also writes extensively that young children are teleologists, indeed making them "intuitive theists" (Kelemen, 2004). Children find purpose and design in the world "promiscuously" and, from them, infer a designer. Hume said the same of adults (Guthrie, 1993).

The fourth aspect of agency is that perceiving it is unconscious and uncontrolled. Hassin, Uleman and Bargh (2005), Lillard and Skibbe (2005, 282), and Scholl and Tremoulet (2000) all write that detecting intentionality and animacy is not conceptual but perceptual, and thus rapid and automatic. Seeing one circle pursue another on a computer screen, we cannot help inferring agency.

The fifth aspect of agency is that the threshold for perceiving it is low. As noted, we see even a moving collection of dots as an agent. Mar and Macrae (2006, 118) write specifically that we have a "low threshold" for the intentional stance. Indeed, we scan actively for intentionality. As Nietzsche wrote, "I notice something and seek . . . an intention in it, and above all someone who has intentions, a subject, a doer: every event a deed" (1901/1967, in Cziko 2000, 13).

These five aspects of agency in intuitive psychology (dualism, priority of mind, teleology, unconsciousness, and low threshold) constitute a proclivity for finding disembodied agents everywhere. Now we can see why invisible and intangible spirits are plausible and even compulsory: they are precisely how we conceive agency itself.

Why should we conceive agents this way, when modern biology does not? I end with a Darwinian suggestion that parallels my theory of anthropomorphism, by pointing to a perceptual problem and a strategy for solving it. The problem again is identifying intentional agents in an uncertain world, in which their embodiments are both camouflaged and innumerable and thus defy simple searches. Their goals and purposes, however, are fewer and more consistent: for example, to eat, reproduce, and avoid being eaten. Our strategy, then, is to build our notions of agency around goals, purposes, and corresponding behaviors. The constraint of looking, first, for goal-oriented behavior makes finding the myriad forms in which agents are embodied more nearly possible.

Conclusion

We began with three questions: Where does animism come from? How does it relate to religion? And *was* Darwin's dog an animist? My answers are much the same as in my 1980 paper and ongoing work.

Animism in both senses—belief in spirit beings and giving life to the lifeless—comes from our need to discover agents in an uncertain environment. Animism is basic to religion, if not sufficient for it. As for Darwin's dog, it certainly shared our need to find agents hidden in an ambiguous world. Since it apparently also shared our strategy of betting readily that we've found them, we have little reason to think Darwin was mistaken.

References

Bering, J. 2002. Intuitive conceptions of dead agents' minds. *Journal of Cognition & Culture 2*, 263-308.

Bloch, M. in press. Durkheimian anthropology and religion: Going in and out of each other's bodies. In H. Whitehouse & J. Laidlaw, Eds., *Ritual and cognition: Challenges for the anthropology of religion*. Durham, NC: Carolina Academic Press.

Bloom, P., & Veres, C. 1999. The perceived intentionality of groups. *Cognition, 71*, B1-B9.

Csibra, G., Gergeley, G. , Bíró, S., Koós, O., & Brockbank, M. 1999. Goal attribution without agency cues. *Cognition, 72*, 237-267.

Cziko, G. 2000. *The things we do*. Cambridge, MA: The MIT Press.

Guthrie, S. 1980. A cognitive theory of religion. *Current Anthropology, 21* (2), 181-194.

Guthrie, S. 1993. *Faces in the clouds*. New York, NY: Oxford University Press.

Hassin, R., Uleman, J., & Bargh, J. 2005. *The new unconscious*. Oxford, UK: Oxford University Press.

Kelemen, D. 2004. Are children 'intuitive theists'? *Psychological Science, 15*, 295- 301.

Kelemen, D., & DiYanni, C. 2005. Intuitions about origins. *Journal of Cognition & Development*, 6 (1), 3-31.

Kuhlmeier, V., Bloom, P., & Wynn, K. 2004. Do 5-month-old infants see humans as material objects? *Cognition, 94* (1), 95-103.

Lahelma, A. in press. Communicating with 'stone persons.' In E. Walderhaug & L. Forsberg, Eds., *Cognition and signification in northern landscapes*. Bergen: University of Bergen.

Lillard, A., & Skibbe, L. 2005. Theory of mind. In R. Hassin, J. Uleman, & J. Bargh, Eds., *The new unconscious*, 277-305. Oxford, UK: Oxford University Press.

Mar, R., & Macrae, C. N. 2006. Triggering the intentional stance. In G. Bock & J. Goode, Eds., *Empathy and fairness*, 110-132. London, UK: Wiley, Chichester.

Scholl, B., & Tremoulet, P. 2000. Perceptual causality and animacy. *Trends in Cognitive Sciences*, *4* (8), 299-309.

Turchin, V. 1998. Agent. *Principia Cybernetica Web*, May 23. Filename: AGENT.html.

Wegner, D. 2005. Who is the controller of controlled processes? In R. Hassin, J. Uleman, & J. Bargh, Eds., *The new unconscious*, 19-36. Oxford, UK: Oxford University Press.

PART VI

GODS IN BODIES

Not Myself Today

A Cognitive Account of the Transmission of Spirit Possession Concepts

Emma Cohen

Introduction

In the last two decades, the scientific study of religion has seen the rapid expansion of a multi-disciplinary network of scholars interested in applying theories and findings from cognitive science (particularly cognitive, evolutionary and developmental psychology) to research on religious thought and practice cross-culturally. The broad set of questions now guiding this scholarship stems from a central concern to explain how and why cross-culturally recurrent forms of religious thought and practice emerge, stabilize, evolve, and spread in the ways they do. By considering the constraining and enabling effects of our evolved cognitive architecture upon the transmission of culture, such approaches promise to complement and bridge biological and sociological explanations of cultural phenomena in general, and religious phenomena in particular (see Barrett, this volume).

In this paper, I present some recent research findings on the cognition of spirit possession. The research problems emerged during eighteen months of ethnographic fieldwork with an Afro-Brazilian religious group in Belém, Northern Brazil (2002-2004). Observations of this community's concepts of spirit possession, together with a survey of anthropological literature on spirit possession phenomena cross-culturally, yielded a host of empirical questions and theoretical speculations about the possible causal role of cognition in the spread of certain forms of thinking about spirits, bodies and possession (Cohen, 2007). Reformulating these questions as testable hypotheses, Justin Barrett and I have initiated a program of experimental investigation of the cognitive underpinnings of possession concepts[1].

The context

Spirit possession is a term that has been used to describe and account for many different kinds of phenomena in many different cultural contexts,

1 We gratefully acknowledge the support of a British Academy Small Research Grant (SG-42034) and the John Templeton Foundation.

from the kinds of symptoms associated with sleeping sickness in West Africa to the dramatic trance episodes of films such as the *Exorcist*. Here I focus on *possession trance*, which, according to Erika Bourguignon, is "a state of relatively brief duration, from a few minutes to a few days at most" during which "the individual loses his or her identity for the duration, an identity which is replaced" (Bourguignon 1976, 46). Contrary to Bourguignon's description, however, possession trance is not invariably associated with a complete replacement of identity. It is this aspect of possession trance—the notion of what happens to one's identity when one is possessed—that has become the focus of our investigations.

Conceptual building blocks

How is possession trance conceptualized? What kind of mental capacities does it take? Certain properties of the self (and other) appear to be crucially and fundamentally relevant to thinking about possession, namely, body and agency. In contrast to embodied human hosts, or mediums, spirits are agents that do not have bodies. The widespread, cross-cultural recurrence of ideas about disembodied agents (e.g., spirits, souls, gods, etc.) suggests that the mental tools employed in the representation of persons readily facilitate the conceptual fissure of body and agent. The work of development psychologist, Paul Bloom (2004), on what has become known as "intuitive dualism" sheds some light on the possible cognitive mechanisms at work here. Research in developmental psychology points to the existence of two sets of early-emerging cognitive systems relevant to our representation of persons. One—naïve psychology—is activated in the perception and representation of the social world of intentional agents. The other—naïve physics—deals with problems in the physical world, delivering assumptions about the world of solid, cohesive bodies, or objects. Both systems are foundational to the representation of persons, entities that are at the same time social and physical. It has been suggested that the duality of perception generated by these discrete sets of mechanisms makes Cartesian mind-body dualism natural and intuitive (e.g., Bloom 2004, 2007). We readily perceive and represent minds and bodies as autonomous. Even as adults we have difficulty in fully and consistently integrating the outputs of our naïve physics and naïve psychology in our person representations. So, while we may not believe in the existence of such things as persons without bodies, we have no trouble readily comprehending such concepts.

Having achieved the conceptual fissure of minds and bodies, how do we then think about their reconfiguration and recombination in possession? What are the cognitive constraints and possibilities? A number of options are available. The spirit agency may displace the host agency from the body;

or, spirit and host agencies may merge in one body; or, spirit and host agencies may oscillate in one body, and so on. What is particularly apparent from the cross-cultural record, however, is that although there are many different possibilities—at least in principle—for the ways in which agents and bodies may be recombined in possession, there is one configuration that appears with considerably more frequency than any other. This configuration assumes that when a spirit possesses a medium, the medium's soul/mind/spirit/agency is completely displaced. In the case of *displacement*, the spirit's entrance marks the ousting, or eclipse, of the host agency. There is only one active agent in one body at any given moment. An *oscillation* model, in which spirit and host intermittently control the body, tends to feature strongly in scary films, where the afflicted host and evil demon struggle to gain control over the body. *Fusion*, in which spirit and host agency merge, appears in the ethnographic record, including Brazil, but is rare. Indeed, the spiritual leader of the Afro-Brazilian group with whom I conducted fieldwork taught *fusion* as the "theologically correct" account of possession. Yet across the rank and file population, displacement was the predominant description of possession.

The problem and investigation

The puzzle, then, is why is *displacement* so common cross-culturally? Related, why does the displacement concept persist even in the face of theological correction and instruction? One possible answer is that intuitive assumptions about the relationship between minds and bodies structure mental models of possession. For example, perhaps there is a universal intuitive expectation that there can only be one mind controlling a body at a particular time. Two minds simultaneously controlling a body, two minds merging together, and so on, are cognitively cumbersome concepts and difficult to implement in social perception and cognition (for example, in the prediction and explanation of behavior). To investigate this possibility, we conducted a study that explored whether the displacement model was spontaneously used by naïve adults when presented with novel mind-body scenarios. To investigate further why displacement enjoys such transmissive success, we explored whether it is better remembered than the other candidate accounts.

In the first study, participants were told about two fictitious characters called Ann and Beth. They were presented with ten scenarios in which Beth's mind goes into Ann's body and asked to reason about the post-transfer girl's behavior on a variety of tasks. The tasks in half of the items depended heavily on mental aptitudes, and in the other five 'control' items tasks hinged more strongly on physical aptitudes. So, for example, one 'mental' item read as follows:

> Ann is very good at maths. She regularly gets excellent marks on 7-point quizzes—usually around 6 out of 7 of her answers are correct.
>
> Beth is very poor at maths. She regularly gets poor marks on 7-point quizzes—usually around 2 out of 7 of her answers are correct.
>
> Once when the girls were in maths class, somehow Beth's mind went into Ann's body. How well do you think that the girl will do on the maths test?

All the items followed a similar structure, with example control items including aptitudes such as visual acuity, sprint speed, and so on (Cohen & Barrett, in press).

Unsurprisingly, responses showed that participants reasoned differently on the physical and mental items. When Beth's mind goes into Ann's body, Ann does not simply become Beth. Physical aptitudes are retained, but mental performance is transformed. But precisely how is this transformation represented? Do people reason (consistently) about the transfer as entailing a displacement or a fusion?[2] A participant analysis showed that there were significantly more 'displacers' (i.e., participants who used a displacement model in four or five of the five mental items) than 'fusers' (i.e., participants who used a fusion model in four or five of the five mental items). Four out of 51 participants consistently offered fusion answers and 30 out of 51 participants consistently reasoned about the mind-transfer as entailing a complete displacement. Of the 17 participants who offered a mix of fusion and displacement responses, 12 used displacement most and four used fusion most.

Importantly, no possession model was specified in this task. We did not wish to activate people's specific models of possession, but to identify the assumptions that pertain to the elemental conceptual building blocks of possession concepts. The fundamental assumption driving our investigations is that concepts of possession, spirits, and so on, do not have special cognitive supporting structures of their own, but they are supported—and constrained—by the same cognitive structures that guide ordinary, everyday thinking about persons, bodies, and minds and the relationships between them. Possession concepts appear to exploit the cognitive tools we have for solving other common problems in our social and physical environments.

Similarly, using a standard narrative recall task and without specifying a possession model, we investigated memorability of the various body-mind configurations represented by possession concepts. Participants listened to a short recorded narrative featuring various types of fictitious beings who had

---

2 In the maths item example given, a 2 represents a displacement response. Any other point on the scale, except 6, represents a fusion response.

the ability who fuse with, oscillate with, and displace other beings in/from a single body. Descriptions controlled for structural similarity, complexity and length, and the order in which each item was heard was counterbalanced across participants. Two hypothesis-blind coders recorded the recall rate for each item - a total of 31 participants recalled displacement accurately; 12 recalled fusion; and 11 participants recalled the oscillation concept (Cohen & Barrett, under review).

These findings offer preliminary support for the hypothesis that displacement predominates cross-culturally, and is more easily grasped in the Afro-Brazilian context, because it is supported by ordinary cognition. People are more likely to infer spontaneously that possession entails displacement because this notion is consistent with a one-mind-controlling-one-body expectation. The potential for the concept to spread is further enhanced because, relative to the other candidate concepts, it is more memorable. It appears, therefore, that our cognitive tools bias the emergence and memorability, and therefore the transmission, of concepts that concern minds and bodies in general, and possession in particular.

Possession perception

The cognitive factors contributing to religious phenomena we observe on the ground are rarely singular, however, but are complex and interdependent, and it is often only through attention to the finer details of each case that we can begin to build a comprehensive explanation for the observed phenomena. Closer observation of the ways in which people in the Afro-Brazilian context comprehend and represent possession by spirits in *actual* possession episodes yields a much more complex picture than these cult participants' definitional accounts of possession might suggest.

It appears that the conceptually 'easy' displacement model of possession is often difficult to implement in the real-time perception of a possessed medium. Although observers explicitly accept the verisimilitude of the possession trance and affirm a displacement of identity, they do not consistently attribute all behaviors during the possession episode to the possessing spirit. For example, if someone danced poorly while possessed, blame was often directed toward the host. Furthermore, there is some evidence that people are unable to shut off affective elements of their relationship with a host normally when the host was possessed. Fondness, or contempt, for a medium apparently 'carried over' into the possession episode.

A possible explanation for these apparent inconsistencies may be accounted for by another set of neuro-cognitive mechanisms. Cognitive neuroscientists are demonstrating how our highly sophisticated face recognition architecture is linked through an automatic neural pathway to person familiarity assessment regions and person identity semantic and emotional systems (e.g., Gobbini et al. 2004; Paller et al. 2003; Shah et al. 2001). Indeed, the high automaticity of this pathway suggests that we cannot simply choose to attach a novel identity file to a familiar face. Despite explicitly acknowledging that someone is possessed and therefore displaced, the observer therefore experiences difficulty in fully dissociating the normal host identity from the host's body.

This brief example illustrates that without an appreciation of the complex ways in which our evolved cognitive mechanisms inform and constrain thought and behavior, we would be ill-equipped to understand what might off-handedly be labeled "inconsistencies" in people's beliefs. Ethnography and cognitive science offer equally indispensable and interdependent methodologies for the generation of truly relevant, explanatory, and grounded theories about culture.

Conclusion

This research represents a naturalistic approach to the evolution of cultural phenomena. How do religious concepts emerge, stabilize, and spread? By recognizing that they are cognitively constructed and maintained, supported by natural, ordinary cognitive mechanisms and processes, we can gain some traction on this key anthropological question. Certain concepts spread better than others, as is demonstrated by ethnographic and cross-cultural comparative research. One plausible explanation is that these successfully spreading concepts (e.g., displacement concepts of possession) effectively exploit the evolved cognitive mechanisms we use to make sense of our everyday social and physical worlds. The mind-body dualism, for example, that is fundamental to many varieties of possession concepts appears to be supported by ordinary cognitive capacities to do with the perception and representation of physical objects and social agents. Those concepts that are less well supported by our cognitive tools (e.g., fusion concepts of possession) are less likely to enjoy success in cultural transmission, all else being equal. Such hypotheses are amenable to cognitive scientific investigation. The data presented here suggest that, while a comprehensive explanation of the emergence and spread of possession concepts requires an appreciation of wider social and cultural processes, the stability of these concepts is explained in part by cognitive constraints.

So, even apart from being well-represented across the globe, ideas about spirit possession really aren't all that exotic. Have you ever been accused of 'losing your mind' or being 'out of your mind'? Maybe you just haven't been feeling yourself lately. Have you ever pondered that by combining that person's mind in that person's body, you'd have found your perfect mate? Perhaps not, but such notions—and the kinds of comedic novels and films that they inspire—form readily, are easily comprehended and spread rapidly, and may have much more in common with cross-culturally recurrent ideas about possession by spirits than you may have previously considered.

References

Bloom, P. 2004. *Descartes' baby: How the science of child development explains what makes us human*. New York, NY: Basic Books.

Bloom, P. 2007. Religion is natural. *Developmental Science, 10*, 147-151.

Bourguignon, E. 1976. *Possession*. Chandler & Sharp Series in Cross-cultural Themes. San Francisco: Chandler & Sharp Publishers.

Cohen, E. 2007. *The mind possessed: The cognition of spirit possession in an Afro-Brazilian religious tradition*. New York, NY: Oxford University Press.

Cohen, E., & Barrett, J. Under review. *When minds migrate: Conceptualizing spirit possession*. Manuscript submitted for publication.

Cohen, E., & Barrett, J. In preparation. *Conceptualizing possession trance: Ethnographic and experimental evidence.*

Gobbini, M. I., Leibenluft, E., Santiago, N., & Haxby, J. V. 2004. Social and emotional attachment in the neural representation of faces. *NeuroImage, 22*, 1628-1635.

Paller, K. A., Ranganath, C., Gonsalves, B., LaBar, K. S., Parrish, T. B., Gitelman, D. R., et al. 2003. Neural correlates of person recognition. *Learning & Memory, 10*, 253-260.

Shah, N., Marshall, J. C., Zafiris, O., Schwab, A., Zilles, K., Markowitsch, H. J., et al. 2001. The neural correlates of person familiarity: A functional magnetic resonance imaging study with clinical implications. *Brain, 124*, 804-815.

Dualism, Moral Judgment, and Perceptions of Intentionality

Gretchen Koch

The central question I'll be addressing in this paper is this: If people are intuitive dualists—they feel introspectively that they are separable from their bodies, distinct from them—what relationship might this attribution have to the way we make moral judgments about others? The separate essence of a person is what I'll be calling a soul, and for reasons to be explained, I place this entity in the category of the supernatural. The developmental psychologist Paul Bloom (2004) makes a very compelling argument in his book *Descartes' Baby* that we are born intuitive dualists, and this intuition stays with us throughout life. He argues that it even contributes to forming some of our beliefs about controversial political issues regarding life and death, such as abortion, cloning, and euthanasia. We find it easy to contemplate the idea of out of body experiences, possession, and life after death because, as he argues, we already tend to operate as if the mind and the body are separate, and the mind constitutes the actual person. Therefore it follows that this mind is immaterial, yet has some kind of causal relationship with the body which subverts the body to it but does not allow the direct equation of mind to brain—the mechanistic functions whereby a materialist views the mind as functioning. We can speak quite easily of wanting to have Einstein's brain, for example, not appearing to be bothered by the thought that actually having Einstein's brain would mean that *our* brain—and hence we—would no longer exist. Whatever a person is, they don't seem intuitively to be inextricably entwined with their physical form, and the essence of a person doesn't seem to be something we can touch and see, but rather something which occupies, something mysteriously unsubstantial—something we call a soul.

Why is the soul best described as supernatural? I would argue because it is an example of top-down agency, a mind built from skyhooks rather than cranes, to use the terminology of Dan Dennett (1996). In this way, the soul falls into a category of spirits, ghosts, and gods, in which the mental precedes the material. It is a non-reducible force which acts on the material without relying on physical laws, and its character is best understood in terms of whys, not hows. Arthur C. Clarke's (1962) third law proclaims that "Any sufficiently advanced technology is indistinguishable from magic" (39). I would suggest that, at least as far as supernatural agency is concerned, we might modify it to say that "Any sufficiently elevated crane is indistinguishable from a skyhook." This goes against Pascal Boyer's (2001) theory of supernatural concepts as minimally counter-intuitive violations of ontological categories, but if it is not useful, then we end up with (what seems to me to be) a strange dichotomy that either souls are not intuitive, or they are not supernatural. If our intuition of "person" does not necessarily connect mind and body, then it's not problematic to imagine a person as mind existing *without* a body, or in someone else's body.

Recent research by Emma Cohen (this volume) gives credence to the idea that we intuitively view people as A) distinguishable from their bodies, in such a way that B) if they inhabit other bodies, they do so completely rather than being fragmented or diffused. Are we only truly free, and hence morally responsible, as immaterial entities unbound from the body, from society? This may be an intuitive belief as well, and the philosopher Eddy Nahmias (2006) recently made a case along these lines—that the real threat people perceive to their free will is not determinism, as has been alleged by philosophers such as Shaun Nichols, but rather reductionism. Determinism doesn't entail, for example, that nothing we do matters, that our decisions are meaningless, or that we are not responsible for our actions. Determinism doesn't prevent consciousness from being causal, and we at once treat other people as the agents who perform their own actions *and* as if their actions are determined. People need reasons for doing things—if there is no reason, why do anything at all? So determinism, Nahmias says, is not really the problem. What people are really afraid of is reductionism—their desires, passions, beliefs, convictions all being "explained away" as the result of mechanistic processes—and epiphenomenalism—"the view that our brain states cause everything we do while our conscious mental processes—including our self-critical capacities—play no causal role in our decisions or actions" (Nahmias 2006, 227).

What the "folk" believe about intentionality these days is a hot topic among some philosophers, to the point that they've even found it worthwhile to conduct experiments and surveys in order to determine how the folk actually think, rather than relying on their own (trained) introspections and assuming they are universal. Much has been made of an apparent important discovery in this research so far by Joshua Knobe (2003) concerning perceptions of intentionality in scenarios with a moral valence. The results indicated that when an action taken by an actor in a hypothetical situation has harmful consequences, respondents are more likely to attribute intentionality to the actor than otherwise. To give an example:

> The vice-president of a company went to the chairman of the board and said, "We are thinking of starting a new program. It will help us increase profits and it will also help the environment." The chairman of the board answered, "I don't care at all about helping the environment. I just want to make as much profit as I can. Let's start the new program." They started the new program. Sure enough, the environment was helped.

Now compare:

> The vice-president of a company went to the chairman of the board and said, "We are thinking of starting a new program. It will help us increase profits and it will also harm the environment.' The chairman of the board answered, 'I don't care at all about harming the environment. I just want to make as much profit as I can. Let's start the new program.' They started the new program. Sure enough, the environment was harmed (Knobe & Burra 2006, 117).

If you're like the majority of the respondents, your reaction is to attribute greater intentionality to the vice-president in the latter scenario. In addition, you assess the vice-president as more deserving of blame in the latter scenario than he is deserving of praise in the former. This same result held over a number of different experiments, leading Knobe and others to the conclusion that there is something to this idea that people have some reason why they might consider morally negative acts to be more intentional, more blame-worthy.

What are the possible reasons for this? That's something that will probably be in dispute for quite some time, but there are some tentative evolutionary conclusions we might draw. One is that in terms of assessing the intentions of other people within your community, it might be adaptive to erroneously assume that they intend their harmful behaviors when in fact they don't, rather than the other way around. If you erroneously assess that someone actually intends harm toward you when they don't, then you may have lost good relations with this person. But if you erroneously assume their intentions are not malicious when in fact they are, you may well end up dead. The odds favor a tactic of being overly suspicious, whereas the same conditions don't exactly hold for praise of others when they do something good. In addition, this could also apply when the perceived perpetrator didn't even commit their ill act toward you, but toward someone else, as cheater detection theory would seem to indicate—if being willing to punish non-co-operators on behalf of others is important in terms of reputation, then being unwilling because of some reluctance to perceive the harmful acts of another as intentional may well bring the enmity or at least suspicion of the group against you

The sociologist Roy Baumeister (1997) has developed a concept of what he calls *The Myth of Pure Evil*, which I think fits in well with this view of intentionality. In a meta-analysis of multiple studies examining the viewpoints of both perpetrators and victims in violent or otherwise harmful encounters, he outlines the following characteristics which typically identify the victim's view of an evil agent:

1. Evil is the intentional infliction of harm on people.
2. Evil is driven primarily by the wish to inflict harm merely for the pleasure of doing so. Evil is either gratuitous or simply senseless.
3. The victim is innocent and good—minding her own business, go ing about her day and not bothering anyone else. The evil one bears all of the blame.
4. Evil is the other, the enemy, the outsider.
5. Evil has been that way since time immemorial (Baumeister 1997, 73-74).

Baumeister draws attention to the difference in the way victims and perpetrators characterize the *cause* of the act—perpetrators are much more likely to describe environmental circumstances, such as being tired or angry because of some previous event, the behaviour of the victim, or their physical surroundings. The victim, by contrast, is more likely to specifically address the perpetrator's mentality, saying things like "He did this for no good reason," or "He did this just to hurt me." As Baumeister puts it, "It is more comforting to think that the world contains evil, malicious people who attack innocent victims for no reason than to believe that one's sufferings are the result of one's own poor judgment and ill-advised actions that provoked a violent response from someone else" (Baumeister 1997, 73-74). Note that in this account, the victim is removing the evil act from its social context—outside circumstances are not allowed to be a factor. Evil must be intentional so as to hold the perpetrator fully responsible.

This model of evil fits with the description of the supernatural I gave earlier, in that it represents a casual mind which is independent of and precedes matter—in this case, the behaviour of the body. The ascription of evil is made possible by the dualistic portrayal of the perpetrator's intentionality, and thereby his or her moral responsibility. The prognosis of evil allows us to stop questioning, allows the buck of moral responsibility to stop in one place, with one person. Evil allows us, as Baumeister says, to distinguish ourselves from the perpetrator as well as the perpetrator from any exculpatory circumstances. It acts as an effective blocker against empathy, which can undermine proper condemnation. It might seem odd to consider the *inhibition* of empathy adaptive since so much work has been done lately to think about what adaptive functions it would serve, but in some circumstances it may well be more expedient to form quick, decisive conclusions about other people's behaviour in order to decide whether they should be punished or ostracized, or simply not trusted in the future. The primary elements which have been shown to stimulate empathic reactions are perceptions of similarity and familiarity. If these perceptions can be diminished or eliminated by emphasizing that *he* is responsible for the bad thing whereas *I* am not, a hasty barrier can be constructed which cuts off any thoughts of identification with him which might lead to an unwillingness to condemn or punish.

The relationship of the soul to cognitive empathy is something I believe needs to be further researched—in particular, whether empathy is aided or inhibited by the body/mind division we attribute to others. Uta Frith (1989) calls our ability to attribute invisible causal forces to other people (that is, beliefs, emotions, desires) "mentalizing," and it is a capacity in which she has found people with autism to have a notable deficiency. Mentalizing is an ability which we (what some people with autism and Asperger's that I've talked to refer to as "neurotypicals" or "NTs") habitually use as a shortcut in discerning the reasons for other peoples' behaviour in order to navigate our social environment. A person with a mentalizing deficiency must therefore take what is usually a more tedious route of relying on behaviourism and trial and error, at least until they have gained considerable experience in the world (for quite a few, deliberate training) in how to "read" other people's intentions and emotional states. This has been described as a lack of empathy, but it is not just empathy in the sense of a sympathetic reaction to someone who is suffering. Though it may include this, the deficiency is more a matter of being unable to practice perspective taking (what has been called cognitive empathy, though this is a somewhat problematic term given that all empathy would seem to entail some kind of cognition). It seems possible that those with autism are less likely to share our intuitive dualism, however to my knowledge no intensive research has been conducted in order to establish or refute this

We generally seem to accept the idea that evolution should shape us to believe in what is true—to take the world as it really is—rather than that mistakes or misapprehensions should be adaptive. But it may well be that the soul is something we couldn't help evolving, because the shortcuts that come with it in terms of understanding—and in some cases blaming—other people are irresistible to replication and perpetuation. The locus of free will, of humanity as we understand it, is intuitively resistant to reduction because we are afraid that if that boundary between mind and body is breached, so too will our ability to describe the actions of others as right and wrong, intentional and unintentional. This is an area of cognition which is ripe for future research in our attempt to understand the nature of supernatural agency.

References

Bloom, P. 2004. *Descartes' baby*. New York, NY: Basic Books.

Baumeister, R. 1997. *Evil: Inside human violence and cruelty*. New York, NY: Henry Holt & Company.

Boyer, P. 2001. *Religion Explained*. New York, NY: Basic Books.

Clark, A. 1962. *Profiles of the future*. New York, NY: Harper & Row.

Dennett, D. 1996. *Darwin's dangerous idea*. New York, NY: Simon & Schuster.

Frith, U. 1989. *Autism: Explaining the Enigma*. Oxford: Blackwell.

Knobe, J. 2003. Intentional action in folk psychology: An experimental investigation. *Philosophical Psychology, 16*, 309-324.

Knobe, J., & Burra, A. 2006. The folk concepts of intention and intentional action. *Journal of Cognition & Culture, 6* (1-2), 113-132.

Nahmias, E. 2006. Folk fears about freedom and responsibility: Determinism vs. reductionism. *Journal of Cognition & Culture, 6* (1-2), 215-237.

iPods, Gods, and the Adolescent Brain

Candace S. Alcorta

"When that sign is carved on the body the abstract is not only made substantial but immediate…and if the mark is indelible, as in the case of the subincision, the excised canine, the lopped finger, the scarified face, chest or back, it is ever-present. As the abstract is made alive and concrete by the living substance of men and women, so are men and women predicated by the abstractions which they themselves realize."

(Rappaport, 1999, 149)

Introduction

Humans are born with incompletely developed brains; in contrast to other primates a large proportion of human brain growth occurs after birth. By the second year of a human infant's life, only about 50% of brain development is complete. The brain does not reach its maximum size until approximately 15 years later (Giedd et al. 1999), and is subsequently reduced through "pruning". This delayed brain maturation provides a unique opportunity for environmental stimuli to influence patterns of brain development. Human brain growth is not uniform. Different parts of the human brain mature at different times (Giedd et al. 1999). Since the maturation rates of various brain structures differ, the optimal developmental periods for shaping neural interconnections through experientially-based "firing" of synapses differ, as well. As a result, environmental stimuli are processed differently and have different impacts on the brain at various stages of development (Kolb, Forgie, Gibb, Gorny, & Rontree 1998). The learning of music, language, and religion exemplify this process.

Music and Language Development

Throughout the world, mothers, fathers, and other caregivers sing to infants; universally such songs exhibit a common slow, high-pitched, and rhythmically exaggerated style. Newborns prefer song to speech; this preference for song appears to be innate. Even two day old infants born from congenitally deaf parents who sign and do not speak or sing prefer such songs (Trehub 2001).

By age 3 children are able to recognize "happiness" as represented by the musical forms of their culture, and by 6 years of age they readily employ both tempo and mode to identify sadness, fear, and anger in music (Trehub 2001). This ability to "read" the emotions encoded in their culture's musical conventions, like the ability to "read" facial expressions, seems to remain unchanged throughout the remainder of life (Trehub 2001).

Language learning occurs slightly after that of music and appears to build on many of the capacities developed during music acquisition. The associations between sound patterns, meaning, and syntactic structure that are critical elements in language are first developed in relation to music (Koelsch & Friederici 2003). The pitch, tone and cadence of speech, collectively referred to as speech prosody, are the first elements attended to in linguistic communication (Trehub 2001). Likewise, the rhythms of a culture's speech reflect the predominant musical rhythms of the culture (Patel 2003). Brain studies show that children first learn to process structure in music around the age of 5. The processing of structure in language follows a similar developmental trajectory, but occurs approximately four years later (Patel, Gibson, Ratner, Besson, & Holcomb 1998).

The development of both our music and language capacities depends on the maturation of functional brain regions responsible for specific components of these capacities. At each specific stage of brain development, associational networks are sculpted from a broad range of possibilities as environmental, social, and cultural inputs selectively fire and reinforce specific neuronal interconnections and infrequently fired synapses are "pruned" away. In this cumulative process, emergent capacities build upon previous learning.

iPods and Gods

Adolescent interest in music is universal. Karaoke clubs in Thailand and Tokyo, teen "raves" in Argentina and America, and the ubiquitous "earbuds" that have become a standard feature of adolescent anatomy all attest to the importance of music during adolescence. A recent national survey of 1000 U.S. teens aged 13-18 found that "music is high on the average teen's to-do list. Their love of music is second only to their love of friends and even ahead of their love of family....75 percent of (U.S.) teens spend two or three hours a day downloading or listening to music online" (Olse 2006).

Although contemporary teens in secularized Western societies are more likely to be listening to hip-hop than hymns, in most traditional cultures music is inseparable from religious ritual. Anthropologist Maurice Bloch has described music, chanting, and dance as "distinguishing marks of ritual" (1989, 21). Among the Igbo of Africa a single word, "nkwa", refers to both (Becker, 2001). It is only within the last 200 years of Western civilization that secular music has emerged as an entity separate from religious ritual (Cross 2003), and even in contemporary, highly secularized Western societies music remains a fundamental and universal element of all religions. In their recent nationwide survey of U.S. congregations, sociologist Mark Chaves and his colleagues (1999) found music to be the single most consistent feature of contemporary worship across all U.S. faiths, and the growing popularity of Christian "rock" among U.S. teens over the last several decades has brought rock music full circle from its gospel origins. Music is a central component in even the most fundamentalist religions. "Even the Taliban, who prohibited nearly all public displays of sensory stimulation, promoted a cappella religious chants" (Atran & Norenzayan 2004, 717). The significance of music for religion was perhaps best expressed by the 11th century Persian Sufi mystic Ghazzali:

> The heart of man has been so constituted by the Almighty that, like a flint, it contains a hidden fire which is evoked by music and harmony, and renders man beside himself with ecstasy. These harmonies are echoes of that higher world of beauty which we call the world of spirits, they remind man of his relationship to that world, and produce in him an emotion so deep and strange that he himself is powerless to explain it. (Becker 2001 145)

Music has the ability to evoke strong emotions of awe and rapture; it also conjoins and entrains those who experience those emotions. Individuals listening to the same music share the same emotions and the autonomic responses in heart rate, respiration, skin conductance, and pulse rate they engender (Harrar & Harrar 1977). Such shared autonomic functions highly correlate with the ability to empathize, an important element in cooperation (Levenson 2003). Music not only elicits emotion, but also evokes memories associated with those emotions. A musical phrase, like Proust's madeleines, can instantly recall a person, an event, or a year. The universal importance of music in religious ritual is likely to derive from its ability to invest places, symbols, and beliefs with shared emotional meaning.

Throughout the world the developmental period deemed most appropriate for "learning religion" is adolescence. Adolescent rites of passage are found in 70% of the world's societies and occur in cultures as diverse as Australian hunter-gatherers, African agriculturalists, and American industrialists (Lutkehaus & Roscoe 1995). Although the duration, intensity, and performance of these rites differ widely from culture to culture, all share a common structure, and all include music as a common element.

Abstractions, Algorithms and the Adolescent Brain

Adolescence appears to be an "experience expectant" (Greenough 1986) developmental period for investing abstract beliefs and symbols with emotional and social significance. Emotional intensity peaks during this developmental period. Adolescents react more quickly and with greater intensity to environmental stimuli than do either children or adults, and they perceive events as relatively more stressful than individuals at other life stages (Spear 2000). Even though adolescents are physically and immunologically more robust and resilient than younger children, mortality rates rise by nearly 200% during the teenage years. This is largely due to increases in "homicides, suicides, and accidents (that) collectively account for more than 85% of all adolescent deaths" (Spear 2000, 421). Adolescence is also the developmental period when social interest heightens, mental processing speeds increase, and abstract and symbolic reasoning develop (Spear 2000).

These behavioral attributes of adolescence derive from changes in the brain structures responsible for emotional, social, and executive processing. The prefrontal and temporal cortices of the brain do not attain their maximum volumes until around 16 or 17 years of age (Giedd 1999). While the temporal lobe functions in the processing of music, language, and facial recognition, the prefrontal cortex is responsible for various "executive" functions of the brain, including planning, impulse control, abstract and symbolic reasoning, and social judgment. The amygdala, critical to emotional processing, also shows volume increases during this time (Spear 2000).

During adolescence, neural networks linking these structures are shaped and defined through growth, pruning, and myelination. The simultaneous maturation of these brain regions provides a unique developmental window for investing abstract and symbolic constructs with incentive value and for imbuing them with both social and emotional significance.

As adolescents transition from the predominantly kin-based world of childhood to the expanded adolescent peer group of unrelated individuals, they face the difficult task of sorting potential allies from adversaries. In humans and other mammalian species, "the time around puberty seems to be essential for the acquisition of those social skills needed to adapt to unfamiliar conspecifics in a non-stressful and non-aggressive way" (Sachser, Durschlag, & Hirzel 1998, 891). Adolescent rites of passage not only transmit social knowledge and values; they also render such values "sacred" by investing them with emotional significance. These emotionally-weighted belief systems constitute social algorithms. Since these are shared among all initiates, they provide a ready guide for the prediction and coordination of social behaviors (Alcorta 2006).

An important outcome of the algorithms fostered through adolescent rites of passage is enhanced cooperation. Recent research conducted by Sosis and Ruffle (2003) on Israeli kibbutzim provides empirical evidence that participation in religious ritual is significantly and positively correlated with cooperative behaviors. As the costliness of such rituals increase, the degree of commitment and cohesion among ritual participants increases, as well. Prolonged, intense, and emotionally evocative adolescent rites of passage are more common in non-state societies that frequently engage in external warfare (Sosis, Kress, & Boster, in press). Such rituals appear to achieve greatest adherence to cooperative group goals—precisely the motivation and commitment you would want if you were frequently counting on your fellow initiates during war.

Conclusion

Humans appear to possess an innate predisposition to "learn" music, language, and religion, with a unique developmental window of "experience expectancy" for each. All of these abilities are at once individual and social; each derives from innate, genetically-encoded neurophysiological capacities that require socialization experiences for their development. "Learning" religion, like learning music and language, is a cumulative process. The cultural encoding of emotional meaning in music during infancy, and the development of language-based cognitive beliefs in socially omniscient supernatural agents during childhood are fundamental elements in this process (Bering, 2004). Religion engages these developed musical and linguistic abilities during adolescence in the construction of emotionally-weighted socio-symbolic systems capable of motivating the individual behaviors and decisions that structure non-kin social interactions (Alcorta & Sosis, 2005). The abstract rules and institutions of societies are made substantial through the neurophysiological encoding of algorithms that define and motivate social behaviors. Adolescence provides an experience expectant developmental period for such encoding. Music-based religious ritual is the means by which such encoding is optimally achieved. Religion's ability to imbue abstract cultural symbols with shared motivational and social meaning provides a foundation for the creation of the cooperative, non-kin social relationships that lie at the heart of human culture.

References

Alcorta, C. 2006. Religion and the life course: is adolescence an experience expectant period for religious transmission? In P. McNamara, Ed., *Where God and science meet: How brain and evolutionary sciences alter our understanding of religion*, Vol. 2, 55-79. Westport, CT and London: Praeger Publishers.

Alcorta, C., & Sosis, R. 2005. Ritual, emotion and sacred symbols: The evolution of religion as an adaptive complex. *Human Nature, 16*, 323-359.

Atran, S., & Norenzayan, A. 2004. Religion's evolutionary landscape: Counterintuition, commitment, compassion, communion. *Behavioral & Brain Sciences, 27*, 713-730.

Becker, J. 2001. Anthropological perspectives on music and emotion. In P. Juslin & J. Sloboda, Eds., *Music and emotion*, 135-160. Oxford, UK: Oxford University Press.

Bering, J. M. 2004. The evolutionary history of an illusion: Religious causal beliefs in children and adults. In B. Ellis & D. Bjorklund, Eds., *Origins of the social mind: Evolutionary psychology and child development*, 411-437. New York, NY: Guilford Press.

Bloch, M. 1989. *Ritual, history and power*. London, UK: Athlone Press.

Chaves, M., Konieszny, M. E., Beyerlein, K., & Barman, E. 1999. The national congregations study: Background, methods and selected results. *Journal for the Scientific Study of Religion, 38*, 458-476.

Cross, I. 2003. Music as a biocultural phenomenon. In G. Avanzini, C. Faienza, D. Minciacchi, L. Lopez, & M. Majno, Eds., *The neurosciences and music*, 106-111. Annals of the New York Academy of Sciences, Vol. 999. New York: New York Academy of Sciences.

Giedd, J., Blumenthal, J., Jeffries, N. O., Catellanos, F. X., Liu, H., Zijdenbos, A., et al. 1999. Brain development during childhood and adolescence: A longitudinal MRI study. *Nature Neuroscience, 2*, 861-863.

Greenough, W. T. 1986. What's special about development? Thoughts on the bases of experience-sensitive synaptic plasticity. In W. T. Greenough & J. M. Juraska, Eds., *Developmental neuropsychobiology*, 387-408. New York, NY: Academic Press.

Harrar, G., & Harrar, H. 1977. Music, emotion, and autonomic function. In M. Critchley & R. A. Henson, Eds., *Music and the brain: Studies in the neurology of music*, 202-216. Springfield, IL: Charles C. Thomas.

Koelsch, S., & Friederici, A. D. 2003. Toward the neural basis of processing structure in music. Comparative results of different neurophysiological investigation methods. In G. Avanzini, C. Faineza, D. Minciacchi, L. Lopez, & M. Majno, Eds., *The neurosciences and music*, 15-28. Annals of the New York Academy of Sciences, Vol. 999. New York: New York Academy of Sciences.

Kolb, B., Forgie, M., Gibb, R., Gorny, G., & Rontree, S. 1998. Age, experience and the changing brain. *Neuroscience & Biobehavioral Reviews, 22*, 143-159.

Levenson, R. W. 2003. Blood, sweat and fears: the autonomic architecture of emotions. In P. Ekman, J. J. Campos, R. J. Davidson, & F. B. M. de Waal, Eds., *Emotions inside out*, 348-366. Annals of the New York Academy of Sciences, Vol. 1000. New York: New York Academy of Sciences.

Lutkehaus, N. C., & Roscoe, P. B., Eds. 1995. *Gender rituals: Female initiation in Melanesia*. London, UK: Routledge.

Olsen, S. 2006. Teens and media: a full-time job. Retrieved March 14, 2007, from <http://news.com.com/2100-1041_3-6141920.html>

Patel, A. D. 2003. Rhythm in language and music. Parallels and differences. In G. Avanzini, C. Faienza, D. Minciacchi, L. Lopez, & M. Majno, Eds., *The neurosciences and music*, 140-143. Annals of the New York Academy of Sciences, Vol. 999. New York Academy of Sciences, New York.

Patel, A. D., Gibson, E., Ratner, J., Besson, M., & Holcomb, P. J. 1998. Processing syntactic relations in language and music: An event-related potential study. *Journal of Cognitive Neuroscience, 10* (6), 717-737.

Rappaport, R. A. 1999. *Ritual and religion in the making of humanity*. London, UK: Cambridge University Press.

Sachser, N., Durschlag, M., & Hirzel, D. 1998. Social relationships and the management of stress. *Psychoneuroendocrinology, 23*, 891-904.

Sosis, R., & Ruffle, B. 2003. Religious ritual and cooperation: Testing for a relationship on Israeli religious and secular kibbutzim. *Current Anthropology, 44*, 713-722.

Sosis, R., H. Kress, , & J. Boster, 2007. Scars for war: Evaluating alternative signaling explanations for cross-cultural variance in ritual costs. *Evolution & Human Behavior, 28*, 234-247.

Spear, L. P. 2000. The adolescent brain and age-related behavioral manifestations. *Neuroscience & Biobehavioral Reviews, 24*, 417-463.

Trehub, S. E. 2001. Musical predispositions in infancy. In R. Zatorre & I. Peretz, Eds., *The biological foundations of music*, 1-16. Annals of the New York Academy of Sciences, Vol. 930. New York: The New York Academy of Sciences.

Once More, With Feelings

The Importance of Emotion for Cognitive Science of Religion

Nicholas J. S. Gibson

Although many disciplines could be brought to bear in studying the evolution of religion, any attempt to discuss the origins of religious concepts must eventually engage with research on the cognitive representation of these concepts. Research at a cognitive level of analysis involves modeling the flow and transformation of information. The goal of the study of religious cognition, therefore, is to provide a description and explanation of religion-related knowledge, beliefs and attitudes, behaviors, and experience in computational terms (Gibson 2006). Unfortunately, although the cognitive science of religion (CSR) is concerned with both the origins and the representation of religious concepts (Barrett 2000), the field does not seem to be in step with current theory in cognitive psychology. In this chapter I will address the failure to consider affective cognition within CSR in the hopes that this corrective will allow more fruitful dialogue with evolutionary theories.

The Need for Multilevel Models of Religious Cognition

Everyday experience suggests the close link between emotions and cognition (see Epstein 1994). For example, emotions can exert considerable influence on thinking, and the interpretation of events can effect what emotions are felt. While people are capable of reasoning in a rational and dispassionate manner under certain restricted circumstances, this is certainly not the only—or the preferred—sort of processing that people carry out. Nor is the very knowledge on which people draw upon in making judgments necessarily affect-free. In fact, most languages (though curiously not English) use different words to distinguish between a conceptual or propositional way of knowing and a schematic or experiential way of knowing, as for example *wissen* and *kennen* in German. James (1890) described these as "knowledge-about" and "knowledge of acquaintance" (221). Cognitive psychologists have reached a consensus that an adequate description of human information processing requires a multilevel cognitive architecture (Williams, Watts, MacLeod, & Mathews 1997). In dual-level theories, one level corresponds to verbal, rational, propositional, conceptual, affect-free, or "cold" cognition, while the other level corresponds to nonverbal, irrational, experiential, schematic, affect-laden, or "hot" cognition.

Any cognitive account of religion must therefore deal with propositional- and affective-level information processing. In recognition of the neglect of emotion and affect in psychological theories of religion (see Hill 1995; Watts 1996; Watts & Williams 1988), several proposals have been advanced for the adoption of multilevel theories of cognition from general psychology as helpful conceptual frameworks for the study of religion (e.g., Hall 2004; Hill & Hood 1999). The most promising of these to emerge thus far is Watts' (2002, 2006) proposal to apply the Interacting Cognitive Subsystems model (ICS; Barnard & Teasdale 1991; Teasdale & Barnard 1993) to religious cognition. ICS is a highly specified and empirically tested cognitive architecture consisting of nine subsystems: three sensory and proprioceptive subsystems (*acoustic, visual,* and *body-state*), two intermediate structural description subsystems (*morphonolexical, object*), two meaning subsystems (*propositional, implicational*), and two effector subsystems (*articulatory, limb*). Each of the subsystems is specialized for the storage and processing of a single type of information corresponding to a different aspect of subjective experience. The two meaning subsystems are of specific interest here: the propositional level corresponds to intellectual belief, to "knowing something 'with the head,'" while the implicational level corresponds to an affective, "holistic, intuitive, or implicit sense of knowing something 'with the heart' or 'having a gut feeling for it'" (Barnard & Teasdale 1991, 24). The model allows for discrepant meanings between the two levels, consistent with the common experience of conflict between "head" and "heart".

Cognitive psychologists have much work to do in testing and extending ICS and other competing models of cognition, and it behooves the wise CSR scholar to keep abreast of developments in the field. Whatever the specifics, however, it seems clear that for theories of religion involving cognitive representation to be psychologically plausible they must—at the least—distinguish between hot and cold cognition. Unfortunately this has yet to happen to any significant degree within CSR.

The Absence of Emotion in CSR Theories

The CSR literature has often taken a normative approach to religious cognition. That is, researchers have focused on disparities between what people *should* believe doctrinally and what they actually do seem to believe (e.g., Slone 2004). Barrett and Keil (1996), for example, tested people's recall for stories involving God and found that people made inferences about God's powers consistent with an anthropomorphic, theologically incorrect concept of God, despite affirming theologically correct concepts on a questionnaire. From this the authors concluded that adults have two different concepts of God, one theologically correct and the other more intuitive and used in automatic online processing.

The problem with normative models is that it becomes much harder to see beyond the blinkers to what is actually being investigated—so in this case the religion investigated within CSR is reduced to cold cognition concerning the counterintuitive attributes of gods. Tellingly, Barrett's (2000, 29) definition of religion as "a shared system of beliefs and actions concerning superhuman agency" contrasts with other definitions of religion (e.g., Thouless 1924/1961) in omitting any emotional or relational component. One notable exception is Pyysiäinen's (2001, 2003, 2004a) helpful work on emotion and religion. Yet even here there seems to be a confusion of automatic (or implicit) processing with affective processing. For example, Pyysiäinen (2004b) tries to map the two concepts proposed by Barrett and Keil (1996) onto a conglomeration of dual-process theories of cognition. Although it is helpful to draw the attention of workers in CSR to these various theories, it is less helpful to suggest that they are all describing the same two aspects of cognition. Cold cognition and hot cognition alike can proceed above or below the level of conscious awareness, and automatic processing certainly need not entail hot cognition (just think of any non-affective but well-learned task such as solving mathematical problems). So, as J. L. Barrett (personal correspondence, March 1999) agrees, while the theologically correct concept probably corresponds to concepts held on the propositional level, the automatic online inferences consistent with an anthropomorphic concept need not indicate involvement of affective cognition.

While asking "Why would anyone believe in God?" (Barrett 2004) is certainly a key endeavor for research into religious cognition, there is also a need to integrate this work with religious believers' affective evaluations of and responses to the character and intentions of gods. Recent experimental data suggests that evangelical Christians not only have more accessible and salient representations of God than atheists, but also hold information about God in mind in a way that is consistent with the experience of an affective and intimate relationship (Gibson 2006). Our goal should not simply be to understand how people represent the counterintuitiveness of supernatural agents, therefore, but also to understand in cognitive terms what is going on relationally in the believer's mind (see Baldwin 1992). Such an approach also makes sense from both an evolutionary and a developmental perspective, given that the capacity for affective cognition (and with it the cognitive tools required to relate to other agents) is phylogenetically and developmentally prior to the capacity for explicit propositional thought.

Why Are Emotion and Relationality Relevant to Current Topics in CSR?

Even if affective evaluations of God are worthy of investigation as part of the big picture of religious cognition, one might nevertheless argue that they are irrelevant to current research questions within CSR. The following two examples are intended to illustrate why such an argument is not tenable.

When Do People Use Minimally Counterintuitive Concepts?

A consideration of how people's personal goals and desires influence the mode of information processing (see Kunda 1999) suggests an alternative account of Barrett and Keil's (1996) data. The amount of time and effort people devote to making inferences or judgments will depend on their goals and motivations. People may not invoke God's supernatural properties while processing a story about God listening to birds singing while a plane is taking off (a task that has nothing to do with relationality) but might well be motivated to do the extra cognitive work to process God's counterintuitive properties if personal goals or motivations (including threat-avoidance) were involved. So, rather than representing a specific concept, participants' tendency to anthropomorphize God's counterintuitive properties may instead represent a processing heuristic (cf. Tversky & Kahneman 1974).

This hypothesis is easily testable. Blocked goals or perceived injustice are two specific instances in which people are more likely to automatically invoke God's supernatural powers. For example, 63% of Americans report occasional anger against God (Davis, Smith, & Marsden 2005), often as a response to natural disasters, illness, death, abuse, war, murder, divorce, abandonment, or violation of expectations such as unanswered prayers or personal failures (Exline & Rose 2005). Since there is no point in getting angry at someone who has no power to act, it seems likely that anyone who gets angry at God for not acting to avert some disaster is presuming God's omnipotent power.

When Good Gods Go Bad

Anger toward God is a good example of how lived religion does not always fit normative models of how it is predicted to work. Kirkpatrick (2005), for example, draws on the work of theologian Gordon Kaufman to suggest that—for the believer—God functions as an ideal attachment figure. Yet it is clear that for some believers—especially those with an insecure attachment—God is far from a positive figure. Rather, for those who are angry at God, God is characterized as punishing, rejecting, and angry. Such feelings can lead to rejection of God or what Novotni and Petersen (2001) have called emotional atheism (Exline, Fisher, Rose, & Kampani 2005).

Data like these cast doubt on evolutionary theories that rely on an assumed positive relationship between gods and believers. For example, Atran

(2002; Atran & Norenzayan, 2004) has hypothesized that concepts of supernatural agents emerged during evolution to deal with the existential fears that accompanied more sophisticated cognition. Atran and Norenzayan (2004) describe an experiment in which participants primed with a story involving the death of a child made significantly stronger ratings of strength of belief in God's existence and the efficacy of supernatural power than participants primed with a religious or neutral control story. What is not clear here is whether reduction in people's existential anxieties is conferred simply by belief in a given god, or whether a positive and beneficial relationship with the god is necessary. Indeed, for a person whose experience has led them to believe in a punishing and rejecting God, it is hard to imagine replicating Atran and Norenzayan's results.

Author's Note

This work was supported by John Templeton Foundation grant 10701 to Fraser Watts and John Polkinghorne. Correspondence concerning this chapter should be addressed to Nicholas Gibson, Psychology and Religion Research Group, Faculty of Divinity, West Road, Cambridge, CB3 9BS, UK. E-mail: njsjg2@hermes.cam.ac.uk.

References

Atran, S. 2002. *In gods we trust: The evolutionary landscape of religion*. Oxford, UK: Oxford University Press.

Atran, S., & Norenzayan, A. 2004. Religion's evolutionary landscape: Counterintuition, commitment, compassion, communion. *Behavioral & Brain Sciences, 27* (6), 713-770.

Baldwin, M. W. 1992. Relational schemas and the processing of social information. *Psychological Bulletin, 112* (3), 461-484.

Barnard, P. J., & Teasdale, J. D. 1991. Interacting cognitive subsystems: A systemic approach to cognitive-affective interaction and change. *Cognition & Emotion,* 5 (1), 1-39.

Barrett, J. L. 2000. Exploring the natural foundations of religion. *Trends in Cognitive Sciences, 4* (1), 29-34.

Barrett, J. L. 2004. *Why would anyone believe in God?* Oxford, UK: AltaMira Press.

Barrett, J. L., & Keil, F. C. 1996. Conceptualizing a nonnatural entity: Anthropomorphism in God concepts. *Cognitive Psychology, 31* (3), 219-247.

Davis, J. A., Smith, T. W., & Marsden, P. V. 2005. General Social Surveys, 1972-2004 [CUMULATIVE FILE] [Computer file]. Chicago, IL: National Opinion Research Center. Retrieved February 5, 2007, from <http://sda.berkeley.edu/D3/GSS04/Doc/gs040048.htm>

Epstein, S. 1994. Integration of the cognitive and the psychodynamic unconscious. *American Psychologist, 49* (8), 709-724.

Exline, J. J., Fisher, M. L., Rose, E., & Kampani, S. 2005. Emotional atheism: Anger toward God predicts decreased belief. Unpublished manuscript, Case Western Reserve University.

Exline, J. J., & Rose, E. 2005. Religious and spiritual struggles. In R. F. Paloutzian & C. L. Park, Eds., *Handbook of the psychology of religion and spirituality*, pp. 315-330. New York, NY: Guilford Press.

Gibson, N. J. S. 2006. The experimental investigation of religious cognition. Unpublished doctoral dissertation, University of Cambridge, UK. Retrieved March 1, 2007, from <http://prrg.divinity.cam.ac.uk/personnel/nicholas.html#PhD>

Hall, T. W. 2004. Christian spirituality and mental health: A relational spirituality paradigm for empirical research. *Journal of Psychology & Christianity, 23*, 66-81.

Hill, P. C. 1995. Affective theory and religious experience. In R. W. Hood, Jr., Ed., *Handbook of religious experience*, 353-377. Birmingham, AL: Religious Education Press.

Hill, P. C., & Hood, R. W., Jr. 1999. Affect, religion and unconscious processes. *Journal of Personality, 67* (6), 1015-1046.

James, W. 1890. *Principles of psychology*, Vol. 1. New York, NY: Henry Holt.

Kirkpatrick, L. A. 2005. *Attachment, evolution, and the psychology of religion*. New York, NY: Guilford Press.

Kunda, Z. 1999. *Social cognition: Making sense of people*. Cambridge, MA: The MIT Press.

Novotni, M., & Petersen, R. 2001. *Angry with God*. Colorado Springs, CO: Piñon Press.

Pyysiäinen, I. 2001. Cognition, emotion, and religious experience. In J. Andresen, Ed., *Religion in mind: Cognitive perspectives on religious belief, ritual, and experience*, 70-93. Cambridge, UK: Cambridge University Press.

Pyysiäinen, I. 2003. *How religion works: Towards a new cognitive science of religion*. Leiden, Netherlands: Brill.

Pyysiäinen, I. 2004a. *Magic, miracles, and religion: A scientist's perspective*. Walnut Creek, CA: AltaMira Press.

Pyysiäinen, I. 2004b. Intuitive and explicit in religious thought. *Journal of Cognition & Culture, 4* (1), 123-150.

Slone, D. J. 2004. *Theological incorrectness: Why religious people believe what they shouldn't*. Oxford, UK: Oxford University Press.

Teasdale, J. D., & Barnard, P. J. 1993. *Affect, cognition, and change: Re-modelling depressive thought*. Hove, UK: Erlbaum.

Thouless, R. H. 1961. *An introduction to the psychology of religion* 2nd ed. Cambridge, UK: Cambridge University Press. Original work published 1924.

Tversky, A., & Kahneman, D. 1974. Judgment under uncertainty: Heuristics and biases. *Science, 185,* 1124-1131.
Watts, F. N. 1996. Psychological and religious perspectives on emotion. *International Journal for the Psychology of Religion,* 6 (2), 71-87.
Watts, F. N. 2002. Theology and psychology. Aldershot, England: Ashgate.
Watts, F. N. 2006. Implicational and propositional religious meanings. Unpublished manuscript, University of Cambridge, UK.
Watts, F. N., & Williams, J. M. G. 1988. *The psychology of religious knowing.* Cambridge, UK: Cambridge University Press.
Williams, J. M. G., Watts, F. N., MacLeod, C., & Mathews, A. 1997. *Cognitive psychology and emotional disorders,* 2nd ed. Chichester, England: John Wiley.

Narrativity, Emotions, and the Origins of Religion

Tom Sjöblom

The Origins of Religion

Humans are storytelling animals. With this I do not only mean that we—among all animal species—are the only ones capable of storytelling. I want to make a stronger claim and argue that what makes us a storytelling species is of fundamental importance for our cognitive evolution and the origins of symbolic and cultural behavior. Here I will discuss my argument in terms of the origins of religion.

How religion got started was one of the founding questions of the academic study of religions in the late 19th century. These early scholars were inspired in their work by the work of Charles Darwin to the extent that one of them, the English social anthropologist R.R. Marett, argued that without Darwin there would be no science of religion to begin with (Marett 1912, 8). For what comes to the issue of the origins of religion, at least, Marett certainly had a point. As pointed out by Eric Sharpe (1975/1986), these early efforts to apply Darwinian insights into the study of religions were guided by the idea that individual experiences were at the heart of religion. However, the time was certainly not yet ripe for this kind of analysis and the suggestions of these early Darwinians were discredited by their critics as unscientific and beyond verification. Indeed, even Sharpe himself argues as late as 1986 that "psychologizing" will not lead us anywhere in the study of early religious behavior. This attitude led to the abandonment of Darwinian approaches in Cultural Studies and with that also to the abandonment of questions dealing with the origins of culture and religion (Capps 1995, 53-104; Sharpe 1986/1975, 47-71).

Sharpe actually thought that the mind of other peoples, past and present, will always stay closed to us and this is why we should confine the study of religions to observing religious behavior in its different types and forms (Sharpe 1986/1975, 71). Indeed, in the early decades of the last century the data for discussing the origins of culture was certainly not yet available. Likewise, psychology was in its infancy and the human mind was little more than an uncharted territory for the scholars of that period (see e.g., Cole 1996). Nevertheless, I would argue that Marett and his companions were right in insisting that discussing the origins of religion is fundamentally a psychological issue and has to do with the evolution of human cognition (see e.g., Marett 1909, 143-169). In contrast to what Sharpe is arguing, the combination of these two has now become possible through the introduction of biological thinking into Cultural Studies as well as the growth of archaeological and fossil data available to us (see e.g., Barkow, Cosmides, & Tooby 1992; Dennett 2006); Hinde 1999; Pinker 2002; Plotkin 2002; Sperber 1996). This has made the origins of religion once more actual for students of religion working in a naturalistic mode. In what follows I will try to lay down my version of the tale in the form of a working hypothesis (see also e.g., Atran 2002; Boyer 2001; Dawkins 2006, 161-207; Dennet 2006, 97-115; Guthrie 1993; Mithen 1996).

The Narrative Mind

As pointed out by Daniel Dennett in his most recent book *Breaking the spell*, in order to get anywhere in science we must know what questions to ask (Dennett 2006, 19). What comes to the origins of religion as the two essential questions we must deal with appears to be, first, what kind of mind it takes to "have" religion and, second, when in the course of evolution that kind of mind emerged in our ancestors. My suggestions to these questions are that what is needed is a *narrative mind* which emerged with the appearance of early modern humans over 200,000 years ago and that some of the cognitive programs involved derive from even earlier periods (Dunbar 2004, 31-34, 186-200; Henshilwood & Marean 2003, 630-631; McBrearty & Brooks 2000, 453-563; Sjöblom 2003/2004, 187-190).

Having a narrative mind means that we are driven to experience the world in narrative format. However, we must be careful what this means. It is true that, while all of us will probably never become great storytellers, we do communicate in everyday social interactions mainly through narratives, although we may only rarely be aware of it (Abbott 2002, 1; Bruner 1991, 1-21; Dautenhahn 2002, 97-123; Schank 1990). But we must not confuse the product with the process behind it. Narrativity as a cognitive quality is both more and less than communicating with actual stories. It is less, because not everything produced by the narrative mind is represented in the form of stories. It is also much more, because it appears to be the decisive cognitive boost that enabled early modern humans to turn into creatures that not only create and understand symbols, but also organize their environment symbolically in the form of culture (see Carrithers 1991, 310-315; Henshilwood & Marean 2003, 627-651; McNeil 1996, 331-360).

It is still very much an open question what particular cognitive processes are responsible for narrativity. In this respect we move in an uncharted and debated territory. However, the basic framework is largely agreed upon and it includes such features as metarepresentation, cognitive fluidity, and analogical thinking (see Gentner, Holyoak, & Kokinov 2001; Mithen 1996; Sperber 2000). It also entails a capacity to cognize many-sided interactions between agents carried out over a considerable period, a preference to represent descriptive and abstract relationships in terms of social interaction, an intentional stance towards one's environment, and that we judge what is important for us not on the basis of its truth value or logic, but on the basis of its relevance (Bruner 1991, 1-21; Carrithers 1991, 310; Dennett 1987; Sperber & Wilson 1995; Thagard & Shelly 2001, 335-362). It is the last mentioned that is of special interest in the context of discussing the origins of symbolic behavior, like religion, as much of the cognitive power attached to symbols seems to be derived from how they invite us to show special attention to certain entities by providing these with emotional significance (see e.g., Bloom 2004, 65-95; Dissanayake 1995/1991, 39-63; Tooby & Cosmides 2001, 6-27).

Emotional communication

The roots of emotional signaling goes far back in the evolutionary history of our species. Indeed, inherited emotion processes or *affect programs* are found even in lower animal species. (Lazarus 1991, 26-29; Maynard Smith & Harper 2003). What appears to be unique to us humans is the level of empathy – the capacity to feel within or in another agents feeling – we can achieve and how we are able to exploit this capacity in social communication (see Escalas & Stern 2003, 567; Wispé 1986, 318). Indeed, our capacity for empathy is so great that we are able to produce extra-somatic gadgets in order to consciously inspire emotional responses, whatever our own emotional state and even whether we are ourselves present or not (see Bloom 2004, 65-95). It is this capacity of investigating emotional signals into cultural artifacts that can be held as a sign of symbolically organized behavior and the emotional origins of religion (see Greenspan & Shanker 2004, 5; Tooby & Cosmides 2001, 6-27).

The earliest known uncontested evidence for symbolically organized behavior comes in the connection of the so-called Herto skulls. These skulls were discovered in 1997 from Middle Awash in Ethiopia by Tim White and his colleagues and the discovery was reported in a series of articles in the journal *Nature* in 2003 (see Clark et al. 2003, 747-752; Stringer 2003, 692-695; White et al. 2003, 742-747). The skulls belong to anatomically modern humans, two adults and one child, which were found together with some artifacts. Two things make these skulls interesting. First, radioisotopically the fossils have been dated to between 160,000 and 154,000 years ago, which places them among the earliest known representatives of early modern humans. Second, the skulls bear clear signs of cultural modification. They have been cut-marked and polished in a manner reminiscent of the handling of skulls in the mortuary practices of some modern day tribes in New Guinea. This has led the experts to conclude that what we see in Herto is the evidence of an early mortuary ritual (Clark et al. 2003, 251; Gibbons 2003, 1641; Stringer 2003, 692; White et al. 2003, 745; but see Trinkaus 2005, 213-214).

In addition to the general recognition of that human cognition appears to have been fully evolved for symbolic behavior around 200,000 years ago, the Herto skulls tell us little how such symbols create emotional responses. A clue to this can be found in the form of the earliest representational art known to us. This is the so-called Temple of Python, a ritual cave situated in the Tsodilo Hills in Botswana, and dated to have been in use around 70,000 years ago (Vogt 2006, 1-4). According to Sheila Coulson, the archaeologist responsible for the excavations, a huge rock carving of a snake dominates the cave and our Upper Palaeolithic ancestors came apparently far away just to sacrifice stone artifacts for the divinity represented by the stone python.

That snakes and other animal representations dominate early religious art is interesting when we remember that the ultimate function of affect programs is to enhance our survival in a potentially hostile world (Lazarus 1991). Feelings that evoke anxiety in us (like fear, disgust, and anger) seem to have special potential to guide our attention and behavior. They are more easily ignited than other types of emotions and harder to extinguish. They also enhance our level of alertness, activate behavior, and focus our attention toward what ever has been the triggering cue, while the so called positive emotions appear to have a soothing function (Levenson 1999, 481-504; Hatfield, Cacioppo, & Rapson 1994, 28-32).

What I am suggesting is that in order to explain the origins and survival of religion, we must turn our attention to this kind of innate emotional triggers. The early evidence for religious behavior suggest that by imitating in symbolic representations everything that ignites our natural affect programs is the principle cognitive mechanism for creating relevance to religious behavior and to make it special. The transference of natural emotions to cultural representations is made possible by the means of narrativity, so it is to the evolution of narrativity that the origin of religion is to be connected. Stories combine in them language-based data with representational cues that ignite emotional responses in us. This has made them a powerful—maybe even the optimal—tool for communicating relevance into transmitted beliefs and traditions. This is why religious traditions even today prefer narratives as the basic tool for transmitting their traditions.

References

Abbott, H. P. 2002. *The Cambridge introduction to narrative*. Cambridge, UK: Cambridge University Press.

Atran, S. 2002. *In gods we trust: The evolutionary landscape of religion*. New York, NY: Oxford University Press.

Barkow, J. H., Cosmides, L., & Tooby J., Eds. 1992. *The adapted mind*. New York, NY: Oxford University Press.

Bloom, P. 2004. *Descartes' baby: How child development explains what makes us humans*. London, UK: William Heinemann.

Boyer, P. 2001. *Religion explained: The evolutionary origins of religious thought*. New York, NY: Basic Books.

Bruner, J. 1991. The narrative construction of reality. *Critical Inquiry, 18*, 1-21.

Capps, W. H. 1995. *Religious studies: The making of a discipline*. Minneapolis, MN: Fortress Press.

Carrithers, M. 1991. Narrativity: Mindreading and making societies. In A. Whiten, Ed., *Natural theories of mind*, 305-317. Oxford, UK: Basil Blackwell.

Clark, J. D., Beyene, Y., WoldeGabriel, G., Hart, W. K., Renne, P. R., Gilbert, H., et al. 2003. Stratigraphic, chronological and behavioural contexts of Pleistocene Homo Sapiens from Middle Awash, Ethiopia. *Nature, 423*, 742-747.

Cole, M. 1996. *Cultural psychology: A once and future discipline*. Cambridge, MA: The Belknap Press.

Dautenhahn, K. 2002. The Narrative Intelligence Hypothesis: In search of the transactional format of narratives in humans and other social animals. *International journal of cognition and technology*, 1 (1), 97-123.

Dawkins, R. 2006. *The god delusion*. London, UK: Bantam Press.

Dennett, D. C. 1987. *The intentional stance*. Cambridge, MA: The MIT Press.

Dennett, D. C. 2006. *Breaking the spell: Religion as a natural phenomenon*. London, UK: Allen Lane.

Dissanayake, E. 1995. *Homo aesteticus: Where art comes from and why*. Seattle, WA: University of Washington Press.

Dunbar, R. 2004. *The human story*. London, UK: Faber & Faber.

Escalas, J. E., & Stern, B. B. 2003. Sympathy and empathy: Emotional responses to advertising dramas. *Journal of Consumer Research 29*, 566-578.

Gentner, D., Holyoak, K. J., & Kokinov, B. N., Eds. 2001. *The analogical mind*. Cambridge, MA: The MIT Press.

Gibbons, A. 2003. Paleoanthropology: Oldest members of Homo Sapiens discovered in Africa. *Science, 300* (5626), 1641.

Greenspan, S. I., & Shanker, S. G. 2004. *The first idea: How symbols, language, and intelligence evolve from our primate ancestors to modern humans*. Cambridge, MA: Da Capo Press.

Guthrie, S. 1993. *Faces in the clouds*. New York, NY: Oxford University Press.

Hattfield, E., Cacioppo, J. T., & Rapson, R. L. 1994. *Emotional contagion.* Cambridge, UK: Cambridge University Press.
Henshilwood, C. S., & Marean, C.W. 2003. The origin of modern behavior: Critique of the models and their test implications. *Current Anthropology, 44* (5), 627-651.
Hinde, R. A. 1999. *Why gods persist: A scientific approach to religion.* London, UK: Routledge.
Lazarus, R. 1991. *Emotion and adaptation.* New York, NY: Oxford University Press.
Levenson, R. W. 1999. The intrapersonal functions of emotion. *Cognition & Emotion, 13* (5), 481-504.
Marett, R. R. 1909. *The threshold of religion.* London, UK: Methuen & Co.
Marett, R. R. 1912. *Anthropology.* London, UK: Williams & Norgate.
Maynard Smith, J. & Harper, D. 2003. *Animal signals.* Oxford, UK: Oxford University Press.
McBrearty, S., & Brooks, A. 2000. The revolution that wasn't: A new interpretation of the origin of modern human behaviour. *Journal of Human Evolution, 39,* 453-463.
McNeil, L. D. 1996. Homo inventans: The evolution of narrativity. *Language & Communication, 16* (4), 331-360.
Mithen, S. 1996. *The prehistory of the mind.* London, UK: Phoenix.
Pinker, S. 2002. *The blank slate.* London, UK: Penguin Books.
Plotkin, H. 2002. *The imagined world made real.* London, UK: Penguin Books.
Schank, R. C. 1990. *Tell me a story: Narrative and intelligence.* Evanston, IL: Northwestern University Press,
Sharpe, E. J. 1986. *Comparative religion: A history.* London, UK: Duckworth Press. Original work published 1975.
Sjöblom, T. 2003/2004. Wordpower: Narratives, tradition and religion. *Temenos, 39-40,* 185-208.
Sperber, D. 1996. *Explaining culture: A naturalistic approach.* Oxford, UK: Blackwell Publishers.
Sperber, D., Ed. 2000. *Metarepresentations: A multidisciplinary perspective.* Oxford, UK: Oxford University Press.
Sperber, D., & Wilson, D. 1995. *Relevance,* 2nd ed. Oxford, UK: Blackwell Publishers.
Stringer, C. 2003. Out of Ethiopia. *Nature, 423,* 692-695.
Thagard, P., & Shelly C. 2001. Emotional analogies and analogical inferences. In D. Gentner, K. J. Holyoak, & B. N. Kokinov, Eds., *The analogical mind,* 335-362. Cambridge, MA: The MIT Press.
Tooby, J., & Cosmides, L. 2001. Does beauty build adapted minds? Toward an evolutionary theory of aesthetics, fiction and the arts. *SubStance, 94/95,* 6-27.

Trinkaus, E. 2005. Early modern humans. *Annual Review of Anthropology, 34,* 207-230.
Vogt, Y. 2006. World's oldest ritual discovered. Worshipped the python 70,000 years ago. *Apollon: Forskningsmagasin fra Universitet vid Oslo.* Retrieved on February 27, 2007, from <http://www.apollon.uio.no/>
White, T. D., Asfaw, B., DeGusta, D., Gilbert, H., Richards, G. D., Suwa, G., et al. 2003. Pleistocene Homo Sapiens from Middle Awash, Ethiopia. *Nature* 423, 742-747.
Wispé, L. 1986. The distinction between sympathy and empathy: To call forth a concept, a word is needed. *Journal of Personality & Social Psychology, 50* (2), 314-321.

Memes, Genes, and Dead Machines

Evolutionary Anthropology of Death and Burial

William W. McCorkle, Jr.

Archaeologists speculate that humans between forty thousand and a hundred fifty thousand years ago disposed of dead bodies in ritualized ways—often involving non-utilitarian grave goods and special tools (Clark et al. 2003; Mithen 1996, 20-21, 198-199; Pearson 1999). This tendency to handle human bodies in special ways and in variable cultural forms is puzzling. Recent attempts to explain this recurrent behavior include the argument that (human) corpses trigger an evolutionarily based system, or "biological warning system" (BWS) involving the human sense of smell. This system's behavioral outputs often include handling dead bodies in ways that either assist in fending off predators or prevent accidental gestation by (human) survivors (Boyer 2001, 212-215; Mithen 1996, 154).

Humans are capable of differentiating between ten-thousand different scents that are received in the posterior of the nose, in what is called the olfactory epithelium. The olfactory epithelium then sends a variety of 'neural messages' via the olfactory bulb (behind the nose) which are routed to either the neocortex (where higher level thinking is found) or to more ancestral parts of the brain that instigate actions like fight or flight (see Axel 2006, 69-75). In the above theory, signals to the latter regions would trigger the BWS, which would tend to generate representations of the corpse, and anything related to it, as a contaminant.

Are dead bodies really dangerous?

The contagiousness of the corpse appears *prima facie* instinctive to humans in the historical and ethnographic record. However, this apparent instinct contradicts the actual toxicity of a dead body. In recent reports by the *World Health Organization* and the *Centers for Disease Control and Prevention* (PAHO) (Fisher 2005; Morgan & Fisher 2004; PAHO 2003, 2004; Wisner & Adams 2002) scientists stated that dead bodies are not in fact as dangerous as people seem to believe. In fact their reports asserted that "psychological trauma to the living" should be a much more important focus for relief organizations working at major disaster scenes (Fisher 2005, 1). Nevertheless, people in areas like these prioritize the disposal of the resultant dead bodies, apparently compelled by some sense of contagion to do so. And, as noted above, this disposal includes the performance of elaborate rituals (many with no historical precedence).

The evolution of mortuary ritual behavior

The specific special handling of dead bodies differs between cultures so there may be no reason to believe that dead bodies stimulate an input/output (black box) scenario in humans that produces an unvarying response. In fact it makes more sense to view mortuary rituals as independent cultural forms occurring over time and space. Pascal Boyer (2001) argues persuasively that *religious* (or counterintuitive) representations are the cumulative result (time and space) of natural selection that favors certain representations over other ones. In addition, the search for a single origin of religion or ritual is itself an exercise in futility, since these kinds of successful representations are a synchronic and diachronic process from a multitude of sources. If we are to take evolutionary theory seriously there simply *is no one origin for mortuary behavior*; there are potentially an infinite number of them happening at various times and places throughout human history.

How might we empirically test whether corpses trigger a BWS, yet argue that smell is not the deciding factor? One way to explore the problem of smell and the triggering of BWS is to tease out smell from other mental systems that might be triggered by corpse stimuli such as systems related to agency.

From a very early age children are able to differentiate between the mere movement of objects and the animacy of objects (Rochat, Morgan, & Carpenter 1997). They are also able to determine whether they are agents or objects as well as make inferences about the probable intention behind their movement (theory of mind) (Karmiloff-Smith 1992). The root of these abilities is probably related to survival and conspecific fitness, not only intuitive physics and spatial awareness but also distinguishing between potential predators and prey.

When dead bodies do tell tales

In a recent dissertation experiment (McCorkle 2007), 78 subjects were given a series of six vignettes with a common theme of the handling of various types of dead bodies. The subjects were then tested on instruments measuring "disgust" and different psychological traits (e.g., neuroticism, psychoticism, and extraversion). According to preliminary results, those with high psychoticism or tough-mindedness in this subject pool (P/TM) appeared not to be bothered (disgusted) by the handling of dead bodies, unless the variable of agency was manipulated. In other words, they didn't mind handling dead bodies or body parts unless the corpses triggered certain types of agency or related systems.

This was apparent in vignette number five of the study, where the high P/TM subjects didn't mind handling dead skeletons or parts until the skeleton appeared to be "looking back at them" (question number eight). The subject clearly felt very little empathy towards dead bodies; however, when the variable of agency, or in this case agency, person-file, and theory of mind were stimulated, the high P/TM subject scored high towards the stimuli. In other words, the high P/TM was extremely bothered by the perceived (imagined) agency of the skeleton.

High P/TM subjects scored average (75) on the Haidt, Rozin, and McCauley "disgust" inventory. They scored high for environmental hazards like fluids and cleanliness, but scored low on dead bodies and parts. Extremely low P/TM subjects scored the same average (74, 75) on the Haidt/Rozin/McCauley inventory, yet they scored the opposite: high on dead bodies, parts and low on fluids, cleanliness.

Individual variation and explanation of ritual behavior

These preliminary results suggest that there is a measurable index relating the P/TM scale of the Eysenck (Eysenck Personality Inventory-Revised, EPQ-R) (see Eysenck & Eysenck, 1994) and behavioral responses towards dead bodies. Robert Hare suggests, appealing to fMRI experiments on extreme psychotic subjects, that the low emotional response towards corpse stimuli may be related to low activity in the limbic system in human brains (Kiehl et al. 2001). The limbic system, an ancestral system involved in emotion, memory, and instinctual behavior, does not appear to "fire" the same way in normal subjects as in extreme psychotic subjects (Hare 1999).

From an evolutionary perspective, the P/TM results suggest a reason why there is variation within and between cultures towards reactions to dead bodies (Metcalf & Huntington, 1991). Individuals do not react the same way to dead bodies based upon the preliminary evidence from this study (as well as from the archaeological and ethnographic evidence). One of the reasons might be that the stimuli trigger *various* systems (agency, animacy, theory of mind, and the collection of data on agents, or person-file system) that inform behavioral outputs. Boyer reasons that these systems are activated based upon the evolved cognitive architecture of human minds, developed from the ancestral environment where a host of different environmental stimuli (e.g., predatory/prey awareness, social intelligence, and biological contamination) mutually reinforced human conspecific fitness (Barrett 2004, 32-44; Boyer 2001 203-228; Mithen 1996, 166-170, 198-202).

This would be extremely important in the ancestral environment of humans where certain locations were dangerous and informed human behavior. Saying it is dangerous to go near the lake because of tigers is not as memorable a representation as saying that the river is haunted by the ghosts of the people that died there. Mortuary rituals, behavior that involves the stimulation of the above mentioned systems, then operate on an evolutionary model to maintain the survival of the species, or conspecific fitness. If dead bodies activate certain systems that evolved from the ancestral environment, then it is also plausible to suggest that the kinds of behaviors (mortuary rituals) resulting from this stimulation reinforce salient representations vis-à-vis danger, warning, social bonds, and biological contamination. Therefore, these representations transmit successfully, though they might take (theoretically) infinite amount of cultural forms.

Corpse, concept, and contagion triggers

Based upon anecdotal and experimental data, this research seems to provide evidence to support the hypothesis that human beings do not respond to dead bodies in the same way. Furthermore, this difference seems to be a measurable index based upon certain personality traits (specifically P/TM) that are innate, developmental, and culturally constructed. It is possible that certain biological inferences concerning contamination from dead bodies may have been plausible from an early period of humans; however, these inferences appear to have taken other more salient forms, rather than by smell and taste.

Empirical evidence suggest that humans make inferences about dead bodies being dangerous based on mental systems that handle agency and predation, rather than inferences about toxicity. In addition, the various mental systems that are stimulated by dead bodies might be parasitic upon biological warning/contagion systems (BWS) and thereby successfully spread and contribute to conspecific human fitness.

The encoding and decoding of cultural representations

A possible explanation for ritual behavior towards dead bodies is that the stimuli (corpse) encode information in various systems involved in agency, animacy, ToM, and the collection of data on agents (person-file). The encoding of the information is tagged as very important and thus these systems act upon the BWS as parasitic to spread the encoded data, now tagged as extremely significant. So, when corpse stimuli are encoded, they are tagged as dangerous and important utilizing the BWS; however, when it is decoded by individuals (post hoc explanation and cultural behavior) these behaviors appear meaningful in some instances and meaningless in others, yet they are tagged contagious for memorable transmission. In addition, encoding is performed into specific cognitive systems and decoded back as garbled, but extremely important, information to the subject, resulting in various behaviors and *post hoc* explanations about such behaviors.

This would be extremely important in the ancestral environment of humans where certain locations were dangerous and informed a human's behavior. Saying it is dangerous to go near a certain bush because of people that have died from eating it is not as memorable a representation as saying that the bush is a dangerous location and haunted by the people that died there. The bush and its location remains dangerous and contagious when the bush is tagged with certain violations of ontological categories (e.g., the bush lives, haunts, hears, kills, etc.) (Boyer 2001). Furthermore, because of the encoding/decoding hypothesis, individual cognitive processes might be involved in the biological deviation from a standard activity in much the same way as immune systems develop or closer to cultural behaviors seen in memetic transmission (e.g., food taboos, diseased individuals, xenophobia). These rituals then operate on an evolutionary model that employs difference to maintain the survival of the species, or conspecific fitness. An analogy might be that if one behavioral group caught a virus, all the behavioral groups wouldn't perish.

If a culture made certain areas taboo because people get killed there from time to time, the importance of the taboo and the association of dead bodies makes it a memorable public representation. If one culture made a certain area taboo and another did not, the later culture might keep dying because of potential dangers in this geographic location (predators/agents). The culture that associated the taboo with death might live to spread its genes and memes another day. This would be a direct evolutionary benefit for variation between cultural behaviors. Specifically mortuary ritual (and perhaps rituals in general), then, may be a vehicle for transmitting these vital representations horizontally and vertically throughout culture.

References

Axel, R. 2006. The molecular logic of smell. *Scientific American, 16*, 69-75.

Barrett, J. L. 2004. *Why would anyone believe in god?* Walnut Creek, CA: AltaMira Press.

Boyer, P. 2001. *Religion explained: The evolutionary origins of religious thought.* New York, NY: Basic Books.

Clark, J. D., Beyene, Y., WoldeGabriel, G., Hart, W. K., Renne, P. R., Gilbert, H., et al. 2003. Stratigraphic, chronological and behavioural contexts of Pleistocene Homo Sapiens from Middle Awash, Ethiopia. *Nature, 423*, 471-452.

Eysenck, H., & Eysenck, S. 1994. *Manual of the Eysenck personality questionnaire.* San Diego: EdITS/Educational and Industrial Testing Service.

Fisher, J. 2005. Disposal of dead bodies in emergency conditions. *World Health Organization Technical Notes for Emergencies* No. 8.

Hare, R. 1999. *Without conscious: The disturbing world of psychopaths among us.* New York, NY: Guilford Press.

Karmiloff-Smith, A. 1992. *Beyond modularity: A developmental perspective on cognitive science.* Cambridge, MA: The MIT Press.

Kiehl, K. A., Smith, A. M., Hare, R. D., Mendrek, A., Forster, B. B., Brink, J., et al. 2001. Limbic abnormalities in affective processing by criminal psychopaths as revealed by functional magnetic resonance imaging. *Biological Psychiatry, 50,* 677-684.

McCorkle, W. W. 2007. *From corpse to concept: A cognitive theory of the ritualized treatment of dead bodies.* Unpublished Dissertation, Queen's University of Belfast, Belfast, Ireland.

Metcalf, P., & Huntington, R. 1991. *Celebrations of death: The anthropology of mortuary ritual,* 2nd ed. Cambridge, England and New York: Cambridge University Press.

Mithen, S. 1996. *The prehistory of the mind: A search for the origins of art, religion, and science.* London: Phoenix.

Morgan, O., & Fisher, J. 2004. Infectious disease risk from dead bodies following natural disasters. *Revista Panamericana Salud Pública/Pan American Journal of Public Health, 15* (5), 307-312.

Pan American Health Organization. PAHO. 2003. Unseating the myths surrounding the management of cadavers, Disaster Newsletter, No. 93, October 2003. PAHO, USA.

Pan American Health Organization. PAHO. 2004. Management of dead bodies in disaster situations. Washington, D.C.: PAHO, USA Disaster Manuals and Guidelines on Disasters Series, No. 5.

Pearson, M. P. 1999. *The archaeology of death and burial.* College Station, TX: Texas A&M University Press.

Rochat, P., Morgan, R., & Carpenter, M. 1997. Young infants' sensitivity to movement information specifying social causality. *Cognitive Development, 12,* 441-465.

Wisner, B., & Adams, J., Eds. 2002. Environmental health in emergencies and disasters. World Health Organization Technical Notes for Emergencies. WHO, Geneva.

PART VII

METHODOLOGY

Keeping 'Science' in the Cognitive Science of Religion

Needs of the Field

Justin L. Barrett

Consider if someone "explained" language by arguing that language was an adaptation. Satisfied? Would that exhaust scientific treatment of language? Or suppose someone argued that people have language because it serves important social functions. Or that people have language because they were socialized to use language. I imagine that we wouldn't find any of these "explanations" as terribly satisfying even if they captured something true. They ignore something crucial. What constitutes language cannot be divorced from the cognitive science of language. Similarly, as human social phenomena, what constitutes religion cannot be sensibly divorced from the cognitive science of religion.

Cognitive science (broadly construed to include information processing of both the relatively affect-free and the more affect-rich sorts) can be thought of as a bridge over a deep gorge. On one end is a biological valley and on the other a social one. The rocks below include mind-blind behaviorism (perhaps blanketed in neo-Darwinian moss so that they don't seem quite so sharp or dangerous), relativist social constructionism looking suspiciously like blank slate, and historical particularism that creates the illusion of a safe crossing but shifts under a hiker's weight, collapsing into the rushing currents, and not being available for any other trekkers. For a genuinely scientific, productive field to explain religious phenomena, one must cross the bridge—human cognition. The behaviors upon which natural selection acts are cognitively mediated. Social inputs and outputs are cognitively mediated.

I do not mean to imply that all projects in the Evolution of Religion need be cognitive, but all do need to be compatible with what we know about human cognition and should not assume cognitive contributions are merely trivial details.

So, now that you are convinced that the cognitive science of religion is the critical bridge that we must all use and care for, please allow me to make some observations about where it needs our collective attention to remain strong. I see three, interrelated, critical needs of cognitive science of religion: more empirical support for major theories, more cross-trained scholars able to conduct empirical projects, and more empirical projects addressing specific issues in religion and theology. Simply, we need more *science* in the cognitive science of religion.

Testing Out Major Theories

Although one of the attractive promises of Cognitive Science of Religion is to inject the study of religion with empirically testable theories, theoretical projects have outpaced empirical ones. Consequently, many theories in the area rest on weak evidential footing. Without shoring up this foundation, scholars may become disillusioned with what is presently widely considered to be a highly promising area. Finding examples of the time-lag from theoretical pronouncement to empirical substantiation in this field is not difficult. For instance Pascal Boyer's theories concerning the transmission of "minimally counterintuitive concepts" first appeared in the early 1990's (e.g., Boyer 1993) but did not receive empirical treatment until almost a decade later. In this theory Boyer observes that largely intuitive concepts—those that fit cross-culturally ordinary and early developing conceptual structures in human minds—are more readily remembered and transmitted than radically counterintuitive concepts without natural cognitive underpinnings. Boyer goes on to predict, however, that concepts that slightly deviate from intuitive expectations are even more memorable and transmittable than completely intuitive concepts. I am happy to report that a handful of refereed journal articles presented experimental data relevant to Boyer's predictions have now appeared (e.g., Barrett & Nyhof 2001; Boyer & Ramble 2001; Norenzayan, Atran, Faulkner, & Schaller 2006). So far his central prediction has been cross-culturally vindicated, though more nuance has been suggested as well.

E. Thomas Lawson and Robert McCauley's ritual form hypotheses represent another such example (1990; McCauley & Lawso, 2002). Though appearing in detail in 1990, it wasn't until 2001 that the first systematic, quantitative testing of their predictions appeared (Barrett & Lawson 2001), and their predictions still remain in need of empirical scrutiny. Some of their central predictions have only just begun to be systematically investigated (Barrett 2004a). For instance, McCauley and Lawson predict that religious rituals that participants represent as 'special agent rituals' (such as weddings in Christianity) will tend to be judged as relatively high in sensory pageantry (weddings include more pomp and circumstance than Communion) and as non-repeatable (you only marry the same person once—no need to perform the wedding repeatedly) but potentially reversible (e.g., through divorce). To date, the evidence from Jewish, Muslim, and Hindu informants appears to be on McCauley and Lawson's side (Malley & Barrett 2003).

Numerous other theoretical projects deserve similar empirical attention so that they may be supported, modified, or rejected. Indeed, on page after page of Barrett's (2004b) *Why Would Anyone Believe in God?* we see testable, under-supported (but sensible) claims being made.

What the field requires, then, is rigorous application of scientific hypothesis testing. Particularly needed are cross-cultural and child developmental projects to give us greater confidence that theories are resting on panhuman and not culturally specific features of human cognition.

Part of the reason for the lag between theoretical pronouncement and empirical substantiation is the time, expense, and difficulty in conducting rigorous, ecologically valid and theoretically meaningful projects—especially with a cross cultural component. But I fear this isn't the only reason for the lag. Unfortunately, I perceive in my field a general tendency to attempt to solve theoretical problems through argumentation alone. Rather than systematically test Lawson and McCauley's claims, for instance, we would rather explain how they just don't seem right (or do seem right), cherry picking historical cases or ethnographic anecdotes instead of doing the hard work of systematic data collection. Where is the *science* in the cognitive science of religion?

Cross-trained Scholars

More charitably, perhaps the single greatest reason we do not see more hypothesis testing in cognitive science of religion is that we have a shortage of scholars with strong knowledge and skills in multiple disciplines. Identifying just which of Scott Atrans's (2002), Boyer's (2001), or Barrett's (2004a, b) many claims are evidentially suspect often requires familiarity with the cognitive or developmental psychological literature. Few comparative religionists or anthropologists of religion have this familiarity. On the other hand, few psychologists have a deep understanding of either religion or culture in order to identify critical questions for testing or how cognitive insights might matter to the study of religion. Even once the problems have been identified, we still suffer a shortage of scholars with the skills to design and implement relevant experiments and other designs.

To address this shortage I encourage us, as a community of scholars, to find ways to share insights and methodological techniques across disciplines. Particularly, those of us with training in scientific methods (who are in the minority in this field) need to pursue ways to offer our skills to those with humanities backgrounds, either through collaboration or in assisting with cross-training and retooling. Might we find ways to share research designs, protocols, and instruments? Similarly, those of us with students might find ways to insure they receive training in religion *and* in cognitive science, including experimental and other quantitative methods. We need more *scientists* in the cognitive science of religion.

Specific Projects in Religion & Theology

My third suggestion for the cognitive science of religion is that we conduct more empirical projects on specific topics in religion and theology. What I am suggesting is a strategic move for the field.

To date, most prominent projects in the cognitive science of religion have aimed at making general, cross-religious and cross-cultural claims about religious phenomena. We have asked why religious rituals appear the way they do *generally*, why people believe in gods *generally*, why religion *generally* concerns morality, and so forth. Seeing these general treatments through with strong evidential bases would be a major accomplishment for the study of religion. But this emphasis on the general has led some observers of the field to suggest that the cognitive science of religion can say little or nothing about particular matters. So, the cognitive science of religion might be able to tell us why people generally believe in gods but not why Muslims have the kind of monotheism they have or why ancestor-spirit concepts are what they are in Melanesia. We can argue that these observers are wrong about the cognitive science of religion's explanatory potential or we can *show* them.

Frustration with a historic inability to generate empirically testable, plausible general accounts of religion and culture has helped to fracture the academic study of religion and culture. Many scholars are automatically suspicious of general accounts of religion and identify themselves with particular religious traditions, people groups, or geographical regions. To demonstrate to these particularists that cognitive science of religion is productive, we must produce in their neighbourhoods. The cognitive science of religion has many examples of this sort of scholarship, but we need more. Brian Malley's (2004) application of cognitive insights to Biblicism in an American Baptist community and Emma Cohen's (2007) treatment of spirit possession in an Afro-Brazilian group are fine examples of how cognitive perspectives can explain local phenomena. So too is McCauley and Lawson's (2002) application of their cognitive theory of religious ritual form to the Pomio Kivung movement from Harvey Whitehouse's (1995) ethnography.

Relatedly, much of the popularizing attention given to cognitive and evolutionary treatments of religion has been both generalizing and anti-religious in tone. If popularizers such as Daniel Dennett (2006) and Richard Dawkins (2006) can get mileage out of the scientific findings in the field to attack religious belief, theirs is a perfectly legitimate intellectual enterprise. Nevertheless, anti-religious rhetoric and application, if unswervingly maintained within the field, may distance the field from potential scholarly allies and audiences.

Many people who study religion and theology do so because they find value in religious beliefs, in terms of utility or truth. Empirical projects that bring cognitive scientific tools and insights to problems, practical and theological, will enhance the field by showing first, that the field is not an ideological platform but a scientific enterprise; and second, that insights from the field may potentially hold positive (as well as negative) implications for particular theologies and/or religious efforts.

To illustrate, as religions spread into new cultural contexts, clergy and theologians are presented with problems regarding how to best adapt to or accommodate these new groups of people. Should religious rituals be modified in terms of the symbols, objects used, roles given to different classes of people, frequency, physical context, and so forth? As much as these theologians are concerned with the consequence of proposed modifications on religious belief, attitudes, commitments, and the spread of ideas, their concerns are cognitive ones. Though the cognitive science of religion has produced two different prominent theories of religious ritual (McCauley & Lawson 2002; Whitehouse 2004), to my knowledge no application of these theories to particular theological problems have been undertaken, particularly using empirical methods. Potential projects such as this could demonstrate that the cognitive science of religion is not merely useful in addressing cross-cultural regularities or in attacking religious belief, but useful too in solving practical theological problems.

Here, too, I see the need for more science, not less. Rather than passively succumbing to a stereotyped science-religion divide, the field would benefit from applying scientific insights and methods to problems inspired by theological perspectives and religious problems.

Conclusions

I am not proposing that all scientific study of religion must take a cognitive scientific perspective. I do, however, see the cognitive science of religion as the most promising tool for giving evolutionary and other biological perspectives more precision, and social perspectives more rigor.

Nor am I proposing that all scholars in the cognitive science of religion must begin conducting experiments and other quantitative work. A great strength of the field has been its methodological and disciplinary pluralism. My encouragement, rather, is that we find ways to ground our theorizing in solid, scientifically gathered empirical evidence. I see the relative shortage of quantitative hypothesis testing, particularly in cross cultural and developmental research designs as worrisome.

Not all scholars in the field must be cross-trained in multiple disciplines or be trained in experimental methodologies. Collaborative projects across disciplines, bringing scientific methods to bear on theorizing about religion, could shore up the evidential weak spots. We do need, however, more people equipped to do this challenging scientific work and must find ways to either recruit or train such individuals.

Finally, I am not proposing that cognitive scientists of religion all begin turning to theological problems or appealing to religious organizations for funding. Rather I encourage those of us in the field to be open to scholars with such interests and welcome opportunities to turn the tools of science to theological and religious problems.

What I am urging is that evolutionary and other scientific approaches to explaining religious phenomena do not ignore cognitive scientific perspectives. The cognitive science of religion offers the greatest promise for a comprehensive, bridging science of religion. Further, for the cognitive science of religion to properly execute this function, it needs to stay cognitive, scientific, and relevant to religion.

Acknowledgements

The author thanks Emma Cohen for comments on an early draft and the John Templeton Foundation for support.

References

Atran, S. 2002. *In gods we trust: The evolutionary landscape of religion.* New York, NY: Oxford University Press.

Barrett, J. L. 2004a. Bringing data to mind: Empirical claims of Lawson and McCauley's theory of religious ritual. In B. C. Wilson & T. Light, Eds., *Religion as a human capacity: A festschrift in honor of E. Thomas Lawson,* 265-288. Leiden, Netherlands: Brill.

Barrett, J. L. 2004b. *Why would anyone believe in God?* Walnut Creek, CA: AltaMira Press.

Barrett, J. L., & Lawson, E. T. 2001. Ritual intuitions: Cognitive contributions to judgments of ritual efficacy. *Journal of Cognition & Culture, 1* (2), 183-201.

Barrett, J. L., & Nyhof, M. 2001. Spreading non-natural concepts: The role of intuitive conceptual structures in memory and transmission of cultural materials. *Journal of Cognition & Culture, 1* (1), 69-100.

Boyer, P. 2001. *Religion explained: Evolutionary origins of religious thought.* New York, NY: Basic Books.

Boyer, P. 1993. Cognitive aspects of religious symbolism. In P. Boyer, Ed., *Cognitive aspects of religious symbolism,* 4-47. Cambridge, UK: Cambridge University Press.

Boyer, P., & Ramble, C. 2001. Cognitive templates for religious concepts:

Cross-cultural evidence for recall of counter-intuitive representations. *Cognitive Science, 25*, 535-564.
Cohen, E. 2007. *The mind possessed*. New York, NY: Oxford University Press.
Dawkins, R. 2006. *The God delusion*. London, UK: Bantam Press.
Dennett, D. C. 2006. *Breaking the spell: Religion as a natural phenomenon*. New York, NY: Viking.
Lawson, E. T., & McCauley, R. N. 1990. *Rethinking religion: Connecting cognition and culture*. Cambridge, UK: Cambridge University Press.
Malley, B. 2004. *How the Bible works: An anthropological study of American Biblicism*. Walnut Creek, CA: AltaMira Press.
Malley, B., & Barrett, J. L. 2003. Does myth inform ritual? A test of the Lawson-McCauley hypothesis. *Journal of Ritual Studies, 17* (2), 1-14.
McCauley, R. N., & Lawson, E. T. 2002. *Bringing ritual to mind: Psychological foundations of religious forms*. Cambridge, UK: Cambridge University Press.
Norenzayan, A., Atran, S., Faulkner, J., & Schaller, M. 2006. Memory and mystery: The cultural selection of minimally counterintuitive narratives. *Cognitive Science, 30*, 531-553.
Whitehouse, H. 1995. *Inside the cult: Religious innovation and transmission in Papua New Guinea*. Oxford, UK: Oxford University Press.
Whitehouse, H. 2004. *Modes of religiosity: A cognitive theory of religious transmission*. Walnut Creek, CA: AltaMira Press.

Evolutionary Psychology, Neuroscience and the Study of Religion

Uffe Schjødt

Instead of browsing thousands of experimental studies on neural correlates of different cognitive phenomena, and picking out empirical support for whatever the evolutionary psychologists are claiming must underlie religious behavior, I suggest that brain scanning experiments on religious behavior itself would be far more informative. This paper introduces current work in the neuroscience of religion; it discusses problems inherent to the discipline, and presents some preliminary results of my fMRI studies on prayer.

Introduction

The mainstream of today's cognitive science of religion follows the hugely popular trend of evolutionary psychology. Religious behavior is understood to be a product of the evolutionary palette of evolved properties of the human mind. Some researchers have argued that religion draws on specific cognitive systems (Persinger 1987), but most cognitive scientists support the idea that religion draws on multiple and much older mechanisms. From this perspective, a wide range of cognitive systems underlying both normal and pathological behavior might explain why some features of religious behavior seem to be universal traits of human culture. Thus, ritual rigidity in religious practice may utilize the same system underlying OCD pathology (Boyer 2003; Boyer & Liénard 2006); representing supernatural beings takes a theory of mind system (Boyer 1994; Lawson & McCauley 1990; Mithen 1996); counterintuitive features of gods survive in the cognitive apparatus parasitizing on hardwired categorical domains (Boyer 1994); supernatural concepts are interactions of different intelligences (Mithen 1996); dogmatic teachings are encoded by a semantic memory system, while religious experiences are stored by an episodic memory system (Whitehouse 2002); representations of ritual structure are the result of a task-specific inference system of action-grammar (Lawson & McCauley 1990; McCauley & Lawson 2002), and anthropomorphizing is a product of a hyperactive agency detection device (Barrett 2004; Guthrie 1993).

By breaking the religious phenomenon into multiple sub-phenomena, evolutionary psychology with its numerous evolved cognitive mechanisms is able to put the pieces together again with an impressive amount of detail. Drawing on evolutionary psychology, cognitive scientists of religion indeed offer a rich description of the religious mind.

However, as intriguing as these hypothesized mechanisms might seem, they often have trouble connecting to the physiological reality of the brain. When asked about the ontological status of these systems, researchers often look for answers among neuroscientific studies, but rarely do they propose anything concrete. This is unfortunate.

In my Ph.D. project, I am applying the experimental methodology of cognitive neuroscience on religious behavior to make concrete claims about what is going on in the brain of religious practitioners. This paper introduces current work in the neuroscience of religion; it discusses problems inherent to the discipline, and presents results from my fMRI studies on prayer.

Brain, mind and religion

In the last few decades a neuroscience of religion has grown from being a mere curiosity in the broader study of religion to having its own field of research. Today two lines of research run almost independently of each other dealing with the cross-section of Brain, Mind and Religion from two widely different angles, one experimental and one theoretical.

Experimental studies: Brain scans

Experimental research on religious behavior has undergone incredible technological advances. Like other branches of the cognitive sciences, experimenters are now using brain scanning technologies like fMRI, PET, EEG and SPECT to measure brain activity during religious experience and practice.

Most experiments have been carried out by researchers from experimental psychology, psychiatry or neurobiology, answering simplistic either-or-questions of whether religious experience is mainly emotional or cognitive, if religious experience is uniquely different from non-religious cognition, or if religious practice has clinical effects on the practitioner.

One research team has argued that religious experience is caused by particular areas of temporal cortex (Persinger 1987), others have found that recitation of religious texts seems to be a cognitive attributional phenomenon activating dorsolateral prefrontal cortices (Azari et al. 2001), while yet others have demonstrated neurofunctional activities associated with emotional and regulatory effects, arguing that religious experience is an altered state phenomenon (Newberg 1998). A new study has demonstrated that multiple brain areas seem to be involved in mystical experience, both emotional and cognitive (Beauregard & Paquette 2006).

A common perception in this line of research is the idea that religious experience and prayer are generally comparable to meditation regarding its effects on the brain and body. This idea has played an important role in designing experiments using extraordinary subjects assumed to be best capable of practicing religion or having a religious experience. So far, most studies have indeed used expert participants like nuns (Beauregard & Paquette 2006), monks (Newberg et al. 2001) or experienced meditators (Lazar et al. 2000) to get the strongest effects possible.

Unfortunately this approach has made it difficult to gain insights on the effects of common religious practice Extraordinary practice of experts may be an entirely different kind of behavior from the everyday practice reported by scholars of religion.

No experimental study to my knowledge, has adopted any of the well established typologies of religion to explore the neurofunctional correlates of common religious practice in a systematic way.

Theoretical work: evolutionary psychology

Cognitive theories of religion have also made enormous advances over the last decades, drawing primarily on evolutionary psychology to hypothesize brain correlates of numerous cognitive mechanisms involved in different aspects of religious behavior. Unlike the experimental line of research dealing only with expert practitioners, the hypotheses advanced by cognitive theorists aim at explaining universal aspects of religious phenomena.

However, most of these theories have failed to produce direct evidence for their claims. In most cases theorists refer to experimental insights on more basic cognitive aspects to indirectly support their hypotheses of religion, but rarely do these studies inform us on the specifically religious about religious behavior. One example of this approach is the hypothesis that brain area *superior parietal cortex* (SPC) is the neural substrate of an evolved mechanism for agency detection and thus involved in representing supernatural agency (Boyer 2003). The experimental evidence supporting this hypothesis is on basic agency detection using moving shapes on a screen as stimuli (Blakemore, Boyer, Pachot-Clouard, Meltzoff, & Decety 2003).

A meta-analysis of SPC activity and cognition shows that SPC is associated with a variety of cognitive tasks like attention to moving dots, resting, reading of proper vs. pseudo-words, and finger movement imitation.[1] One

1 Searching on anatomical location 36 -44 65 (Talairach) within a radius of 20 mm, which is a standard perimeter of location uncertainty due to pre-processing of fMRI data.

possible reason why this is so, is that the SPC serves a multipurpose function in brain processing. Thus, even though agency detection in fact is part of SPC function, inferences about particular correlations between religious thought and SPC will be somewhat dubious. If representing supernatural beings actually does draw on a basic agency detection system in SPC, this does not inform us on the inherently religious about representing supernatural beings, but rather on a fundamental aspect of human cognition. Representing gods is probably far from the basic perceptual task of detecting intentional behavior.

The fact that very simple agency detections in minimalistic experimental setups seem to show subtle differences in brain activations cannot really offer anything to the understanding of religion, and telling us that frontal or temporal cortices generally seem involved in different kinds of religious behavior is hardly surprising. This would be like claiming that religious writings are dependent on human hands, and that verbally transmitted myths and rituals are partly due to our mouth anatomy. In that way, we could claim that religion is parasitic upon our basic human anatomy, which is not all that informative.

Instead of browsing thousands of studies reporting neural correlates of different cognitive phenomena, and picking out empirical support for whatever the evolutionary psychologists are claiming must underlie religious behavior, I suggest that experiments on religious behavior itself are far more informative.

However, in dealing with complex cognitive tasks like religious behavior, one should be cautious making inferences about single activations like the above mentioned SPC activation. Only if the study is heavily hypothesis-driven or if entire patterns of activation known to work together in specific cognitive tasks can be shown, will the results be a reliable source of evidence. One example of this is the specific neural pattern associated with social interaction (see sections below). This approach will probably not result in radical new findings; it will most likely not be able to support hypotheses about specific cognitive inference systems underlying specific aspects of religion. It may, though, throw light on some of the more general assumptions in the study of religion such as the interactions between religious thinking and bodily activities and perhaps even some of the more classic typologies of religion.

A factorial fMRI study on prayer

My project combines the theoretical and experimental lines of research. By analyzing the neurofunctional correlates of religious practice among normal practitioners, results will be representative of a larger population, and by using insights from the study of religion, important factors interacting with religious behavior are integrated in the experimental design. Three factors in religious practice seem to stand out as being particularly important for the typologies in the study of religion. These are *Structure, Agency* and *Arousal.* My Ph.D. project includes three experimental studies using fMRI technology to explore the neurofunctional correlates of each of these factors in religious prayer. Reported here is the study of *Structure* in prayer.

On Structure

One of the most robust typologies in the study of religion is the one between highly structured (HS) and minimally structured (MS) religious practice. Since Max Weber first made the distinction (1904/1958) between dogmatic (HS) and charismatic (MS) religion, it has pervaded numerous theoretical takes on religious practice (Whitehouse 2002). In conflict theory, religious institutions with their doctrinal systems (HS) are constantly challenged by charismatic leaders (MS) trying to reform the dogmatic traditions. In ethnography the dichotomy lies between literate (HS) and non-literate (MS) religions or literate versus image-based religion. In classic ritual theory Victor Turner distinguishes fertility rituals from political rituals or communitas (MS) from structure (HS), and recently cognitive theories of religion have adopted the dichotomy and tried to explain it by hypothesizing entrenched cognitive capacities of the human mind (Whitehouse 2000). Thus, according to both Whitehouse's dual memory theory and a good variety of classic theories of religion, structure is one of the main factors modulating religious practice. A neurofunctional study of the interactions between *Structure* and *religious involvement* would therefore be of great interest to the broader study of religion and to the experimental cognitive neuroscience of religion in particular.

Method, Results and Discussion

To analyze the interaction between *Structure* and *Religious involvement,* a two-way factorial design was made using two different prayer types, the Lord's Prayer and a Personal Prayer, corresponding to a highly structured condition and a minimally structured condition. Besides a baseline, the target conditions were contrasted with corresponding non-religious conditions as seen in Table 1. Twenty subjects from a Danish Protestant denomination known to use both types of prayer on a daily basis were asked to perform the tasks during scans.

Table 1.

Two-way factorial design	**Religious involvement**	**No religious involvement**
Highly structured	The Lord's Prayer (LP)	Rhyme (R)
Minimally structured	Personal Prayer (PP)	Wishes to Santa Claus (WSC)

Results showed significant differences between the two types of prayer. Personal Prayer, when contrasted with The Lord's Prayer, Wishes to Santa Claus and baseline, activated a surprisingly distinct pattern of Theory of Mind-related areas known to be involved in representing other people's beliefs and desires. It also activated areas associated with self-referential thinking. Combining these findings, practicing Personal Prayer may be a subjective and interpersonal experience at the same time. This suggests that subjects may represent God as a real person to communicate with about personal matters.

The Lord's Prayer, on the other hand, when contrasted with Personal Prayer, a children's rhyme, and baseline, activated subcortical structures involved in emotion and body regulation. This suggests that reciting the Lord's Prayer may have similar effects on the subject as has been reported in meditation and mantra studies, promoting the so called relaxation response (Benson 1976; Lazar et al. 2000).

The results support the hypothesis that communicating with supernatural beings exploits the neurofunctional substrates underlying normal social cognition. This is an important insight challenging the controversial hypothesis that experiencing the closeness of God takes a separate system in the temporal cortex (Persinger 1987). However, representing God as a real person only seems to apply for Personal Prayer corresponding to a minimally structured and improvised mode of religious behavior.

The study also supports the idea that frequently repeated religious recitations can help influence body states towards relaxation, indicating a pleasant or stress reducing experience. However, even though Personal Prayer and the Lord's Prayer fundamentally share the same intention to achieve support from God, only the Lord's Prayer, corresponding to a highly structured and formalized mode of religion, activates subcortical structures involved in body regulation. The significant differences between the two types of prayer indicate that *Structure* is indeed an important factor in modulating religious thought and behavior.

Exactly how these insights contribute to the ongoing debates of the evolutionary psychology of religion is not yet clear. I shall venture no such claim here. I do recommend, however, that such direct evidence on religious practice should be taken seriously by any evolutionary psychologist, who wants to know what kind of behavior religious practice is, and how it relates to the evolved capacities of the human brain.

References

Azari, N. P., Nickel, J. P., Wunderlich, G., Niedeggen, M., Hefter, H., Tellmann, L., et al. 2001. Neural correlates of religious experience. *European Journal of Neuroscience, 13,* 1649-1652.

Barrett, J. L. 2004. *Why would anyone believe in God?* Walnut Creek, CA: AltaMira Press.

Beauregard, M., & Paquette, V. 2006. Neural correlates of a mystical experience in Carmelite nuns. *Neuroscience Letters, 405,* 186-190.

Benson, H. 1976. The relaxation response. New York, NY: William Morrow & Company, inc.

Blakemore, S-J., Boyer, P., Pachot-Clouard, M., Meltzoff, A. N., & Decety, J. 2003. Detection of contingency and animacy in the human brain. *Cerebral Cortex, 13,* 837-844.

Boyer, P. 1994. *The naturalness of religious ideas: A cognitive theory of religion.* Berkeley, CA: University of California Press.

Boyer, P. 2003. Religious thought and behavior as by-products of brain function. *Trends in Cognitive Science, 7* (3), 119-124.

Boyer, P., & Liénard, P. 2006. Why ritualized behavior? Precaution systems and action-parsing in developmental, pathological and cultural rituals. *Behavioral & Brain Sciences, 29* (6), 595-650.

Guthrie, S. E. 1993. *Faces in the clouds.* New York, NY: Oxford University Press.

Lawson, E. T., & McCauley, R. N. 1990. *Rethinking religion: Connecting cognition and culture.* Cambridge, UK: Cambridge University Press.

Lazar, S. W., Bush, G., Gollub, R. L., Fricchione, G. L., Khalsa, G., & Benson, H. 2000. Functional brain mapping of the relaxation response and meditation. *NeuroReport, 11* (7), 581-1585.

McCauley, R. N., & Lawson, E. T. 2002. *Bringing ritual to mind: Psychological foundations of religious forms.* Cambridge, UK: Cambridge University Press.

Mithen, S. 1996. *The prehistory of the mind: A search for the origins of art, religion and science.* London, UK: Thames and Hudson.

Newberg, A. B., & d'Aquili, E. 1998. The neuropsychology of spiritual experience. In H. G. Koenig, Ed., *Handbook of religion and mental health*, pp. 75-94. San Diego, CA: Academic Press.
Newberg, A. B., Alavi, A., Baime, M., Pourdehnad, M., Santanna, J., & d'Aquili, E. 2001. The measurement of regional cerebral blood flow during the complex cognitive task of meditation: A preliminary SPECT study. *Psychiatric Research, Neuroimaging, 106*, 113-122.
Persinger, M. A. 1987. *Neuropsychological bases of God beliefs*. New York, NY: Praeger Publishers.
Weber, M. 1958. The Protestant ethic and the spirit of capitalism. New York, NY: Charles Scribner's Sons. Original work published 1904.
Whitehouse, H. 2000. *Arguments and icons: Divergent modes of religiosity*. New York, NY: Oxford University Press.
Whitehouse, H. 2002. Modes of religiosity: Towards a cognitive explanation of the socio-political dynamics of religion. *Method & Theory in the Study of Religion, 14*, 293-315.

Furthering the Evolution of Discussion on Religion

Multi-Method Study, Universality, and Cultural Variation

Adam B. Cohen, Peter C. Hill, Azim F. Shariff, & Paul Rozin

Though long acknowledged on a descriptive level, the multidimensionality of religious experience has only recently been furthered empirically (Hill & Hood 1999a; Hill & Pargament 2003). Many researchers now believe that numerous aspects of religion have different brain modules subserving them. Perhaps best articulated by Boyer (2001), such mental systems include goal and agency detection, theory of mind, social relations, fear of contagion, detection of emotional states, moral judgment, supernatural companions, social exchange, and altered states (c.f. Kirkpatrick 1999; Whitehouse 2004). These systems give rise to as diverse a set of religious ideas and practices as ritual; believing in supernatural agents; sacredness and taboo; and mystical experiences. Such analyses provide the basis for our suggestions in this chapter. First, we argue that we need to study religion in a multi-method way. Second, we argue that domains of religion vary across cultures in evolutionarily and culturally important ways.

Multi-Method Study of a Multidimensional Phenomenon

Many theorists and investigators focus their discussion of religion on one dimension, belief in supernatural agents (e.g., Barrett & Keil 1996; Dawkins 2006). In a fascinating description of belief in supernatural agents, Boyer (2001) explained "Religious representations are particular combinations of mental representations that satisfy two conditions. First, the religious concepts *violate* certain expectations from ontological categories. Second, they *preserve* other expectations" (62, italics in original). For example, people who believe in ghosts usually maintain that ghosts can pass through walls and that they are weightless, but also have certain features of a person (they have personalities, perceptions).

This theoretical analysis raises the interesting question of the cognitive structure of beliefs about supernatural agents. Do our minds have one module for processing the physics of the natural world, and another module for supernatural agents? This seems like a cumbersome system to engineer.

There are various theoretical perspectives on whether religious beliefs are explicit, implicit, emotional, or rational. Some evidence suggests that people have one set of beliefs at the explicit, conscious level, and a different system of beliefs at the intuitive level. Barrett and Keil (1996) demonstrated that people's explicit religious schemata may be theologically correct, but their implicit schemata may not. Participants who hear that God responded to prayers from two individuals at once will explicitly report that God is both omniscient and omnipresent, and is therefore capable of such an accomplishment. However, when later recounting the story, it becomes apparent that people's implicit schemata led them to process the story as God helping one person *and then* the other.

William James' view of pragmatism would suggest that some people explicitly choose their belief in religion. James (1907/2003) explained "The pragmatic method is primarily a method of settling metaphysical disputes that otherwise might be interminable.... The pragmatic method in such cases is to try to interpret each notion by tracing its respective practical consequences" (23). Later, considering whether salvation is real, James continued: "Here I take the bull by the horns, and in spite of the whole crew of rationalists and monists, of whatever brand they may be, I ask why not?" (144).

A different theoretical perspective comes from Epstein (1994), who distinguished between rational and experiential cognitive processes. The experiential system operates more automatically than the rational system, and can be the source of intuition and creativity. The rational system is more deliberative and abstract. He argued that "Religion provides perhaps the most impressive evidence of all that there are two fundamentally different modes of processing information.... For many individuals, rational, analytical thinking fails to provide as satisfactory a way of understanding the world and of directing their behavior in it as does religious teaching...religion is better suited than analytical thinking for communicating with the experiential system" (712). Of interest, several scholars have noted the transition in American religion as increasingly based on emotional and experiential criteria (reviewed in Cohen, Hall, Koenig, & Meador 2005).

These perspectives may suggest that religious beliefs and schemata can operate differently at implicit and explicit levels. Some religions place disincentives on the expression, and even ideation, of religious doubt. When an individual perceives the welfare of one's soul as depending on faith, there is strong motivation to minimize one's religious doubts, even to oneself (Edwards & Hall 2003; Hill & Hood 1999b). As a consequence, a discontinuity could emerge between what these individuals allow themselves to consciously believe, and the doubts that they keep suppressed.

Another possibility is that people are unwilling to report certain explicit religious beliefs or doubts. Religious beliefs are often maintained in social environments where individuals may feel obligated to report certain beliefs (Burris & Navara 2002). Under such conditions, subjects' willingness and ability to accurately self-report may be vulnerable to demand characteristics, evaluation apprehension, and impression management (Greenwald et al. 2002).

Psychology of religion's reliance on self-report measures has rendered it largely incapable of tapping implicit beliefs or beliefs that people do not wish to report. New research techniques need to be developed which can distinguish beliefs at different levels of cognition, and which will not depend on people's willingness or ability to report their beliefs. One set of promising avenues include reaction time based studies. Cohen, Shariff and Hill (2007) have developed a reaction time task in which participants classify stimuli as real or imaginary as quickly as they can, and faster reaction times seem to correspond to more confidence in ratings. Variations of such techniques could be developed to tap implicit beliefs as well. Gibson (2005) reported a host of reaction time studies, including versions of a religious Stroop test. Behavioral economics experiments are another avenue. Shariff and Norenzayan (in press 2007) showed that participants who were subtly primed with religion became more behaviorally altruistic. Another interesting possibility could be free association techniques. Pioneered by Freud, free association has fallen by the wayside. But free associations appear to possess some of the advantages proposed by Freud, such as not being quite as rationally considered as explicitly reported attitudes (Rozin, Kurzer, & Cohen 2002). Last, physiological studies could greatly enrich our understanding of religion (e.g., Newberg & Newberg 2005).

Universality and Variability

A multiple systems model of religion also has implications for questions surrounding universality. Some seem to suggest that, if an aspect of religion is evolved, it should show up in all cultures. Many theorists point to the universality of supernatural agents because beliefs about ghosts, ancestors, souls, gods, or God occur in all cultures (e.g., Atran & Norenzayan 2004; Bering 2006; Boyer, 2001; Tremlin 2006).

Universality is informative in evolutionary analyses, but this is not to say that there is not meaningful cultural variability, and even evolved differences between cultures long separated. The notion of cultural universals is somewhat controversial within evolutionary and cultural psychology and anthropology. The logical and empirical requirements for documenting a human universal have often been ignored, though criteria have been proposed

(Brown 1991; Norenzayan & Heine 2005). There may be some benefits, but also some costs, of lumping together very different kinds of beliefs about very different kinds of agents, such as ghosts, gods, God, and souls. We propose that cultural differences can be as informative, and as consistent with evolutionary approaches, as universals.

Human behavior represents a continual, dynamic interplay between flexible, evolved mechanisms interacting with ecological inputs that vary in different environments (Kenrick et al. 2002; Rozin 2000; Tooby & Cosmides 1990). Norms concerning mating systems provide one illustration. Some religions and cultures prescribe monogamy, some polygamy, and a small percentage polyandry. Are we to conclude that mating systems are not evolved strategies because they vary? That would not be appropriate because, in humans and other animals, variations in mating systems correlate predictably with physical and social ecology (Crook & Crook 1988; Orians 1969).

If religion involves numerous mental systems, it is likely that different selection pressures shaped different components. Perhaps some of these systems are more adaptive in some ecological conditions or cultural contexts more than others. Therefore, it seems likely that some components of religion will be more salient in some cultures (Cohen, Kenrick, & Li 2006; Sosis & Alcorta 2003). For example, concepts of warrior-like, jealous Gods are more prevalent in religions that originated in harsh, desert environments in which resources are scarce and unpredictable, whereas other concepts (polytheistic beliefs) are more prevalent in lush rainforests with plentiful resources (Textor 1967).

What is known about dimensions of variability in components of religion? Relevant to discussions about religion promoting social cohesion or group selection (Atran & Norenzayan 2004; Wilson 2002), religious cultures differ in the role that personal religious beliefs and community integration play in the formation of religious identity (Cohen, Siegel, & Rozin 2003; Cohen et al. 2005; Cohen & Hill, in press; Morris 1997). And even if religions share some of the same ultimate goals (e.g. group cohesion), they accomplish them in very different ways, which both reflect and shape cultural and ecological differences (Wilson 2002). Religious variability is therefore ripe for evolutionary analysis, both biological and cultural.

Summary

Evolutionary approaches to religion have resulted in great strides in understanding the different mental systems that subserve aspects of religious belief, emotion, and practice. We suggest several avenues for future research based on this theoretical platform. Research that enables us to supplement self-reports will provide a richer understanding of various aspects of religious cognition. And, more attention to cultural variability will help us understand how ecology and cultural context shapes and is shaped by the evolution of different components of religion.

Author's Note

We gratefully acknowledge the support of a Templeton Advanced Research Program grant, sponsored by the Metanexus Institute on Science and Religion. The views expressed do not necessarily represent those of Metanexus or Templeton.

Authors: Adam B. Cohen is from Arizona State University, Peter C. Hill is from Rosemead School of Psychology at Biola University, Azim F. Shariff is from the University of British Columbia, and Paul Rozin is from the University of Pennsylvania

References

Atran, S., & Norenzayan, A. 2004. Religion's evolutionary landscape: Counterintuition, commitment, compassion, communion. *Behavioral & Brain Sciences, 27*, 713-770.

Barrett, J. L., & Keil, F. C. 1996. Conceptualizing a nonnatural entity: Anthropomorphism in God concepts. *Cognitive Psychology, 31*, 219-247.

Bering, J. M. 2006. The folk psychology of souls. *Behavioral & Brain Sciences, 29*, 453-498.

Boyer, P. 2001. *Religion explained: The evolutionary origins of religious thought.* New York, NY: Basic Books.

Brown, D. E. 1991. *Human universals.* New York, NY: McGraw-Hill.

Burris, C. T., & Navara, G. S. 2002. Morality play – or playing morality: Intrinsic religious orientation and socially desirable responding. *Self & Identity, 1*, 67-76.

Cohen, A. B., Hall, D. E., Koenig, H. G., & Meador, K. 2005. Social versus individual motivation: Implications for normative definitions of religious orientation. *Personality & Social Psychology Review, 9*, 48-61.

Cohen, A. B., & Hill, P. C. 2007. Religion as culture: Religious individualism and collectivism among American Catholics, Jews, and Protestants. *Journal of Personality, 75*, 709-742.

Cohen, A. B., Kenrick, D. T., & Li, Y. J. 2006. Ecological variability and religious belief [Commentary]. *Behavioral & Brain Sciences, 29*, 468.

Cohen, A. B., Shariff, A. F., & Hill, P. C. 2007. *The accessibility of religious beliefs.* Manuscript submitted for publication.

Cohen, A. B., Siegel, J. I., & Rozin, P. 2003. Faith versus practice: Different bases for religiosity judgments by Jews and Protestants. *European Journal of Social Psychology, 33*, 287-295.

Crook, J. H., & Crook, S. J. 1988. Tibetan polyandry: Problems of adaptation and fitness. In L. Betzig, M. Borgerhoff-Mulder, & P. Turke, Eds., *Human reproductive behavior: A Darwinian perspective*, 97-114. Cambridge, UK: Cambridge University Press.

Dawkins, R. 2006. *The God delusion*. Boston, MA: Houghton Mifflin.

Edwards, K. J., & Hall, T. W. 2003. Illusory spiritual health: The role of defensiveness in understanding and assessing spiritual health. In. T. W. Hall & M. R. McMinn, Eds., *Spiritual formation, counseling, and psychotherapy*, pp. 261-275. Hauppauge, NY: Nova Science Publishers.

Epstein, S. 1994. Integration of the cognitive and the psychodynamic unconscious. *American Psychologist, 49*, 709-724.

Gibson, N. J. S. 2005. The experimental investigation of religious cognition. Unpublished doctoral dissertation. Cambridge University, Cambridge, England.

Greenwald, A. G., Banaji, M. R., Rudman, L. A., Farnham, S. D., Nosek, B. A., & Mellott, D. S. 2002. A unified theory of implicit attitudes, stereotypes, self-esteem, and self-concept. *Psychological Review, 109*, 3-25.

Hill, P. C., & Hood, R. W., Jr. Eds. 1999a. *Measures of religiosity*. Birmingham, AL: Religious Education Press.

Hill, P. C., & Hood, R. W., Jr. 1999b. Affect, religion, and unconscious processes. *Journal of Personality, 67*, 1015-1046.

Hill, P. C., & Pargament, K. I. 2003. Advances in the conceptualization and measurement of religion and spirituality: Implications for physical and mental health research. *American Psychologist, 58*, 64-74.

James, W. 2003. *Pragmatism*. New York, NY: Barnes and Noble. Original work published 1907.

Kenrick, D. T., Maner, J.K., Butner, J., Li, N.P., Becker, D.V., & Schaller, M. 2002. Dynamic evolutionary psychology: Mapping the domains of the new interactionist paradigm. *Personality & Social Psychology Review, 6*, 347-356.

Kirkpatrick, L. A. 1999. Toward an evolutionary psychology of religion and personality. *Journal of Personality, 67*, 921-952.

Morris, P. 1997. Communities of assent and descent. *Massah; Journey. Journal of the New Zealand Council of Christians & Jews, 3*, 2-4.

Newberg, A. B., & Newberg, S. K. 2005. The neuropsychology of religious and spiritual experience. In R. F. Paloutzian & C. L. Park, Eds., *Handbook of the psychology of religion and spirituality*, 199-215. New York, NY: Guilford.

Norenzayan, A., & Heine, S. J. 2005. Psychological universals: What are they and how can we know? *Psychological Bulletin, 131*, 763-784.

Orians, G. H. 1969. On the evolution of mating systems in bird and mammals. *American Naturalist, 103*, 589-603.

Rozin, P. 2000. Evolution and adaptation in the understanding of behavior, culture, and mind. *American Behavioral Scientist, 43*, 970-986.

Rozin, P., Kurzer, N., & Cohen, A. B. 2002. Free associations to "food": The effects of gender, generation, and culture. *Journal of Research in Personality, 36*, 419-441.

Shariff, A. F., & Norenzayan, A. 2007. God is watching you: Supernatural agent concepts increase prosocial behavior in an anonymous economic game. *Psychological Science, 18*, 803-809 .

Sosis, R., & Alcorta, C. 2003. Signaling, solidarity, and the sacred: The evolution of religious behavior. *Evolutionary Anthropology, 12*, 264-274.

Textor, R. B. 1967. *A cross-cultural summary*. New Haven, CT: HRAF Press.

Tooby, J., & Cosmides, L. 1990. On the universality of human nature and the uniqueness of the individual: The role of genetics and adaptation. *Journal of Personality, 58*, 17-67.

Tremlin, T. 2006. *Minds and gods: The cognitive foundations of religion*. New York: Oxford.

Whitehouse, H. 2004. *Modes of religiosity: A cognitive theory of religious transmission*. Walnut Creek, CA: AltaMira.

Wilson, D. S. 2002. *Darwin's cathedral*. Chicago: University of Chicago.

Selection, Traditions, Kinship, and Ancestor Worship

Crucial Concepts in the Evolution of Religion

Lyle B. Steadman and Craig T. Palmer

In this paper, we argue that the most significant effect of religion is that it extends kinship behavior to distant kin, first, and then, more recently, to non-kin. This has been achieved through the transmission of traditions, which allows ancestors to influence distant descendants (Palmer & Steadman 1997). All this has been subject to Darwinian selection.

Selection

About 150 years ago, Charles Darwin made the most important discovery ever made in biology: He came to realize that every inheritable trait of every living thing was subject to what he called "selection." That is, when any inheritable trait—which refers to both physical and behavioral features—helps an individual to leave descendants, that trait will tend to increase in frequency in a population over time. Any trait that damages fitness will tend to disappear. Because new variants appear from time to time, where these help individuals to leave descendants they will be amplified and move to fixation over time. Darwin's discovery of this process of variation, inheritance, and selection is recognized today as the fundamental cause of evolution.

The development of every trait of every organism depends on a complex interaction between particular genes and particular environmental factors. The particular genes involved, by being heritable, are subject to selection. This means that all traits influence their own frequency in later generations. But humans are, in contrast to other species, profoundly influenced by traditions: learned behavior copied, often through complex interactions and physiological processes, from ancestors. Unfortunately, this fact has led most social scientists to conclude that Darwinian selection is irrelevant to the study of human behavior. To the contrary, the importance of traditions actually increases the relevance of selection in understanding behavior. This is because not only are the genes involved in every traditional behavior subject to selection, traditions themselves, because they are inheritable, are subject *directly* to selection. A tradition, like any trait, begins for a variety of reasons.

But, when it helps to leave descendants it will tend to increase in frequency. When it does not, it will tend to die out.

Therefore, when we look at any widespread tradition that has been around for multiple generations, we can study how it helped individuals in the past to leave descendants. That examination can explain why that tradition is widespread. Religious behavior is an interesting example, because even now it tends to be highly traditional; that is, individuals tend to acquire the religion of their parents. Regardless of the "truth" of a religion, if it helps individuals to leave descendants, it will tend to increase in frequency along with their descendants. If it does not, it will likely disappear. So, a crucial task in understanding why a particular religion is widespread is to figure out how it helped ancestors of the current followers to leave descendants. However, before we can understand how religion helped humans to leave descendants, we must first understand how human kinship behavior has helped leave descendants. This is because religion undoubtedly originated within the context of kinship behavior.

Kinship

Two individuals are kin *only* when they share a common ancestor. Kin may be closely or distantly related, depending on the number of generations between them and a common progenitor. So, kinship is simple, but the definition of kinship *behavior* is more complex, for not all kinsmen act like kinsmen toward one another. Male lizards, for example, don't care for, or even identify, their own offspring and may even pursue and eat them. Somehow, this is not quite what we mean by kinship behavior.

Perhaps the best way to make explicit what is meant by kinship behavior is to look at maternal investment, a behavior common to all mammals. No mammal would survive without it. The important point about maternal investment is that it is at the expense of both her survival, to some extent, and her future reproduction. Maternal investment is distinguished by sacrifice (i.e., altruism). Because it is now extremely widespread, such sacrifice must have helped mammalian mothers to leave more descendants than alternative behaviors.

Maternal investment exemplifies our meaning of kinship behavior. So what, then, do we mean by kinship behavior? Kinship behavior seems to imply some personal sacrifice aimed at benefiting another individual *because* he or she is your kinsman. However, any sacrifice for just any kinsman does not qualify as true kinship behavior because, if that were so, any sacrifice toward any human would be kinship behavior, for we all share a common ancestor. Indeed, any such behavior directed toward any mammal, because we share a common ancestor, would also have to be considered kinship behavior. But clearly that is not what we mean by true kinship behavior. What we must mean by kinship behavior, then, is that the degree of sacrifice be correlated with the degree of kinship. That is, only when the degree of sacrifice is correlated with kinship distance—meaning the number of birth links separating kinsmen—do we in fact consider it true kinship behavior. Only when siblings are favored over cousins, and close cousins favored over distant cousins do we consider it true—i.e., non-metaphorical—kinship behavior.

While kinship behavior is exhibited by many species—all mammals, for example, depend utterly on their mother's care when young—humans in all societies, through traditions, have extended such behavior to many distant kinsmen. In some societies, the number of kin identified by each individual through the traditional transmission of descent, or family, names can number in the tens of thousands (Palmer & Steadman 1997). Based on the number of people exhibiting such extended kinship behavior today, it must have been highly successful in the past; it must have dramatically increased the success of ancestors to leave descendants.

Thus, a fundamental question about human evolution is: how was kinship behavior selected for? That is, how did the degree of sacrifice, based on how close the kinsman is, help to leave more descendants than alternative behavior? The answer for kinship behavior among close kin, as can be seen in all mammalian species, may be that close kin share a lot of the same genes by common descent, with the closest kin sharing the most. However, when individuals in tribal societies everywhere extend kinship behavior to very distant kinsmen, we are faced with an evolutionary puzzle—for such behavior cannot be explained by the sharing of genes or reciprocal altruism (Palmer & Steadman 1997). So too is the now almost universal occurrence of truly metaphorical kinship behavior (i.e., treating individuals like close kin even when these individuals are not identified as kin at all).

We suggest that traditions can explain this phenomenon. Traditions, like all traits, depend on certain genes—in this case, genes that are involved in large brains, speaking, copying behavior and so on. The genes involved in traditionally promoted kinship-like behavior must be the same genes involved in true kinship behavior. But because humans have been selected to copy their ancestors, and accept detailed instructions from them, ancestors have been able to encourage their descendants both to refer to distant kin and even to non-kin (i.e., individuals not identified as kin) by close kin terms and to sacrifice for them as if they were close kin, to some extent. This appears to be true in all tribal societies, and therefore must have greatly promoted their success in the leaving of descendants. An understanding of this relation between ancestors, traditions, and human kinship is necessary to understand the evolution of religion because evidence suggests that the earliest known form of religion was ancestor worship. The worship of ancestors *is* kinship behavior.

Ancestor Worship

Ancestor worship is distinguished by the claim that dead ancestors are still alive and can influence and be influenced. Ancestor worship has promoted the leaving of descendants in two ways: it encourages cooperation among distant living kin and it encourages obedience to, and transmission of, traditions. These two activities, kinship cooperation and the transmission of traditions, are the basis of every human society (Steadman & Palmer 1995).

Ancestors are the source both of kinsmen and traditions, including traditions that encourage distant kin to cooperate through ancestor worship rituals. Thus ancestor worship has a lot to do with distant kinship cooperation (Steadman, Palmer, & Tilley 1996). Indeed, the transmission of traditions itself is a kinship activity, for such transmission involves cooperation between living ancestors and descendants. Tribal religion, which everywhere appears to include ancestor worship (Steadman et al. 1996), promotes directly this close kinship-like behavior. When descendants come together to worship their common ancestor, they often call each other "children" of that ancestor, making them metaphorical "siblings" of one another. And they often call one another "brother" and "sister."

You may have noticed that in our discussion of ancestor worship we have not used the word "belief." We consider this a step forward in the study of not just ancestor worship, but of religion in general, for no-one can identify another person's religious beliefs. If someone said they believed their dead ancestor was present at a ritual, does that mean they necessarily believe their claim? If someone says she believes in God, does that mean she believes in God? Do fellow worshipers necessarily believe the same thing? And to the same degree? If fellow members of the same congregation cannot identify each other's beliefs, why should we trust anyone who claims to know the beliefs of others? For more than a century, anthropologists have made claims about the beliefs of the peoples they have studied. But why should we accept such claims as true? We can study identifiable behavior, including speech, which, by being identifiable, allows the accuracy of our claims to be evaluated. What anthropologists and others have actually observed is religious behavior, not beliefs. And that behavior is distinguished by claims that cannot be shown to be true. When other individuals communicate acceptance of such claims, we have the identifiable behavior that anthropologists have labeled religious behavior (Palmer & Steadman 2004; Steadman & Palmer 1995). When individuals communicate acceptance of the claim that they can influence their dead ancestors, anthropologists label this behavior ancestor worship.

Modern Religions and Prophets

Modern religions, in contrast to tribal religions, are created by prophets. The most significant, identifiable effect of prophets is that they create kinship cooperation between non-kin. Much cooperation in the modern world is based on the acceptance of messages from a common prophet. On the other hand, much competition in the modern world is based on the acceptance of different prophets.

Kinship-like behavior is encouraged in all modern societies between non-kin, perhaps even more than between distant kin. How has this truly metaphorical behavior come about? We suggest it is the result of the acceptance of the influence of prophets. Within the past several thousand years, prophets have arisen who, based on their supernatural claims—often they claim to speak for the first ancestor, called father or mother—have gained followers who are encouraged to treat each other as if they were brother and sister, regardless of their true kinship relationship. Jesus, when told that his mother and brethren were waiting for him outside, said to his followers, "Who is my mother and my brethren? You are my mother and my brethren when you follow me." He also said, "the only way to the Father … is by me." And, "Leave your mother and father, and follow me."

Thus, prophets create a "family," individuals encouraged to sacrifice for one another *as if* they were true brothers and sisters. The fundamental significance of all successful prophets appears to be that they create a metaphorical family, a set of individuals who are encouraged to sacrifice for one another as if they were close kin.

What is the benefit of this kinship-like behavior between distant or non-kin? The most obvious one is that it reduces competition, including violent competition, among them. They are safer. Secondly, it promotes cooperation (which involves some sacrifice) among them. And this cooperation regularly includes trade and some specialization, which is the basis of a higher standard of living, including longer life. For prophet-created religions —modern religions—this has led regularly to extensive trade and specialization. This trade and specialization, which today includes discoveries in science, medicine and technology, not only benefit the individuals involved, but also their children and future descendants. Today, education is an important part of this strategy, for education is aimed at teaching children the skills and knowledge crucial to these specializations. Modern education is still a kinship strategy of ancestors aimed at leaving descendants.

Conclusion

Religious behavior is distinguished by one or more individuals communicating their acceptance of another person's supernatural claim, a claim that cannot be shown to be true. The identifiable effect of such behavior, the effect that has resulted in leaving descendants, we propose, is that it communicates subordination to another person. When one person communicates his acceptance of another person's claim that goes against his own experiences and senses—such as the obvious contradiction that a person continues to live after he has disintegrated—he is, in fact, communicating his willingness to be subordinate to that person, to accept that person's leadership. Religion everywhere creates hierarchy. The subordination may come to include sacrificing one's life for the religious leader and his fellow followers (Palmer, Steadman, & Cassidy 2006).

We suggest that religion originally evolved as ancestor worship, and that ancestor worship is best seen as an extension of kinship behavior. The significant effect of ancestor worship—the religion of all of our ancestors up to a few thousand years ago—the effect that has helped the individuals involved to leave descendants, is the encouragement of close kinship cooperation between distant kin. A few thousand years ago, some individuals, now called prophets, using supernatural claims, began to encourage such cooperation between *non*-kin, the basis of modern societies.

Traditions, including, or perhaps especially, religious traditions have been involved directly in this extension of kinship behavior. But these are only the mechanisms. The fundamental explanation of why they are widespread is based on the discovery by Charles Darwin, 150 years ago, of selection. If those traditions had not promoted success in leaving descendants, they would not have become widespread.

Authors

Lyle B. Steadman is from Arizona State University and Craig T. Palmer from University of Missouri-Columbia.

References

Palmer, C. T., & Steadman, L. B. 1997. Human kinship as a descendant-leaving strategy: A solution to an evolutionary puzzle. *Journal of Social & Evolutionary Systems, 20* (1), 39-51.

Palmer, C. T., & Steadman, L. B. 2004. With or without belief: A new evolutionary approach to the definition and explanation of religion. *Evolution & Cognition, 10* (1), 138-147.

Palmer, C. T., Steadman, L. B., & Cassidy, C. 2006. Traditional religious ritual sacrifice: Cultural materialism, costly signaling, or descendant-leaving strategy? *Journal of Ritual Studies, 20* (2), 33-42.

Steadman, L. B., & Palmer, C. T. 1995. Religion as an identifiable traditional behavior subject to natural selection. *Journal of Social & Evolutionary Systems, 18* (2), 149-164.

Steadman, L. B., Palmer, C. T., & Tilley, C. F. 1996. The universality of ancestor worship. *Ethnology, 35* (1), 63-76.

Reflections on the Evolutionary Study of Religion

The Importance of Individual Differences

Brian H. McCorkle

This paper was written for the panel "Reactions to the Evolutionary Study of Religion," which occurred near the close of the Evolution of Religion Conference held in Oahu, HI in January, 2007. It focuses on individual differences within the research community and within any religious community. Along the way, some thoughts are offered about working together as a community of individuals with diverse scientific and religious backgrounds and beliefs.

Individual Differences Between Researchers

For our fields to advance, it is vital that we not all agree. None of us are 100% right, nor will we ever be. It is important to periodically return to the philosophy of science as a corrective, which reminds us that scientific models are successively better models of reality, but not reality itself.

Consider your human perceptual model of me if I were standing in front of you. You would never actually see the "real me". First, all you would see is the electromagnetic energy or photons that are rejected by my body. These enter your eye, triggering thousands of separate retinal cells to send signals to a variety of cells in your visual cortex, from which your brain assembles a visual model of me. This process is partial at best (with our visual system registering only a small portion of the electromagnetic spectrum), and can be easily misled (as optical illusions and much fashion advice attests). The best we can do is assemble a working model which we continually revise based on new input, knowledge, and beliefs. We do the same with all our sensory channels. Similarly, scientific models are simply working models which are frequently revised over time. One need only consider the evolution of models of physics and chemistry over the last several centuries to see this process at work.

We should learn from the voluminous studies of healthy group decision-making. For example, consider the Bayesian search methodology developed in the 1960s by the U.S. Navy to find a missing hydrogen bomb and nuclear submarine, both lost at sea. Briefly put, asking experts with different perspectives separately to make firm predictions and calculating a statistical mean of the predictions is more accurate than putting the experts in the same room and developing a consensus by group process. Including information acquired from divergent viewpoints is similar to spatial location, which requires three orthogonal 1-dimensional viewpoints to create 3-dimensional coordinates. A recent study by Fredrickson & Losada (2005) indicated that the most highly productive business teams spent nearly equal amounts of time with individuals advocating for their own views and with individuals inquiring about the views of others, while the least productive teams spent most of the time with individuals only advocating for their own views. Of note, the highly productive teams used positive emotion tone more than negative, but were not completely positive; perhaps the positive exchanges created a working relationship in which they could benefit from vigorous dissent without being hampered by it. This is important because studies of healthy business group decision-making describe the value of dissent. In fact, it appears that true "consensus" (i.e., 100% agreement) can suppress the unique contribution of each individual's unique perspective in the service of creating group harmony. We can not learn from one another if we prematurely agree to think alike.

Individual Differences within Religious Groups

There are a number of factors which predict that even the most dominant religious genes, mechanisms, and memes will be subject to within-group individual variation.

First, *not all believers in sacredness agree*. What about those pesky "non-theist" Buddhists? Jason Sloan has shown that many Buddhists actually show evidence of theistic beliefs, and I would comment that much of the journey along the Buddhist path is a movement from what has been called a theistic folk religion towards non-theism. And then what about those equally pesky "spiritual but not religious" folks who include theists, deists, pantheists, agnostics, and yes, many New Age atheists who find meditation and yoga profoundly spiritual but nonetheless do not believe in divine beings. Then there are people whose feelings about God include anger, betrayal, or abandonment; such feelings require belief in the object of the feeling even though there is no face-level adaptive value for the belief. Sometimes this results from feelings of outright betrayal, such as being the victim of various bad events from early childhood trauma through death. Sometimes anger at God can even appear emotionally healthy, and sometimes it is emotionally overwhelming. This range of negative feelings towards God is quite common in psychotherapy, pastoral counseling, and spiritual direction, and can also include feelings of distance: "Why have you forsaken me?" In fact, the Dark Night of the Soul of St. John of the Cross is actually an essential part of movement along the spiritual path from a naïve folk-religious dualism towards the non-linguistic direct non-dual experience of which mystics in every tradition speak.

Second, *even atheism is not unitary*. As some have said, there is "cool" and "hot" atheism. Some atheists engage in a dispassionate examination of belief and the evidence, and conclude that there is no God. However, Julie Exline's studies of atheism describe a subgroup of atheists whose very professions of disbelief in God revealed their implicit belief in a god at whom they are angry.

Finally, remember what we now know about neuroplasticity, gene-environment mutual effects, and epigenetics. Even though the genome for human psychophysiology was set millennia ago, we can be confident that it is not expressed consistently. Not across *any individual's lifetime*, either in structure (e.g., the hippocampi of London cab drivers; or "neural Darwinism" of language neurons for those not learning second languages in childhood) or in function (e.g., the right caudate nucleus for people symptomatic for Obsessive-Compulsive Disorder and how it changes with treatment; or adaptation to stroke or acquired blindness). Neither is it expressed consistently across *individuals alive at the same time* (e.g., even twin studies consistently show an environmental remainder for many different traits after accounting for the contribution of the identical DNA of monozygotic twins). How much less, then, will it be expressed consistently *across individuals living in different eras*, who develop and go through life in different physical, nutritional/biochemical, and cognitive landscapes.

Let me highlight two major effects that flow from the importance of individual differences:

Effect 1: Even thought experiments need representative sampling.

Evolutionary theories of religion need to account for within-group variation as normative, even for "successful" religious genes and memes (as they are broadly defined).

David Sloan Wilson (2007) describes how Bill Muir bred chickens for productivity in two ways: by selecting the *most productive individual* chicken from within each cage of nine hens to breed the next generation, and by selecting the *most productive group* (i.e., most productive cage of nine hens) to breed the next generation. After repeating these strategies for six generations, those bred from productive individuals fought, pecked each other bloody and nearly featherless, and six of the group of nine hens were actually killed, while individual egg production diminished. However, after six generations the fat happy cooperative hens of the productive group lineage showed a significant increase in productivity.

In this regard, evolution will favor groups with religious cooperation within the group rather than dominance by individuals or individual modes. Religious cultures will need high, low, and "differently religious" individuals for success, individuals for whom religion will definitely involve different functional roles. It may also use different mechanisms in filling those roles: in Montserrat Soler's study of spirit possession in Brazil (this volume), consider the differences in the experience of spirit possession of the people in various roles within the house. Also, just because a religious artifact, meme, or cognitive mechanism existed does not mean that everyone used it or even had it, and just because someone used it does not mean that they always used it. Consider the statement: "In the early 21st century, PowerPoint was the (only) medium for academic presentations, and every academic who used PowerPoint used it for all audiences," a statement which was disproved on both counts just during this conference.

Effect 2: Empirical tests need representative samples.

Early hypothesis exploration is often easiest with "distilled" samples, such as a single group of highly religious people, or two groups that contrast highly religious and non-religious people. This appropriate strategy guarantees the presence of the trait of interest in samples small enough to be reasonable in cost, manageable in size, and easily analyzable. However, such samples inherently have a sample-selection bias. Full hypothesis testing requires a full range of religiosity. This means including high, medium, low, and zero values on the continuum in question. It also means including anguished believers, dubious wonderers, and the whole variety of being "differently religious". Not only is this necessary for true understanding of the population, but it is a necessary prerequisite for advanced statistical modeling such as structural equation modeling or discriminant analysis.

Stirring The Pot

Now, let me briefly explore one of those seemingly divergent views I mentioned above. Let's go back to those pesky "spiritual-but-not-religious" folks. Consider the apparent universality of the experience of opening to "something larger", such as when watching a beautiful sunset. Bob Emmons has described the "spiritual strivings" that don't seem to reduce neatly to other domains. Ken Pargament and colleagues have been exploring the "sense of sacredness", which need not be associated with any particular religion or agent-based spirituality. Then there's the so-called "Perennial Philosophy" of Leibnitz and Huxley.

Finally, there is the universality of mystics in seemingly every religious and spiritual tradition who say, "my experience can not be described accurately in words". And yet, words are the human vehicle for communication and reflective thought, so any theology is of necessity a distorted approximation of that experience. For this reason, mystics often rely on poetic imagery, such as the symbolic language of the psalms and prophets in the Hebrew Bible. Likewise with Christian parables: Jesus says "it's *like* this, not "it *is* this." The Kingdom of Heaven is like a mustard seed; it is not actually an actual single mustard seed located in time and space. There is a Buddhist image of religious teachings being fingers pointing at the moon, but not the moon itself.

As an analogy, chemistry and physics now do a fabulous job of *describing the behavior* of water at an aggregate, molecular, atomic, and subatomic levels, but they can not (yet) explain the ultimate origin of the particles of which water consists. They can not (yet) explain the cause of the Big Bang. They can not (yet) answer <insert your favorite Ultimate Question here>. As for those of us at this conference, all our various fields of scientific inquiry are currently (finally!) doing a great job of describing how the "fingers" of religion develop and function. They do a great job of describing how people stare at "fingers" and misinterpret them and reify them and overvalue them. However, none of us have explicit, reliable, replicable scientific evidence (yet) of whether or not there actually is a "moon" being pointed at or not.

The Mind and Life Institute is a group that, working with the Dalai Lama, has been bringing Western scientists and religious scholars together for collaborative dialogues very similar to the 2007 Evolution of Religion conference in Hawaii (the papers from which are published in this volume). In the foreword to the book describing their 2000 meeting, the Dalai Lama remarked:

> I have often said that if science proves facts that conflict with Buddhist understanding, Buddhism must change accordingly. We should always adopt a view that accords with the facts. If upon investigation we find that there is reason and proof for a point, then we should accept it. However, a clear distinction should be made between what is *not found* by science and what is found to be *nonexistent* by science. What science finds to be nonexistent we should all accept as nonexistent, but what science merely does not find is a completely different matter. (Goleman 2003, xiv, italics original)

What is the logically and scientifically rigorous response? Maybe, just maybe, the Perennial Philosophy is perennial for a reason. Ann Taves (this volume) describes how the field of religious studies has moved from a dominant *sui generis* model (religious experience is a unique thing unto itself) to an attributional model (religious experience shares many things with other domains but is attributed to supernatural sources). Maybe, just maybe, there are *both* attributional *and* sui generis components at the same time. Maybe, just maybe, there *is* more than is currently scientifically observable. Maybe the attribution model helps us do a great job of discovering how the human nervous system and social groupings try to make sense of that "something" in languages, images, and behavior, *and* that "something" is sui generis. I'm not talking about blindly adopting a belief simply because so many others hold it, any more than I would advocate belief in a flat earth. What I'm saying is that we just don't yet know. Absence of evidence does not equal evidence of absence, but also absence of evidence does not equal evidence of presence either. For now, at least, science is truly agnostic on the point; a-gnosis, without knowledge.

Therefore, as intellectually rigorous scientists, whether atheists or believers, we really can say no more than: "Based on the evidence and careful thought, *I personally* [do/do not] believe in the existence of something spiritual, but *science* does not yet have any way to directly and definitively answer the question either way." Anything more is simply personal opinion.

Summary

In summary, let me review the four points that I have tried to make:

First, remember the importance of researchers' within-group variation. We actually *need* to disagree in order to advance.

Second, remember the importance of within-group variation in religion's functional roles and processes, including variation between individuals and variation over time.

Third (and only very slightly tongue-in-check), alternate models of reality may be no more mistaken than your own. Consider the enormous historical changes in models of physics and chemistry.

Finally, for disagreement to be productive, we need a culture of *respectful-yet-active* disagreement. The most elegant and accurate design will not evolve unless the full range of chaotically generated variant positions is allowed. Remember the fat, healthy cooperation of the productive chicken group rather than the bloody, featherless, murderous chickens of the productive individual chickens. Also remember the Fredrickson and Losada study showing mostly positive interactions but including a range of both negative and positive, and of both advocating for one's own views and inquiry into others' views.

References

Fredrickson, B. L., & Losada, M. F. 2005. Positive affect and the complex dynamics of human flourishing. *American Psychologist, 60*, 678-686.

Goleman, D. 2003. *Destructive emotions*. New York, NY: Bantam Books.

Wilson, D. S. 2007. *Evolution for everyone: How Darwin's theory can change the way we think about our lives*. New York, NY: Delacorte Press.

On Psychology and Evolution of Religion

Five Types of Contribution Needed from Psychologists

Nicholas J. S. Gibson and Justin L. Barrett

Of those scholars who identify with cognitive science of religion or evolutionary accounts, fewer than one-fifth have substantial background in psychological theory or methods (based on membership in the International Association for the Cognitive Science of Religion). Given how heavily accounts of religious phenomena in this field rely on evolutionary, cognitive, developmental, and social psychological findings and theories, this paucity of psychologists is lamentable for the health of the field. Specifically, we see five types of contributions needed from the psychologists in the field.

Filling in the Details

Behind accounts of costly-signaling, sexual selection, religion-as-byproduct, and religion-as-group-adaptation theories, we too have to consider that real people really believe, think, feel, and act on the individual and episodic level. And for these grand theories to work, they must plausibly work on the psychological level, too; a level that is not always as simple as it first seems. There are two ways in which psychologists can help achieve this. The first is to ground cultural-level theories within the universal characteristics of human minds and brains, so for example exploring how cognitive constraints in the development of agent concepts impact understanding of counterintuitive properties (e.g., Barrett & Richert 2003) or investigating the relationship between the religious rituals and brain function (see Schjødt, this volume). The second is to integrate models of the universal characteristics of religious cognition with models of individual variation. Whatever the universal constraints of human cognition and neurophysiology, it is individual differences in religious schemas that shape how religious cognition proceeds. Individual content and styles of processing develop within an individual's life history and can be investigated from multiple perspectives. A complete picture of religion cannot just account for the universals of religion or even for variation among religions, but must also be able to deal with individual differences among people. Why are some people more committed than others? Why are some people atheists? Why don't all Christians believe the same counterintuitive ideas? Psychologists are equipped to fill in the details at this alternative level of description.

Identifying Under-Supported Psychological Claims

Psychologists have a special perspective and training to offer the field for identifying suspect or under-supported claims. For instance, much has been made of agency detection as an important component in encouraging religious belief (e.g., Barrett 2004; Dennett 2006; Guthrie 1993). That a cognitive device that posits agency given ambiguous inputs may have a plausible evolutionary account behind it and its ability to reinforce the transmission of beliefs in spirits or ghosts (for instance) appears sensible. Nevertheless, to date, no experimental evidence exists in support of this agency detection device playing any role in religious belief formation or transmission, let alone the role that context effects might impact the relative sensitivity or accuracy of this device. These psychological questions require psychologists to answer them.

Similarly, the two most prominent theories of collective religious activities, Lawson and McCauley's ritual form theory and Whitehouse's Modes of Religiosity theory, both have at their core a number of psychological claims. For instance, Whitehouse (2004) claims that the high repetition and relatively low arousal characteristic of core rituals in the doctrinal mode (e.g., Catholic Mass) inhibit personal innovation in terms of the meanings of the ritual and increase a willingness to accept authoritative proclamations regarding orthodoxy. Certainly this is a psychological process being suggested. Do we have psychological evidence that this indeed happens? Similarly, McCauley and Lawson (2002) argue that the high sensory pageantry in what they term *special agent rituals* generates relatively high arousal and subsequent impressions that the god has really done something in the ritual. These, too, are psychological claims in search of psychological evidence.

The field is rife with such examples of under-supported psychological claims. Though non-psychologists may identify these evidential shortcomings, psychologists are specially trained both to identify and do something about them.

Methodological Tools

To successfully fill in the details, we need experimental methods and techniques that get beyond the explicit and normative sort of pronouncements about religious thought, feelings, and actions that characterize much anthropological, theological, and historical treatments of religion. While these approaches can be helpful in generating theories and models, testing the hypotheses that proceed requires us to turn to psychologists for help.

Psychologists investigating religion have traditionally relied on survey-based self-report measures. When reliable and valid, such instruments have proved their worth in the measurement of many religious dimensions (Hill 2005). Surveys are not without problem, however, and a significant limitation is their tendency to tap into propositional-level "theologically correct" representations rather than more everyday and automatic representations (e.g., Barrett & Keil 1996). A new approach to the investigation of religion that avoids this problem and many others associated with self-report measures is to adapt indirect or implicit measurement techniques from the social cognition and cognition and emotion literatures (Gibson 2006). These techniques typically involve measuring the speed or accuracy of participants in performing tasks and can thus allow inferences to be made about the underlying cognitive structures and processes involved. For example, techniques measuring judgment speed and memory biases in the processing of religious material seem not only to be sensitive to individual differences that self-report measures may not pick up, but also are able to tap into more automatic and affect-laden cognition (Gibson 2006). Other promising approaches so far include the measurement of inferences during narrative processing (Barrett & Keil 1996), manipulation of schema activation (Atran 2002), and subliminal priming (Birgegard & Granqvist 2004). Although we are unaware of any general review of these techniques, there are several helpful reviews of research using such procedures within cognitive, social, and clinical psychology (Eysenck & Keane 2005; Musch & Klauer 2003; Williams, Watts, MacLeod, & Mathews 1997).

Span the Chasm between Cognitive Science of Religion and Psychology of Religion

Another service psychologists could provide to the field is bringing insights from a related field—psychology of religion—into more direct contact with research in the evolutionary and cognitive sciences of religion. Despite the considerable overlap in focus between cognitive science of religion and psychology of religion, there is little dialogue between the two disciplines. Part of this has to do with training: the few psychologists involved in cognitive science of religion tend to be trained as developmental or cognitive psychologists, whereas psychologists of religion are more likely to be trained as clinical, personality, or social psychologists. A further issue is that psychology of religion is poorly institutionalized within psychology generally, so for some workers religion is more of a sideline than a principal research interest. As a consequence, psychologists of religion are in the main unaware of the rapid developments within cognitive science of religion over the last two decades. Going back the other way, cognitive scientists of religion can hardly be said to be unaware of psychology of religion, but there is also a lingering and unjustified suspicion that psychologists of religion are too personally involved in their faith to be able to investigate religion objectively. The following two examples of potential collaboration between the two disciplines illustrate the opportunities and benefits of increased dialogue and cross-fertilization of ideas between the two disciplines.

Religious Concepts and Pro-Social Behavior

Research in psychology of religion has had rather mixed results in documenting that specific religious beliefs generate particular pro-social or moral behaviors. Recently, psychologists working from a cognitive science of religion perspective have begun addressing anew the possibility that religious beliefs—even tacit ones—might encourage pro-social or reputation enhancing behaviors (see Shariff, this volume; and Lanman, this volume). Specifically, evidence is emerging suggesting that implicitly priming people with religious ideas or merely suggesting the possibility of a supernatural agent being present is enough to change behavior in a less self-serving direction. Numerous questions remain concerning just which religious ideas encourage pro-social behavior, how much commitment is required to these religious beliefs, and how robust the behavioral consequences are. Nevertheless, this area represents a potential meeting point between cognitive science of religion and more traditional psychology of religion.

Relationship between Divine Attributes and God Images

Psychologists of religion investigating representations of gods have tended to focus on the character of the Judeo-Christian God (for review see Moriarty & Hoffman 2007). As a consequence they have given little attention to the ways in which people think about the counterintuitive properties of gods or other supernatural agents. Cognitive scientists of religion, by contrast, have largely done the reverse, with questions regarding the representation and transmission of counterintuitive agent concepts taking center stage (Barrett 2000, 2004), but this without much consideration of how believers construe their relationship with God or gods (Gibson, this volume). The superposition of counterintuitive properties with human-like properties raises numerous questions for our understanding of how people relate to gods. For example, why do people still get angry at God for not preventing a tsunami if their automatic everyday representation of God's powers does not include the power to prevent the tsunami? Stated more generally, do ordinary attributional and attachment processes operate with an invisible agent whose behavior is rarely observed directly? Investigations that take seriously both types of attribute and their interaction could enrich theory in both disciplines.

Collaboratively Help Cross-Train

Perhaps the greatest asset psychologists could provide the evolutionary and cognitive sciences of religion is to help increase the number of experimentally and psychologically savvy scholars active in the field. In addition to providing solid training for students, this aim could be addressed by psychologists helping non-psychologists—particularly scholars from the humanities—learn how to construct, conduct, and consume empirical hypothesis tests. In our experiences, many religion scholars with backgrounds in the humanities are eager to have their theories and hypotheses empirically scrutinized. Indeed, this desire for testable, falsifiable theory-making in religion has been a formative impetus for the field. What these scholars often lack is a collaborator with similar interests *and* skills in taking theory and turning it into testable hypotheses using sound research designs.

Some of the most exciting work in this field has been conducted by scholars with just this kind of cross training across the humanities-psychological sciences divide, and typically acquired through collaboration. To illustrate, Scott Atran (2002) and Pascal Boyer (2001) are widely recognized as two leaders in this field. Both had formal training as anthropologists but both subsequently spent considerable time working in collaboration with psychologists.

Psychologists have a lot to give in these collaborative relationships that help humanities scholars cross-train, but they also have a lot to receive. In working closely with comparative religionists or anthropologists, psychologists gain deep exposure to much broader questions than psychologists typically consider. Further, psychologists may learn from their humanities colleagues rich case studies and contextual information that forces them to more rigorously consider the ecological validity of their research designs and the generalizability of their conclusions. Psychologists may not only offer cross-training (e.g., in experimental methods) but receive it, too.

Author's Note

This work was supported by grants from the John Templeton Foundation. Both authors contributed equally to this chapter. Correspondence concerning this chapter should be addressed to Nicholas Gibson, Psychology and Religion Research Group, Faculty of Divinity, West Road, Cambridge, CB3 9BS, UK, e-mail: njsjg2@hermes.cam.ac.uk, or to Justin Barrett, Centre for Anthropology and Mind, Institute of Social and Cultural Anthropology, 51 Banbury Road, Oxford, OX2 6PE, UK, e-mail: justin.barrett@anthro.ox.ac.uk.

References

Atran, S. 2002. *In gods we trust: The evolutionary landscape of religion.* Oxford, UK: Oxford University Press.

Barrett, J. L. 2000. Exploring the natural foundations of religion. *Trends in Cognitive Sciences, 4* (1), 29-34.

Barrett, J. L. 2004. *Why would anyone believe in God?* Oxford, UK: AltaMira Press.

Barrett, J. L., & Keil, F. C. 1996. Conceptualizing a nonnatural entity: Anthropomorphism in God concepts. *Cognitive Psychology, 31* (3), 219-247.

Barrett, J. L., & Richert, R. A. 2003. Anthropomorphism or preparedness? Exploring children's God concepts. *Review of Religious Research, 44* (3), 300-312.

Birgegard, A., & Granqvist, P. 2004. The correspondence between attachment to parents and God: Three experiments using subliminal separation cues. *Personality & Social Psychology Bulletin, 30* (9), 1122-1135.

Boyer, P. 2001. *Religion explained: Evolutionary origins of religious thought.* New York, NY: Basic Books.

Dennett, D. C. 2006. *Breaking the spell: Religion as a natural phenomenon.* New York, NY: Viking.

Eysenck, M. W., & Keane, M. T. 2005. *Cognitive psychology: A student's handbook,* 5th ed. Hove, England: Psychology Press.

Gibson, N. J. S. 2006. *The experimental investigation of religious cognition.* Unpublished doctoral dissertation, University of Cambridge, England. Retrieved March 1, 2007, from <http://www.divinity.cam.ac.uk/pcp/personnel/nicholas.html#PhD>

Guthrie, S. E. 1993. *Faces in the clouds: A new theory of religion.* Oxford, UK: Oxford University Press.

Hill, P. C. 2005. Measurement assessment and issues in the psychology of religion and spirituality. In R. F. Paloutzian & C. L. Park, Eds., *Handbook of the psychology of religion,* 43-79. New York, NY: Guilford Press.

McCauley, R. N., & Lawson, E. T. 2002. *Bringing ritual to mind: Psychological foundations of cultural forms.* Cambridge, UK: Cambridge University Press.

Moriarty, G. L., & Hoffman, L., Eds. 2007. *The God image handbook: Research, theory, and practice.* Binghamton, NY: Haworth Press.

Musch, J., & Klauer, K. C., Eds. 2003. *The psychology of evaluation: Affective processes in cognition and emotion.* Mahwah, NJ: Erlbaum.

Williams, J. M. G., Watts, F. N., MacLeod, C., & Mathews, A. 1997. *Cognitive psychology and emotional disorders,* 2nd ed. Chichester, England: John Wiley.

Whitehouse, H. 2004. *Modes of religiosity: A cognitive theory of religious transmission.* Walnut Creek, CA: AltaMira Press.

Does Talk about the Evolution of Religion Make Sense?

Donald Wiebe

Evolution and the Academic Study of Religion

Evolutionary theory has had a significant impact on the development of the academic study of religion for a very long time, as Jane Ellen Harrison's 1909 essay on "The Influence of Darwinism on the Study of Religions" (on the occasion of the fiftieth anniversary of the publication of *The Origin of Species*) attests. So much so did Harrison perceive this to be the case that she considered giving her essay the title "The Creation by Darwinism of the Scientific Study of Religion." Unlike the nineteenth century study of religion that revolved around either maintaining or refuting orthodoxy, evolutionary theory, she claimed, focused attention on how religious phenomena arose and developed. Thus she wrote: "To us nowadays it is a commonplace of anthropological research that we must seek for the beginning of religion in the religions of primitive peoples...." (Harrison 1909, 496).

Several decades later, in his *Comparative Religion: A History*, Eric Sharpe (1975/1986) echoed Harrison's claim, insisting that it was evolutionary theory that made the scientific study of religion possible. "Viewed in Darwinian perspective," he wrote, "religion became something which it had never been before. From being a body of revealed truth, it became a developing organism" (Sharpe 1975/1986, 48). In attempting "to deduce the development of spiritual culture by analogy from the development of material culture" (Sharpe 1975/1986, 54), Sharpe maintains that students of religion turned to "the observables of religion" (Sharpe 1975/1986, 72) which improved the study of religion by providing it a focus located "not in transcendental philosophy, but in ... this-worldly categories of history, progress, development, and evolution" (Sharpe 1975/1986, 24). And according to Sharpe, by the 1890s, evolution was not simply a theory but an "atmosphere" whose value "as a principle of classification was hardly questioned" (Sharpe 1975/1986, 89).

Nevertheless, Sharpe also claimed that by the mid-twentieth century, evolutionary theory was seriously challenged on ethical, socio-political, and scholarly grounds, so that even though, as Sharpe put it, "[e]volutionary optimism did not immediately disappear—it captured fewer imaginations," and younger scholars in the field tended to specialize, "engaging in close and detailed studies in a limited area rather than on vast comparisons and synthetic pattern-making" (Sharpe 1975/1986, 174). Sharpe therefore claimed that twentieth-century scholars of religion, particularly after the second World War, abandoned evolutionary theory and focused their attention on particular religious traditions and special themes within them rather than take up questions about religion-as-such. In recent decades, however, and inspired by the emergence of the new discipline of evolutionary psychology, attention has once more shifted, and scholars in the field have again turned to the theory of evolution to make sense of religion. Pascal Boyer's *Religion Explained: The Evolutionary Origins of Religious Thought* (2001) and David Sloan Wilson's *Darwin's Cathedral: Evolution, Religion, and the Nature of Society* (2002) are perhaps the best examples of this development in the field.

What becomes clear to anyone who ventures into the literature describing the birth and growth of Religious Studies as an academic/scientific enterprise is that for all its influence in the field, there never was a broadly accepted, mainstream view on what the "evolution of religion" amounted to. Nor do I think such a mainstream view of the notion exists today, although, as I hope to show, the view of it today is clearly different from what it was in the nineteenth and early twentieth centuries. The differences in conceptions of the nature of religion, however, obviously create considerable ambiguity as to what precisely it is that is evolving. And differences of opinion about the level or levels on which evolution occurs simply compounds the ambiguity that afflicts the notion.

Despite these difficulties, it is clear that the notion has made sense to many in the field; however, whether it made "scientific" sense in the past, or makes "scientific" sense in the present, is, I think, open to question. It is not possible here to rehearse the whole history of the role this notion has played in Religious Studies in an effort to resolve that matter. I hope, however, to be able to shed some light on that issue by briefly looking at some of the meanings of the phrase "the evolution of religion" in the early scientific study of religion before turning to the dominant views among contemporary students of religion.

The Evolution of Religion: Divergent Views

Although nineteenth-century students of religion were committed to the development of a scientific approach to the study of religions and religion, many were at the same time religiously motivated people and often tended to read "the evolution of religion" as meaning "religious evolution." C. P. Tiele, one of the founding figures of the scientific study of religion, in his two volume Gifford Lectures entitled *Elements of the Science of Religion* (1897), for example, talks about "religion itself" being entirely independent of the forms in which it appears (Tiele 1897, II 222) and maintains that we may be sure that changes in the outward forms of religion "have been preceded by an inward change which we may define as religious development" (Tiele 1897, II, 38). For him, therefore, the evolution of religion refers essentially to such growth or maturation in religiosity which is envisioned as taking place both at the level of the individual and society. Thus, writes Tiele, "[t]he development of religion is. . .the labour of the human mind to create more perfect forms for the ever growing wants of the religious soul" (Tiele 1897, II 149); and regarding religion and society, he maintains "that religion, as distinguished from the forms its assumes, is constantly developed in mankind, [and its] development may be described as the evolution of *the religious idea* in history, or better, as the progress of the religious man, or of mankind as religious by nature" (Tiele 1897, II 32, emphasis added).

The central idea of "the evolution of religion" in this framework, quite obviously then, is teleological and normative; a matter of personal or societal growth from a primitive to a more perfect form of religious life, where religious needs become more refined and lofty, purer and more worthy; involving a spiritual progress governed by principles neither historical nor mechanical. The use of the theory of evolution here, therefore, seems essentially an attempt to assimilate Darwinism, as Theodore Rozak pointed out, to a spiritual world view in which "evolution becomes the essential context of religion [that is, religion-as-such] in a universe that is seen as a drama of progressively unfolding consciousness" (Rozak 1987, 210).

Closely related to such a view is that which focuses attention on the historical development of particular religious traditions after "religion" first appears as an element in the repertoire of human behaviors. Late nineteenth- and early twentieth-century anthropologists and students of religion, that is, attempted to find an evolutionary pattern among the world's early (primitive or archaic) religious traditions that indicated stages or gradations in a progressive social development. Such socio-cultural evolutionists (for example, E. B. Tylor and J. G. Frazer), it seems, assumed that cultural phenomena were like the elements of the natural world and that it should be possible, therefore, to show that human groups are, objectively speaking, ordered in a hierarchical fashion.

E. E. Evans-Pritchard, however, found such progressivist assumptions highly questionable, having at best, the status of vague hypotheses (Evans-Pritchard 1965, 29). And Ernest Gellner refers to this kind of evolutionary approach to understanding culture and religion as "evolutionism," which he sees as more than simply another theory. As he puts it: "it was a philosophy, a theodicy, a moral vision, a surrogate for religion." These theorists "saw in evolution and progress the key notions in which human life was to be interpreted, and human suffering justified; these notions did not merely explain, they conferred moral meaning and order on the world" (Gellner 1981, xviii).

.....

Contemporary scholars of religion have not abandoned such vague spiritual and metaphysical conceptions of evolution and evolutionism because they are necessarily nonsensical, but rather because they are not primarily concerned with, or exclusively directed to, finding an empirically testable scientific explanation of religion (and religions). Like their forbears, however, they also assume the universal (or near universal) presence of religion in all human societies, but they invoke evolutionary theory in a more strictly scientific—biological—sense in their explanations; they refuse, that is, both metaphysical expansion of the term and metaphorical application of it. For them, religion is in some sense or other a *product* (an adaptation or exaptation) or by-product of the evolutionary development of *Homo sapiens* (individually or collectively) and they seek both an ultimate (in the evolutionary biological, not existential, sense) and proximate (in the causal mechanistic sense) explanation of religion.

Vernon Reynolds and Ralph Tanner (1985), for example, claim there is significant evidence in favor of the hypothesis that religious behavior is an adaptive mechanism at the individual level of behavior, while David Sloan Wilson (2002) makes a similar claim about religion's adaptive benefit at the level of group selection. As Reynolds and Tanner put it: "There are a great many. . .ways in which religious rules affect both survival and reproduction. The difficulty is, of course, in finding a theory that will account for their diversity. Certainly the concept of adaptiveness should not be rejected until it has been thoroughly explored, and there is every reason to test the hypothesis that, where religions touch on the basic processes of human biology, they say things that make adaptive sense now or that have made adaptive sense in the past" (Reynolds & Tanner 1985, 142).

David Wilson, on the other hand, writes: "Evolutionary biology is settling into a middle position that acknowledges the potential for adaptation and natural selection at all levels of the biological hierarchy, especially in the case of human evolution. Group-level adaptation is here to stay in evolutionary biology, and the human social sciences must follow suit to remain true to first principles" (Wilson 2002, 85); and, he continues: "Moral systems provide many of the mechanisms that enable human groups to function as adaptive units. Moral systems include both an innate psychological component and an open-ended cultural component that enables groups to adapt to their recent environments. Belief in supernatural agents and other elements that are associated with religion *can play* an important role in the structure and function of moral communities" (Wilson 2002, 46, emphasis added). According to Richard Dawkins (2006), however, religion is neither a biological adaptation nor exaptation but rather a mere spandrel—a by-product—and therefore of no direct survival value. Indeed, not only is it of no survival value, it is, for Dawkins, a detrimental by-product of the failure of the design properties of the organism with which it is associated, namely, brain "modules" that emerged for dealing with, for example, kinship, reciprocal exchange behavior, forming coalitions, and so on (Dawkins 2006, 179).

Dawkins, nevertheless, acknowledges that because religion is ubiquitous, it is probably the case that it has worked to "someone's" benefit, although he is fairly sure that it was neither us nor our genes that received the benefit. Pushing the biological envelope, he suggests that perhaps the benefit accrues to the meme or memeplex of religion itself. As he puts it: "It may be to the benefit of only the religious ideas themselves" (Dawkins 2006, 165).

Problems for Contemporary Theories of the Evolution of Religion

Despite the appearance of greater scientific cogency in the evolutionary theories of religion presented by contemporary scholars, those theories appear to involve commitments to problematic assumptions, and weakness of argument that threaten the scientific payoff they promise for the student of religion. I set out here some of the criticisms others have raised in these respects; they need serious attention, but may not in the final analysis, constitute knock-down arguments against the search for a purely evolutionary account of what is commonly referred to as religion.

At a very general level, I mention here the concern raised by Mario Bunge over the uncritical commitment to adaptationist theory by those who employ evolutionary psychology as an appropriate framework of analysis. Bunge considers adaptationist theory problematic because it allows one to prove that almost anything is the product of selective pressures in the environment because it is so easy to provide "just so" stories about the origin of particular capacities and skills possessed by us. Thus, for him, evolutionary psychology, on which much talk of the evolution of religion rests, seems an "unborn science of the evolution of cognitive abilities and strategies." As he puts it, "evolutionary psychology is a speculative exercise inspired by "the misreading of biological evolution. . ." (Bunge 1999, 85). Mark Blumberg (2005) in *Basic Instinct: The Genesis of Human Behavior*, raises similar concerns and provides empirical evidence to show that what often passes for "real mechanisms" turn out to be merely imaginary neural modules.

Philosopher Paul Thagard (2005) raises a further significant problem with respect to the evolutionary psychological framework assumed by such explanations of religion in an interesting little essay on "The Emotional Coherence of Religion", namely, that of establishing the character of the selective pressures of what such theorists call the Evolutionary Environment of Adaptation. As he puts it: "We know little about the psychological origins of religion in preliterate cultures. . . [and given] how little is known about the early biological or social development of our species, the dependency relation is so speculative that it is best to say that evolutionary biology has little current role to play in the explanation of the prevalence and nature of religion" (Thagard 2005, 71). Religion may be a psychological or social universal and this certainly constitutes a pressure on scholars to seek for its biological causes, yet we know too little about our deep ancestral heritage, claims Thagard, to draw any conclusive claims.

Another major problem with such evolutionary theories concerns the nature of religion; just what it is that evolved or is evolving has never been clearly delineated. As Lee Kirkpatrick (2005), a psychologist who finds the evolutionary framework attractive, points out in *Attachment, Evolution, and the Psychology of Religion*, "religion" refers to so diverse a range of phenomena that it is not at all clear "how a single well-defined mechanism could possibly explain it all" (Kirkpatrick 2005, 230). He writes: "[Given] the domain-specificity argument in its modern form, in which highly specific mechanisms are designed to solve highly specific adaptive problems, the idea that a single religion mechanism underlies all religious phenomena seems patently untenable" (Kirkpatrick 2005, 230). "It is difficult to imagine," he continues, "how religious belief or experience can be considered an economical, efficient solution to any particular adaptive problem" (Kirkpatrick 2005, 231).

Nor are these the only problems to be considered. Paul Thagard, for example, points out that religion in post-civilizational cultures is not universal and that this, therefore, constitutes a significant anomaly to such theorizing; that is, being "deficient in religiosity," as he puts it, "does not seem, at least in the current world environment, to impede the ability of people to survive and reproduce" (Thagard 2005, 70). He also claims, moreover, that for those who claim that evolution takes place only at the level of genes, there is simply no evidence in support of the evolution of religion, for, as he puts it, there "are no known brain areas dedicated specifically to religious beliefs and practices, and no animal precursors of these areas" (Thagar 2005, 70).

Conclusion

These brief comments on the use to which contemporary scholars of religion put evolutionary theory, I think, reveal considerable improvement on the scientific aspirations of their nineteenth- and early twentieth-century predecessors. Contemporary scholars for, the most part, no longer conceive religion to be a fundamentally spiritual reality whose development can only be properly understood in terms of the normative language of "religious evolution." This kind of understanding of science makes a kind of philosophical, metaphysical, or religious sense but its results lie beyond scientific knowledge. Nevertheless, it is also apparent that all is not well in the current evolutionary theorizing of religion. That patterns of religious behavior might well effect both survival and reproduction at the level of the individual clearly makes sense, and is a claim that is open to falsification and should, therefore, be tested, as Tanner and Reynolds maintain. However, current adaptationist thinking in biology and evolutionary psychology (at the level of the individual organism) seems immune to such testing given the fact that it permits the free creation of imaginary adaptations (and neural modules) to account for them in place of seeking the real mechanisms essential to such explanation. Nor is Wilson's theorizing of religion at the group level of any greater benefit to the scientific student of religion since evolution at the group level tells us of the value of any coherent ideology to such groups, but nothing about the peculiar aspects of religion as one type of ideology. Wilson's suggestions that religions are peculiar super-organisms that are subject to evolution, therefore, is misleading; indeed, it seems to disengage "religion" (religion-as-such?) as an object of evolution from the scientifically legitimate discussion of the value of any ideology that provides group cohesiveness that might thereby generate adaptive benefits at both the group level and that of the individual organism. Within this framework of analysis, then, "religion" is not necessary for group selection to take place, and Wilson's theory of religion, therefore, tells us nothing specific about the role of religion in group selection, but only about the role of ideology in general in that process.

Evolutionary theory in the study of religion, then, can, it seems, deliver a scientific payoff. The inadequacies of current theorizing in the field, however, and our inability to come to a consensus (or anything close to a consensus) on the nature of religion constitute serious impediments to the prospect, but I do not think them insuperable. Resolution of the theoretical inadequacies, in my judgment, rests on recognizing, first, the irrelevance of group selection in accounting for the peculiar character of religious ideologies, and recognition (at the level of the evolution of the individual) that genes and brains alone cannot fully account for human behavior; that genes and brains constitute constraints on human behavior but are not sufficient to explain fully that behavior. Human actions, that is, are not simply physical movements but, rather, intentionally directed and socially meaningful behavior that, even though biologically embodied, requires a social-psychological rather than a merely biological or psycho-biological explanation. As for the "definitional problem": I think this can be overcome by delineating that range of overt human behavior of interest to us as students of religion, which is available to objective examination and analysis, and that is clearly differentiated from human behaviors that are the primary focus of attention of other natural and social sciences. Individual and collective human behavior that is intimately connected to/with, or depends upon, belief in (culturally postulated) superhuman agents/beings (powers or states), I think, fills that bill.

Achieving consensus on the nature of the theoretical problems raised above, and on the definitional problem as "outlined" here, will make it possible, I suggest, to make scientific sense of our talk about "the evolution of religion" without entanglement in matters of "religious evolution."

References

Blumberg, M. S. 2005. *Basic instinct: The genesis of behavior*. New York, NY: Thunder's Mouth Press.

Bunge, M. 1999. Evolutionary psychology. In M. Bunge, Ed., *Dictionary of philosophy*, p. 85. New York, NY: Prometheus Books.

Boyer, P. 2001. *Religion explained: The evolutionary origins of religious thought*. New York, NY: Basic Books.

Dawkins, R. 2006. *The God delusion*. New York, NY: Houghton Mifflin

Evans-Pritchard, E. E. 1965. *Theories of primitive religion*. Oxford, UK: Oxford University Press.

Gellner, E. 1981. Introduction. In A. Singer, Ed., *A history of anthropological thought: Sir Edward Evans-Prichard*, pp. xiii-xxxvi. New York, NY: Basic Books.

Harrison, J. E. 1909. The influence of Darwinism on the study of religion. In A. C. Seward, Ed., *Darwin and modern science: Essays in commemoration of the centenary of the birth of Charles Darwin and of the fiftieth anniversary of the publication of the origin of species*, 494-511. Cambridge, UK: Cambridge University Press.

Kirkpatrick, L. 2005. *Attachment, evolution, and the psychology of religion*. New York, NY: The Guilford Press.

Reynolds, V., & Tanner, R. 1985. The effects of religion on human biology. In J. Durant, Ed., *Darwinism and divinity*, 131-153. Oxford, UK: Basil Blackwell.

Rozak, T. 1987. Evolutionism. In M. Eliade Ed., *Encyclopedia of religion* Vol. 5, pp. 208-214. New York, NY: Macmillan Publishing Company.

Sharpe, E. J. 1986. Comparative Religion: A History. London: Duckworth Press. Original work published 1975.

Thagard, P. 2005. The emotional coherence of religion. *Journal of Cognition & Culture, 5*, 58-74.

Tiele, C. P. 1897. *Elements of the science of religion* 2 volumes. Edinburgh, Scotland: William Balckwood and Sons.

Wilson, D. S. 2002. *Darwin's cathedral: Evolution, religion, and the nature of society*. Chicago, IL: University of Chicago Press.

PART VIII

Philosophical and Theological Themes

Can Religion Really Evolve? (And What Is It Anyway?)

Luther H. Martin

Proposals for employing a Darwinian account of religion as a product of natural selection are not new. Already in 1882, the Dublin anatomist Alexander Macalister (1882) gave a lecture on "evolution in church history" in which he explicated ways in which ritual and organizational "variation" might be explained as adaptations to environment (35). Subsequently, proposals have been made for understanding the evolution of the "mental capacities" for religious ideas and practice (Harrison 1909, 497-498); for the evolution of religious groups themselves (Wilson 2002) and even for religion itself (Richerson & Boyd 2005)—all employing a Darwinian model.

The methodological issue raised by these proposals is whether they are to be understood as isomorphic with or analogous to Darwinian theory. If isomorphic, the appropriateness of applying a theory developed to explain the data of one domain, organic speciation, to those of another, the behavioral and ideational productions of a single species, must be raised. If analogical, the question remains of whether any "useful work is done by substituting the metaphor of evolution for history" (Fracchia & Lewontin 1999, 78)? And whether this application be understood as isomorphic with or analogous to Darwinian theory, what, precisely, are the data to be explained?

Does "religion" really evolve?

Those outside the area of religious studies seem to have little problem discussing the pros and cons of its evolution. To those within the field of religious studies, however, discussions about the evolution of religion seem curiously quaint since scholars in that academic field, over its one-hundred-plus years of existence, have yet to produce anything resembling a consensual definition of *religion* or even of *religions*—apart from their own, of course (à la Macalister, 1882). This is because, as some historians of religion now insist, "religion" is a Western academic (and political) category and not a "natural kind" with any independent existence that might be presumed to have evolved (Smith 1982, xi).

Do religious "groups" evolve?

Some scholars wish to argue more specifically that it is not religions themselves but religious groups that evolve. However, neither the internal coherence of any social formation nor the definition of its boundaries would seem to be sufficiently stable over time to conclude that they could function as adaptive units which might evolve in ways that are either isomorphic with or analogous to biological species. Joseph Bulbulia (2006), nevertheless, contends that religious groups are adaptive because they reduce "the cognitive load of social living" through "co-operative norm-reinforcement" (25). However, alternative social formations perform the same function. That is to say, "co-operative norm-reinforcement" is instantiated not only by religious coalitions but, for example, by adherence to the rules in various sports or by the carefully observed conventions of swingers' clubs. But no one has argued that any of these groups represent an evolutionary adaptation—especially the latter. That "religions" (if I too may beg the categorical question) support group solidarity—at least among their own members—is an observation that is, in other words, true but trivial since any number of other social formations may, and do, contribute also to social solidarity. Such considerations invariably slide, in other words, into an affirmation of the assumed category on the basis of correlate functions.

Some would extend evolutionary explanations even to the development of large-scale cooperation among non-kin (Richerson & Boyd 2005, 203-236). Such cooperation can, however, be explained more parsimoniously by political history, in which, for example, one small-scale society may find it expedient to cooperate with another in competition with a third for, for example, resources insufficient to support all parties. Typically, these negotiations were concluded by strategies, such as an intermarriage, that allowed all members of the new alliance to be represented as trusted kin. Such sociopolitical intrigues were, of course, characteristic of much European feudal history.

A remarkable theoretical account of an alliance between groups of non-kin is preserved in Hebrew epic, whatever one concludes about its facticity. According to this epic, a federation was negotiated by a number of Middle Eastern Bedouin tribes to compete with neighboring tribes for the "milk and honey", i.e., the scarce resources, of their rather barren environment (Ex. 3; 13; 23; 33-34). The basis often given for the "solidarity" of this alliance is religious, i.e., their collective faith in a single deity. Rather, the success of this epic endeavor was made possible by their construction of a descent myth identifying these disparate groups as being "in fact" descendents of a common ancestor (Gen. 12-25). It was this *ex post facto* "discovery" of common kinship that allowed the gods of the previously autonomous tribes to be re-represented as aspects of a single deity in the first place rather than any acceptance of a single deity providing a basis for the federation. Thus, even if we accept the argument that groups, large or small, evolve by adaptation—a plausible position which should not simply be dismissed (Wilson 2002, 12-25)—these arguments tells us nothing about "religion" itself unless the claimed adaptations can be shown to be dependent upon at least one of its distinctive aspects.

Do aspects of "religion" evolve?

Recognizing that there is no such "thing" as religion, many advocates of evolutionary views of religion now consider religion a multifaceted reality to be "fractionated" or dissected into its constitutive behaviors, ideas, or traits, each of which has (or may have) its own evolutionary (or adaptive) history (à la Harrison 1909) (Bering 2005, 412; Bulbulia 2005, 36). But you can't carve up a turkey without having a bird and since religion is not a natural thing to dissect, evolutionary discussions of its aspects seem rather quickly to digress into those of a presumed category.

One of the traits most commonly associated with religion is, for example, morality. The relationship of moral behavior to religion is, however, a non-necessary historical contingency, as the non-theistic legitimization of ethics in ancient Greece and Rome or in Confucian China exemplify. Rather, views of a symbiosis between morality and religion are largely a legacy of the Judeo-Christian tradition and its modern colonial hegemony. Such ethnocentric biases in the study of religion—well documented by scholars of comparative religions—present a potential problem for evolutionary psychologists and cognitive scientists in stipulating the theoretical object for their evolutionary considerations or in their experimental designs (Brown 1999, 154).

Similarly some experimental psychologists have shown that many of the traits typically associated with religion—teleological reasoning, for example, or inferences about an afterlife—are natural expressions of ordinary cognitive capacities that can be elicited experimentally under laboratory conditions. This *a*religious incidence of such traits characterizes, of course, all such evidence adduced experimentally and would seem to present a confound for those who argue an adaptive story for aspects of "religion." In other words, those human traits often taken to be religious are, in fact, ordinary expressions of human cognitive capacities. Unless a necessary or dedicated relationship can be established between such capacities and the target category, nothing has been discovered about the evolution of—or anything else about—"religion".

So what then is religion?

Rather than "top-down" approaches to the question of the evolution of religion that assume the category and that, consequently, privilege its various contents, what would seem to be required is a theoretical stipulation of the necessary characteristic(s) of what is *not* to be considered religious and a "bottom-up" study of whether or not such a differentiating characteristic(s) is indeed an evolved human trait. This is not to propose any kind of essentializing definition for religion but simply an attempt to discern what makes "religion" a distinctive (and predicative) category at all—no matter how "fuzzy" its boundaries. Daniel Dennett (2006) counseled that the starting point for such a consideration might initially be based on "common sense and tradition" (8)—though I might suggest that the insights from the comparative study of religion might better inform such initial inquiries. Whatever else might differentiate the religious from the non-religious, *claims to the authority of superhuman agency that recruit and legitimate otherwise ordinary human behaviors and ideas and that motivate their practice and perseverance* would seem to characterize all religions. The question of the "evolution of religion" would seem, therefore, to turn, at the outset, on that of the adaptive efficacy of representations of superhuman agents and on the acceptance of at least some of these representations as authoritative.

As a number of cognitive scientists have argued, the human brain easily and readily produces representations of superhuman, that is, potentially powerful, non-human agents (Boyer 2001)—from fairies, trolls, and leprechauns to the imaginary friends of young children and even to those of adults, as poignantly portrayed by Jimmy Stewart's 6 foot, 3½ inch invisible rabbit companion in the 1950 film *Harvey*. This ready representation of agency is likely an adaptive response "from the wild" in which survival would depend upon quick identification, on the basis of ambiguous perceptual input, of possible agents in the environment as either friend or foe, predator or protein. Such a response can still be noted, for example, in the common reactive representations of a stick, semi-concealed in the high grass, as a potentially dangerous serpent, even though poisonous snakes may well be known to be absent from the present environment. Selection for such a survivalistic response has resulted in a cognitive bias towards identifying agency even where there is none—as in the suggestive formations of clouds, on the surface features of the moon, or in the lonely shadows of the night.

Although representations of non-human agents by *H. sapiens* seem to be "natural", not all such "naturally" represented agents become re-represented as superhuman beings that might authorize or motivate shared behaviors and ideas. It would seem, consequently, as though "religion" might best be understood as exploitations of such naturally produced representations of agency and their postulation as authoritative in the service of sociopolitical interests. Because of the universal human bias towards the representation of agency, such "religious" authority, once postulated, could readily be accepted, transmitted and developed—along with, of course, the social structures and values thereby legitimated.

While it is undeniable that human beings have evolved capacities for producing culture, including those behaviors and representations typically associated by scholars with religion, it does not follow that religions are themselves adaptive simply because they exist nor that changes in religious traditions over time are evolutionary. Rather, most cognitive scientists have concluded that religion is "not an evolutionary adaptation per se, but a recurring cultural by-product of the complex evolutionary landscape that set cognitive, emotional, and material conditions for ordinary human interactions" (Atran & Norenzayan 2004, 713). The persistence into the modern world of the counterintuitive—even maladaptive—by-products that are characteristic of religious behaviors and ideas would seem to provide yet another confound for those who would argue that religion (or culture) itself is an ongoing adaptive process.

Conclusion

I should like to emphasize that views of religions as evolutionary epiphenomena in no way minimize the impact they have had—and continue to have—for human societies. In fact, an understanding of religion as a strategic exploitation of evolved human capacities and behaviors in service of historically contingent social interests may offer a better explanation for its benevolent as well as its malevolent uses throughout human history than do such arguments for religions as manifestations of some *sui generis* spiritual trait of *Homo religiosus* (Eliade 1969, 9). It might be asked, consequently, what evolutionary theory might contribute to the work of the historian *qua* historian. As Richerson and Boyd (2005) rightly concluded, "well-studied models and well-tested empirical generalizations", such as those supplied by evolutionary theory, can be of value for the work of historians, not only because of "the complexity of the problems" (248) to be solved but also—I might add—because of the fragmented, incomplete, and pre-interpreted evidence with which the historian is confronted. The problem of historians, in other words, is less one of complexity than of deficiency, that is, of how best to connect the insufficient dots of surviving historical materials in order to provide inferences to the best representations of the past.

The historian John Bury (1909) has argued that while general principles may embody the necessary conditions for any particular sequence, they do not provide sufficient conditions, either in biology or in history (539). And the anthropologist Donald Brown (1999) has cautioned that an "attention to particulars" is required if the influence of evolution for human affairs is not simply to become a "vacuous truism" (155). What is required, then, are well-tested theories that might inform and constrain while not imposing upon historiographical method. Even as the historical sciences employ constraining theories for dealing with the complexities and incomplete records of their data—astrophysics in cosmology, for example, or plate tectonics in geology (Edelman 2006, 80-88)—evolutionary theory can constrain the proximate as well as general explanations of historians. But the courses of human history can—and do—fluctuate widely within these constraints. The multiple variables governing the complexity of historical developments cannot, in other words, be explained in terms of biological generalization nor should any one theory—no matter how powerful for its target domain—be expected to explain, or even provide an analogy for, everything. Attempts to explain the histories of religion in terms of Darwinian evolutionary theory, whether isomorphically or by analogy, not only create semantic and theoretical ambiguities but they prove finally to be inadequate.

References

Atran, S., & Norenzayan, A 2004. Religion's evolutionary landscape. *Behavioral & Brain Sciences, 27* (6), 713-730.

Bering, J. 2005. The evolutionary history of an illusion. In B. J. Ellis & D. F. Bjorklund, Eds., *Origins of the social mind,* 411-437. New York, NY: Guilford Press.

Boyer, P. 2001. *Religion explained.* New York, NY: Basic Books.

Brown, D. E. 1999. Human nature and history. *History & Theory, 38* (4), 138-157.

Bulbulia, J. 2005. Are there any religions? An evolutionary exploration. *Method & Theory in the Study of Religion, 17,* 71-100.

Bulbulia, J. 2006. Meme infection or religious niche construction? An adaptationist alternative to the cultural maladaptationist hypothesis. Manuscript submitted for publication.

Bury, J. B. 1909. Darwinism and history. In A. C. Seward, Ed., *Darwin and modern science,* 529-542. Cambridge, England: Cambridge University.

Dennett, D. 2006. *Breaking the spell.* New York, NY: Viking.

Edelman, G. M. 2006. *Second nature.* New Haven, CT: Yale University Press.

Eliade, M. 1969. *The quest.* Chicago, IL: University of Chicago Press.

Fracchia, J., & Lewontin, R. C. 1999. Does culture evolve? *History & Theory, 38* (4), 52-78.

Harrison, J. E. 1909. The influence of Darwinism on the study of religions. In A. C. Seward, Ed., *Darwin and modern science, 494-511.* Cambridge, England: Cambridge University Press.

Macalister, A. 1882. *Evolution in church history*. Dublin, Ireland: Hodges, Figgis.
Richerson, P. L., & Boyd, R. 2005. *Not by genes alone; How culture transformed human evolution*. Chicago, IL: University of Chicago Press.
Smith, J. Z. 1982. *Imagining religion*. Chicago, IL: University of Chicago Press.
Wilson, D. S. 2002. *Darwin's cathedral*. Chicago, IL: University of Chicago Press.

How Sartre Inadvertently Presaged a Proper Evolutionary Science of Religion

Jesse M. Bering

Once a leading intellectual paradigm for thinking about human nature, the philosophical doctrine of *atheistic existentialism* has all but disappeared from contemporary discourse on this topic. Whether or not contemporary scholars view its absence as a lamentable one is debatable, but with modern cognitive science increasingly recapitulating its principal tenets—mostly by accident—it deserves to be revisited by empirical researchers (see also Koole, Greenberg, & Pyszczynski 2006).

An unfortunate history of misapplying the term existentialism has rendered it difficult to repair in a technical sense; the term has been colloquialized to such an extent that its original usage, as applied by specialists, is all but lost to the diluting influences of popular culture. It is today associated with a host of loosely connected ideas linking mortality, meaning, and existence, so that grasping the general notion of an 'existential crisis' requires no special training in the philosophy behind these mundane expressions. Even Jean-Paul Sartre (1946/1956b), in his day, sought to rescue the term from common affectation. In seeking to discipline existentialism as a modern scientific endeavor, however, what is central is its offering of ideas that are significant within the present context and its ability to further our understanding of human cognitive evolution (Bering 2006).

Teleo-Functional Reasoning About Human Beings

Although Heidegger's work is often cited as the first formal approach in this area, it is arguably Sartre whose existential philosophy and literature is the most compatible with recent psychological research. Throughout most of his earlier writings, Sartre refers to the human predisposition for teleo-functional thought, arguing that God is commonly viewed as a superior artisan who first held a concept of man and then created him, just as the manufacturer of a paper-cutter conceives of the artifact in his mind and then creates it for this purpose. His notorious turn of phrase "existence precedes essence" rejects this idea, stating that human beings do not exist 'for' any essential purpose but simply are. Without God, we are forced to choose our own *raison d'être*; there is no intelligent designer who made us with a specific function in mind. We simply exist, and absurdly so, since we are here for no more reason than the condensation that has formed on a glass of water.

Recent evidence nonetheless suggests that this view of human life being without an essential purpose may also be deeply counterintuitive to human psychology. For example, preschoolers prefer to see rocks, clouds, and animals as being 'for' something rather than just existing and, even in adults, escaping this default bias requires scientific knowledge (Kelemen 2004). Most theorists have interpreted such data as reflecting an intentionality heuristic; that is, all else equal, people begin their reasoning about an object's origins in terms of the creative intentions of a mind that designed this object for a purpose. This heuristic may be revised by more parsimonious theories that are able to account for origins without invoking intentionality—in the case of biological organisms, the theory of natural selection—but such revisions require explicit teaching. Thus, children are said to be "intuitive theists" not in the sense of a religious belief system, but in the sense of the psychological processes seamlessly lending themselves to attributions of intelligent design.

Me, By God

Many of the images from Sartre's *Nauseé* (1938/1964) anticipate research by cognitive scientists exploring how *essentialist reasoning* influences people's folk beliefs about natural category membership (e.g., Atran 1995). Our perceptions of objects in the world are meaningfully based on our knowledge of these objects' hidden properties, many of which have to do with their functions. Thus, in *Nauseé*, the protagonist soliloquizes on the presence of a giant root from a chestnut tree growing near his park bench, which by losing its perceived function in the narrator's mind simultaneously loses its identity. ("I saw clearly that you could not pass from its function as a root, as a breathing pump, *to that*, to this compact skin of a sea lion, to this oily, callous, headstrong look," 129.)

Apply this type of reasoning to the individual person, who is supposed to behave and think a certain way because it is his 'job' as a human being to do so, and therein lays the heart of existential absurdity. Moreover, the individual person is often believed to have an essential purpose (e.g., "I feel I was born to be a teacher") that is separate from the essential purpose of the abstract category to which he belongs (e.g., "I believe people are here to love each other"). Reasoning in non-intentional (i.e., naturalistic) terms about one's individual existence does not give any such credence to the possibility of an essential purpose of the self (Bering 2006). Destiny, where life "comes at" the person in codes and symbols hidden behind life events, means that a man must spend a lifetime making sense of God's intentions for his existence. If I speak of "finding myself," it implies a self that I am *meant* to be, if only it could be seen through all the disorienting mist of such codes and symbols. Therefore, one becomes a detective in his own life story, watching as his own essential purpose clarifies and reveals itself in an unending succession of events. Without God, this changes: Life happens and that is all. Intentionality recedes to the surface.

The evolutionary theorist may say that human beings exist in order to genetically reproduce—that this is in fact their purpose just as the purpose of the root from Sartre's chestnut tree is to serve as a 'breathing pump' for the whole organism. Yet to argue that this *particular* root has a purpose that is different from all other roots is the same as arguing that a *particular* person has a purpose that is different from all other people.

Consider an evolutionary botanist studying a dense forest of trees, all of which are representatives of the exact same genera and species. This scientist has a curious theory regarding this type of tree, one in which each tree in the forest—say, this one standing over here versus that one next to it versus that one in the copse farther away, and so on—was designed by nature to have a function distinct from that of all of the other trees in this forest. "This specific tree is designed to do this," he might say, "whereas that one is designed to do this other thing." In a forest of tens of thousands of trees, natural selection has seemingly designed each one to perform a function that is distinct from that of every other tree. As evidence for his theory, the scientist points out that each tree is growing in a specific place, receives different amounts of patterned sunlight on its leaves, and different amounts of precipitation on the basis of its exposure. "How can this be a coincidence?" he asks. "Obviously these events are related to its purpose, and it is our task to determine this purpose." In this sense we might say that each tree is here in the forest for a reason even though it is not intelligently designed; the reason reveals itself through its 'biographical' experiences. "Ah, I see now!" he might shout upon observing a particular tree breaking the fall of another. "So that's why nature made this tree!"

This botanist would, of course, be the laughing stock of all. And yet is this not how most people reason about the purpose of each individual man, about the whole of his unique existence? If one of the trees in the forest were to die before its hypothesized function was met, this scientist would say that it died "too soon" just as the death of a young person might prompt a chorus of the same verse from the members of a family in mourning. (Or indeed that its death was, as it were, its designed function in relation to others' unique design.) In the case of the tree, it is absurd because such uniqueness is fundamentally incompatible with evolutionary theory: adaptations do not occur at the species level, and certainly not at the level of the individual organism.

The implication here is that, from both an evolutionary and an existential perspective, the individual person is appropriately classified in the same manner as the individual tree; it is strange to say that either has an essential purpose that can be uncovered by studying the events to which it is subjected.

Cognitive scientists have shown little interest so far in determining why human existence is seen through such a special lens; one that, when held over other natural categories such as trees, immediately strikes both scientist and layperson as absurd. One might counter that not all people reason this way. But this is to get lost in debate about the nature of belief. We can say, however, that if the atheist's private psychology truly reflected his propositional beliefs about the non-existence of God, he would feel absolutely no private sense of 'why me?' when he is told that he will die within the month from an aggressive disease. If this violates his expectations of what his life should otherwise have been—say, the important book he has yet to write—then on what godless principles of biological amorality does he base this even fleeting question of why me? (For a more detailed treatment of implicit theism in atheistic belief systems, see Bering 2002a).

The Cognitive Problem of Death

In other places, as well, Sartre's work sketches out cutting-edge questions in the cognitive sciences. In *The Wall* (1937/1969), he describes how a materialist who believes he will be executed the following day tries to imagine what it will be like to be dead, only to find it impossible to simulate his own psychological nonexistence. Earlier authors writing in the existential tradition, including Goethe (1852/1998), Freud (1915), and de Unamuno (1912/1954), arrived at this same conclusion—that it is impossible to imagine one's own psychological death. The idea that afterlife beliefs are grounded in this basic inability to mentally represent a permanent state of non-consciousness has been the subject of several recent theories (Bering, 2002b; Bering & Bjorklund 2004; Gilbert 2001; Nichols, in press). Research findings on this topic parallel Sartre's intuitions; even self-proclaimed materialists find it cognitively effortful to reason that one can never know that they have died (Bering 2002b).

Hell is Other People (Because They Can't Understand Us)

Sartre's play *No Exit* (1946/1989), in which three strangers find themselves in the unenviable position of having just been cast to hell *en groupe*, is an exercise in advanced social cognitive theory and anticipates recent discoveries in the study of self-esteem, shame, and reputation (e.g., Leary 1999; for a full review of *No Exit* from an evolutionary cognitive science perspective, see Bering, in press). After confessing his own sins, Garcin attempts to gain the others' trust by creating an atmosphere of mutual understanding; this, he reckons, is their best hope of dismantling the psychological traps so carefully laid for them in hell, where each constantly questions the intentions of the others. "There were days when you peered into yourself, into the secret places of your heart, and what you saw there made you faint with horror," says Garcin to Inez. "You are of my kind" (42). Indeed, in a recent study, participants who were given the impression that they shared a subjective experience with an objectively similar person reported significantly more liking of that person than those who did not share this "I-sharing" experience (Pinel, Long, Landau, Alexander, & Pyszczynski 2006). The authors reason that I-sharing attenuates the social anxiety of 'existential isolation'—because subjectivity can never be shared by others, we tend to be guarded against them for fear they will not fully understand us.

Essential Purpose as Others' Creation

In *Being and Nothingness* (1943/1956a), Sartre expounds in great detail on these topics. This occurs especially in the third chapter ("The Look"), in which he argues—before social psychology began articulating any similar point—that the self is a social construction whose identity and value are forged through others' subjective evaluations. Sartre would hold that whenever another person looks at me, my subjectivity is momentarily dissimulated by this person's glance. I become an object; I am only what he sees: a *professor*, a *fool*, an *atheist*, a *casuist*, *ugly*, a *foreigner*; his subjectivity is in turn revealed to me because I am forced to take his perspective as someone who mentally represents me as an object to be classified. But none of these classifications are, in reality, part of an essential nature that *is* me in any biological sense; rather they are psychological attributions that are dependent on another person's mind seeing me in these terms. I am only a professor so long as others say that I am; I may cease being ugly if others cease looking upon me as so; and I may revise my religious beliefs on my deathbed and believe again in God. The trouble, according to Sartre, is that most people act in 'bad faith' because they confuse others' objectifications of them with their own essential nature and, as a consequence, behave within the boundaries of these ascribed roles.

Wherefore Free Will? The Computerized Brain and the Delusional Self

In another work, *The Flies* (1946/1989), Sartre targets the quandary of morality in the absence of a human nature designed by God. In doing so, he foreshadows the many earnest attempts of recent evolutionary theorists who argue that good and evil, the soul, the afterlife, and God are byproducts of the evolved human mind rather than ontological realities. Unlike Sartre, however, many of these writers, including several contributors to this volume, struggle to articulate a non-determinist morality that allows any room for free will. This is because, when followed to its full, logical conclusion, evolutionary psychology can lead only to a determinist moral philosophy. This is not to say that evolutionary processes themselves are deterministic; rather, they are epigenetic, both phylogenetically and ontogenetically. But when it comes to the discrete social behaviors of individual human beings, and the psychological forces that are responsible for such behaviors, the subjective self is impotent to affect the person's biological destiny.

If a married, middle-aged man hires a prostitute, it is because the decision is in accordance with his present physiology, which arises as a consequence of his unique developmental experiences, which occurred within a particular cultural environment in interaction with a particular inherited genotype, which he inherited from his particular parents, who inherited genetic variants of similar traits from their own particular parents, *ad infinitum*. Furthermore, this man's brain acted without first consulting his self-consciousness; rather his neurocognitive system enacted evolved behavioral algorithms that respond, either normally or in error, in ways that favored genetic fitness in the ancestral past. "The brain is not just like a computer. It is a computer" (Tooby & Cosmides, 2005, 16).

In the example, this man's self merely plays the role of spectator in his body's sexual affairs; thus, there is no-one here to personally hold accountable for his behavior even though he may be exposing his wife to a sexually transmitted disease and exploiting a drug addict for his own pleasure; there is only the embodiment of a man who is helpless to act in any way that is contrary to his particular nature, which is a derivative of a more general human nature.

In this sense, evolutionary psychology is antithetical to Sartre's humanistic thesis; here, the self is only a deluded homunculus that thinks it is participating in a moral game when in fact it is just an emotionally invested audience member. Thus, just as he did with any religious portrayal of a human nature purposefully crafted by God, Sartre (1946/1956b) similarly derided any biological portrayal of a universal human nature. In his view, this would excuse the individual from accountability in the moral domain; if there is, in reality, no free will, then the individual stands outside of judgment; attributing responsibility to others becomes a meaningless convention that reflects only a naïve psychology of the causes of their behaviors (e.g., Nichols 2006; Wegner 2002).

Conclusion

Sartre's rejection of a biologically based human nature was an unfortunate dismissal of an inconvenient fact, because in so doing he divorced his atheistic existentialism from what was to become an empirically rich science of psychology. This science now provides ample space for the many issues raised by Sartre. The phenomenological cognitive processes specific to reasoning about the nature of personal existence can now be subjected to rigorous and innovative experimental designs. This scientific frontier is where Sartre shakes hands with Darwin and, ultimately, where Darwin will be theoretically reconciled with God.

If, as cognitive scientists, we are serious about arriving at the deep evolutionary core of religion in the human mind, then rather than tracking the spread of supernatural concepts as they parasitize brains, trick our agent-detection systems, and tender irrational beliefs, we should instead be focusing our investigation on the following question: Why is the individual's subjective worldview so completely saturated with private symbolic meaning? That is to say, we must focus on the individual's relationship with God—even if the latter is naught but an illusion, or if the relationship has gone sour. Such would be the very profitable beginnings of a new existential cognitive science based on central and sound evolutionary tenets.

References

Atran, S. 1995. Causal constraints on categories and categorical constraints on biological reasoning. In D. Sperber, D. Premack, & A. J. Premack, Eds., *Causal cognition: A multidisciplinary debate*, 205-233. New York, NY: Oxford University Press.

Bering, J. M. 2002a. The existential theory of mind. *Review of General Psychology*, 6, 3-24.

Bering, J. M. 2002b. Intuitive conceptions of dead agents' minds: The natural foundations of afterlife beliefs as phenomenological boundary. *Journal of Cognition & Culture*, 2, 263-308.

Bering, J. M. 2006. The folk psychology of souls. *Behavioral & Brain Sciences*, 29, 453-462.

Bering, J. M. in press 2007. Why hell is other people: Distinctively human psychological suffering. *Review of General Psychology*.

Bering, J. M., & Bjorklund, D. F. 2004. The natural emergence of reasoning about the afterlife as a developmental regularity. *Developmental Psychology*, 40, 217-233.

de Unamuno, M. 1954. *Tragic sense of life*. New York, NY: Dover. Original work published 1912.

Freud, S. 1915. Thoughts for the times and war and death. *The standard edition of the complete psychological works of Sigmund Freud*, 14, 274-301.

Gilbert, D. T. 2001. Why economists are not afraid to die. Paper presented at the First International Conference on Experimental Existential Psychology, Amsterdam, The Netherlands, August 2-4, 2001.

Goethe, J. W-V., Eckermann, J. P., & Moorhead, J. K. 1998. *Conversations with*

Goethe. New York, NY: Da Capo. Original work published 1852.
Kelemen, D. 2004. Are children 'intuitive theists?' Reasoning about purpose and design in nature. *Psychological Science, 15,* 295-301.
Koole, S. L., Greenberg, J., & Pyszczynski, T. 2006. Introducing science to the psychology of the soul: Experimental existential psychology. *Current Directions in Psychological Science, 15,* 212-216.
Leary, M. R. 1999. Making sense of self-esteem. *Current Directions in Psychological Science, 8,* 32-35.
Nichols, S. 2006. Folk intuitions of free will. *Journal of Cognition & Culture, 6,* 57-86.
Nichols, S. in press. Imagination and immortality: Thinking of me. *Synthèse.*
Pinel, E. C., Long, A. E., Landau, M. J., Alexander, K., & Pyszczynski, T. 2006. Seeing I to I: A pathway to interpersonal connectedness. *Journal of Personality & Social Psychology, 90,* 243-257.
Sartre, J. P. 1989. *No exit and other plays*. New York, NY: Vintage. Original work published 1946.
Sartre, J. P. 1969. *The wall: And other stories*. New York, NY: New Directions. Original work published 1937.
Sartre, J. P. 1964. *Nauseé.* New York, NY: New Directions. Original work published 1938.
Sartre, J. P. 1957. *Existentialism and human emotions*. New York, NY: Philosophical Library.
Sartre, J. P. 1956a. *Being and nothingness*. New York. NY: Philosophical Library. Original work published 1943.
Sartre, J. P. 1956b. Existentialism is a humanism. In W. Kaufman, Ed., *Existentialism fromDostoevsky to Sartre,* 287-311. New York, NY: The World Publishing Co. Original work published 1946.
Tooby, J., & Cosmides, L. 2005. Conceptual foundations of evolutionary psychology. In D. M. Buss, Ed., *The handbook of evolutionary psychology,* 5-67. Hoboken, NJ: John Wiley & Sons.
Wegner, D. M. 2002. *The illusion of conscious will.* Cambridge, MA: The MIT Press.

Four Arguments That the Cognitive Psychology of Religion Undermines the Justification of Religious Belief

Michael J. Murray

Over the last decade a handful of cognitive models of religious belief have begun to coalesce in the literature. Attempts to offer "scientific explanations of religious belief" are nothing new, stretching back at least as far as David Hume, and perhaps as far back as Cicero. What is also not new is a belief that scientific explanations of religious belief serve in some way to undermine the justification for those beliefs.

Do these contemporary cognitive models of religion show us that religious beliefs are nothing but "a trick fobbed off on us by our genes?" Our first reaction to such a question should be: well if they do, it is not clear how. These models, if correct, show *not one thing more* than that we have certain mental tools (perhaps selected for, perhaps spandrels) which under certain conditions give rise to beliefs in the existence of entities which tend to rally religious commitments. But pointing that out does nothing to tell us about whether those beliefs are *justified* or not. After all, we have mental tools which, under certain conditions, give rise to belief in the existence of palm trees and electrons. We don't regard those belief forming mechanisms as unreliable, nor (typically) the beliefs formed as unjustified. So what is it about religious beliefs, formed by HADD (hypersensitive agency detection device—see below), our penchant for minimally counter-intuitive entities, our attachment to full-access strategic agents, and so on, that makes us think that religious beliefs are epistemically unjustified? This paper considers four arguments for this claim.

Argument 1

> In the most widely endorsed cognitive account of the origins of religious belief, those beliefs are spawned—or at least nurtured—into existence by a mental tool often described as a "hypersensitive agency detection device" (HADD). HADD is triggered by various environmental stimuli including apparently purposeful motion, configurations of matter, or physical processes with no apparent natural

> cause. When triggered, HADD spawns belief in unseen agents that are taken to be the causes of the motions, configurations or processes. Evolutionary theorists hypothesize that such a mental tool would be adaptive since it would lead our ancestors to be especially sensitive to cues that might signal a predator. Furthermore, it would be adaptive for HADD to err on the side of excessive false positives since the cost of these would, for obvious reasons, be much greater than the cost of any false negatives. And indeed it does err in this way, thus explaining our tendency to immediately assume that bumps in the night are caused by some*one*.
>
> In light of the fact that HADD is hyperactive in this way, it generates many false positives and is thus unreliable. Of course, beliefs that are outputs of a mechanism known to be unreliable are unjustified, at least unless those beliefs have some sort of independent evidence supporting their truth. Thus religious beliefs, spawned by HADD and not supported by independent evidence (and that covers the religious beliefs embraced by most folks), should be rejected as unreasonable or unjustified.

While this argument might be modified into a formidable objection as it stands, it fails. The problem with it is that it treats HADD as a belief-forming mechanism whose reliability can be assessed without reference to the contexts in which it is activated. This is wrongheaded, since belief forming mechanisms will routinely vary in reliability as the context changes. My visual system is generally reliable in helping me form beliefs about my physical environment, except in low light conditions, or when it comes to things that are very distant or small, etc. Similarly, HADD is quite reliable as a belief-forming mechanism in some conditions and perhaps not in others. In fact, in the ordinary course of things, it seems that when HADD triggers beliefs in agents, those beliefs *are* reliable. When you hear footsteps in the hall outside your room, or a knock on the door, or a whistled tune, you form beliefs in unseen agents, and you are right. However, it is also true that HADD has a tendency to misfire under some conditions. Can we distinguish conditions under which HADD is reliable from conditions under which it is not? Perhaps. We need not undertake the task of identifying all of those conditions. Instead we can conclude for now that religious beliefs spawned by HADD are unjustified only if HADD is likely to be unreliable in the contexts in which religious beliefs are generated. No scientist or philosopher has presented us with any such argument and, in fact, it is hard to see how such an argument could be formulated.

Argument 2:

> Whatever cognitive tools are involved in spawning religious belief, one thing is clear: the beliefs spawned are obviously mutually incompatible. Any cognitive tools which give rise to mutually incompatible beliefs in this way are obviously unreliable, and any beliefs arising from them would then have to be taken to be unjustified (at least absent some sort of independent evidence of their truth). As a result, religious beliefs arising from these tools cannot be reasonably accepted absent independent justification.

One aspect of this argument is obviously correct: religious beliefs across times and cultures are largely mutually inconsistent. But for this argument to succeed it would have to presume something that is just as obviously false, namely, that the mental tools identified by cognitive scientists give rise to these inconsistent beliefs *all on their own*. When environmental conditions stimulate HADD, Theory of Mind, memorability and transmissibility via minimal counterintuitiveness, etc., the outputs of these tools are still highly non-specific. HADD tells me there is "an agent"; my beliefs about what sorts of fauna inhabit these parts lead me to conclude that the agent is a bear or a tiger or the bogeyman. If you conclude that it is a bear and I conclude that it is the bogeyman, this doesn't show HADD to be unreliable, it shows that my mom was wrong to teach me that there is a bogeyman. Likewise, no one doubts that divergent cultural traditions play an enormous role in giving religious concepts their specific contours. If the mutually exclusive aspects of these beliefs creep in from cultural sources, this does nothing to undermine the reliability of these cognitive tools, it just shows that the cultural traditions are false.

What this shows is that for this second argument to succeed, one would need to show that the mutually incompatible aspects of these beliefs arise from the workings of the cognitive tools, and not the accretions or specifications that are introduced through cultural influences. It seems unlikely that this is the case.

Argument 3:

> Cognitive psychological accounts of religion can account for the origin of religious belief in a way that makes no reference to and requires no causal connection with supernatural reality. However, properly justified belief requires that the target of the belief be causally connected to the belief itself in certain ways. Since these accounts show us that none of those ways are in fact in play in the origins of religious belief, beliefs so generated are unjustified.

This is a complex objection and it merits a more detailed response than I can give here. I have space for only the following two points. First, philosophers who are concerned about questions of the justification of belief fall into two basic categories: internalists and externalists. Internalists argue that whether or not a belief is justified depends entirely on facts "inside the head" (for example, facts about the extent to which the belief is properly supported by other beliefs one has). Externalists argue that justification depends on whether or not the belief has the right relation to facts about the external world. For some, the right relation consists only in *reliability* while for others the right relation will require that there be *certain causal connections* between the external world and the belief formed. I point this out only to make it clear that even if these psychological accounts do show that there is no direct causal connection between religious beliefs and their target, only some epistemological theories would take that to be relevant to the justification of those beliefs.

Should externalist epistemologists who argue for the importance of causal connections between the belief and its target take religious belief formed by HADD (etc.) to be similarly unjustified? No. Perhaps God set up our environment and the course of evolutionary history in such a way that we come to have cognitive tools that lead us to form beliefs in a supernatural reality (let's call this the "supernaturalist explanation of religion"). If that is the way things work, then my beliefs would have a connection, albeit an *indirect* one, to the target of the belief, and a connection of that sort would not undermine the justification of the belief. We can see this by way of an analogy: Jones is a candidate in a local election. The voters in this district don't pay much attention to this election and typically don't know who the candidates are until they enter the voting booth. Wanting to become known to the voters beforehand, Jones programs an automatic dialing machine which calls each home in the district and delivers a short message introducing Jones and his campaign slogan. Because of this, all of the voters become aware of Jones and his campaign. If Smith were to stumble into Jones' campaign headquarters and find the machine, could Smith conclude that the beliefs of the voters are unjustified because they were caused directly by the machine rather than directly by Jones? Of course not. The *direct* cause was a self-contained mechanism. But since Jones was the remote cause of the machine doing what it does, the beliefs are perfectly well justified. For all we know, God is likewise the indirect cause of the religious beliefs we have—beliefs that are directly caused by the cognitive tools psychologists have identified.

However, some scientist critics of religious belief are not satisfied with this response. For them, and this is the second point, something else is at stake in this argument, which they put like this:

> In responding to Argument 3, the religious believer might push back by saying that "for all we know" God is the indirect cause of our religious beliefs, and in this way a proper causal connection between belief and target is preserved. That might tempt the religious believer into thinking that there is no better reason to affirm the "naturalist" explanation of religion over the "supernaturalist" explanation of religion. But that's not right. We do have reason to favor the naturalist explanation and the reason is: it's more parsimonious! Thus, while it is possible that the supernaturalist is right, it is more reasonable to assume that the naturalist is right.

This argument aims to press the superiority of the naturalist explanation on grounds of simplicity. But while simplicity is a scientific virtue, it is a virtue only when all other things are equal, something that is rarely the case. When we choose between competing hypotheses, we also need to take into account the other theoretical virtues of the competitors including the extent to which the hypotheses cohere with our over-arching worldview. To borrow an example, it is, all other things being equal, simpler to assume that there are no other minds but my own (and that the behavior of other apparently minded things is caused by purely mechanical processes) than it is to accept that there are many minds. But we don't accept the "one mind" over the "many mind" hypothesis because such a hypothesis doesn't cohere with many other things we are committed to. The Christian might be committed to the idea that all humans have minds because they are created in the image of God. The naturalist/physicalist might be committed to the idea that things that are physically alike are alike in other respects (including mental ones) and thus that all humans (like me) have minds. In either case, other considerations override considerations of parsimony in leading us to our view.

How does this affect the argument above? The answer is: the theist might say that the belief that God is the remote cause of supernatural beliefs fits in quite well with other reasons they have for thinking that religious belief is true (e.g., that without a God, many things just don't make sense: the existence of objective morality, why there is something rather than nothing, why the universe is fine-tuned for life, and so on). For them, that explanation would be more reasonable even if not simpler. Of course, for the naturalist, things might be different. However, all of this shows simply that psychological explanations of belief of the sort we have been considering do nothing on their own to undermine the justification of religious belief.

Argument 4:

> While some belief forming mechanisms honed by natural selection can be supposed to be reliable, others cannot. The ones that can are those that produce beliefs "visible" to natural selection—beliefs about the physical world generated by the operation of the senses, for example. If my visual system produces beliefs that are largely incorrect, natural selection will catch up with me. Because of this, I can have some confidence that my visual systems are reliable. But supernatural beliefs generated by HADD and other cognitive tools are not subject to the winnowing power of natural selection in this way. If these cognitive tools were to mislead us systematically about the nature of supernatural reality, natural selection would do nothing to cure us of these illusions. As a result, we have no reason to think that their reliability would have been similarly honed. We ought thus to regard religious belief so spawned to be unreliable.

This argument makes two fundamental mistakes. First, it assumes that natural selection can indeed winnow reliable from unreliable belief forming mechanisms. Unfortunately, there is no reason to think this. The only way that natural selection can winnow these belief forming mechanisms is by winnowing the behaviors that they produce. Behaviors, in our case, arise from the interplay of beliefs *and desires*. Because of this, false beliefs can be as adaptive as true beliefs *as long as they are paired with affective systems that, together with the false beliefs, give rise to adaptive behaviors like feeding, fleeing, fighting, and reproducing.* Since false beliefs can be as adaptive as true ones, there is no reason to think that natural selection will select for reliable belief forming mechanisms and against unreliable ones.

The second mistake is that even if our imaginary scientist is right about the role evolutionary pressures play in giving us true beliefs about our environment, there is no reason to think that evolutionary pressures would lead us to false beliefs concerning religious reality. If the "supernaturalist explanation of religion" is correct, then our coming to believe that there is supernatural reality is something that leads us to true belief because those beliefs are true. God set up the natural conditions so that, *pace* the objection, natural selection does select for reliable religious belief forming mechanisms.

Does Evolution Threaten the Soul?

Gretchen Koch

Near the beginning of his book *Freedom Evolves,* Dan Dennett (2003) describes what he calls the Peril of Paulina, after a former student who conveyed the importance of a scholar's responsibility and care in presenting ideas and information for public consumption, even when the information is true (17). In her case it was a hypothetical of discovering a cure for AIDS which could only work under certain conditions and might be at least part based on faulty calculations or reasoning. Given these circumstances it is critical for a researcher to present such ground-breaking information with a concern for her audience, and how they will receive it. Dennett (2003) uses this idea to compare the job of an academic to that of an engineer designing a bridge who knows that the safety of thousands of people depends on the integrity of the structure. "When we academics aspire to have a greater impact on the "real" (as opposed to "academic") world," he says, "we need to adopt the attitudes and habits of those more applied disciplines. We need to hold ourselves responsible for what we say, recognizing that our words, if believed, can have profound effects for good or ill" (17). What impact can academics investigating the relationship of evolution to religion expect to have on the "real world"? How are we to interpret our responsibility toward those who read our explanations of what they find most meaningful in the world in terms other than those which they might embrace?

The past two years have brought books from Sam Harris, Richard Dawkins, and Daniel Dennett attempting, at least in part, to use science to demonstrate that religion is harmful or at least not necessarily beneficial to humankind. And people are responding—none too enthusiastically, in some cases. The word "scientism" is being bandied about quite a lot,[1] as well as accusations that the explanations being given do not properly take into account more esoteric theological doctrines. The biologist and blogger, PZ Myers (2007), refers to this sort of complaint as "The Courtier's Reply," and mocks it in this fashion:

---

1 For example: Leon Wieseltier's review of *Breaking the Spell* in the New York Times Feb. 19, 2006 or Marilynne Robinson's review of *The God Delusion* in Harper's Magazine Nov. 2006.

> I have considered the impudent accusations of Mr. Dawkins with exasperation at his lack of serious scholarship. . .We have entire schools dedicated to writing learned treatises on the beauty of the Emperor's raiment, and every major newspaper runs a section dedicated to imperial fashion; Dawkins cavalierly dismisses them all. . . . Dawkins arrogantly ignores all these deep philosophical ponderings to crudely accuse the Emperor of nudity. Until Dawkins has trained in the shops of Paris and Milan, until he has learned to tell the difference between a ruffled flounce and a puffy pantaloon, we should all pretend he has not spoken out against the Emperor's taste. His training in biology may give him the ability to recognize dangling genitalia when he sees it, but it has not taught him the proper appreciation of Imaginary Fabric.

The significance of this caricature, of course, is its implication that those who criticize scientific explorations of religion such as that of Dawkins because they do not consider finer theological schemas are dodging the question of the existence of a thing, with concerns about the nature of that thing which are irrelevant to the thing's existence. In the case of the naked emperor, the thing is the clothing. In the case of Dawkins' (2006) book *The God Delusion*, the thing is God, or religion (it's not always clear which). Does this criticism have merit? It really depends on what we think a scientific inquiry into religion, especially from an evolutionary viewpoint, ought to tell us. Ought it cover the gamut of religious doctrines, explaining everything from animal sacrifice to process theology? Or would it be more reasonable to expect that the discovery of theological incorrectness, such as D. Jason Slone (2004) has described, might indicate a disconnect between the explicit, reflective beliefs recorded and observed by clergy and the "folk religion" that appears to be a by-product of our folk psychology, expecting to find that the latter is much more easily explicable in evolutionary terms? This paper will take a look at the relationship between such an approach and the way people perceive cognitive and evolutionary inquiries into religion.

My research concerns folk intuitions of the soul, and what properties of folk psychology contribute to our belief in it. Is it required for free will? What is its relationship to belief in an afterlife? Does it play a role in what we consider moral and immoral? What discoveries by scientists about how the mind and body works are perceived as threats to its existence, and why? With regard to the debate on evolution vs. intelligent design, there is one particular aspect of the soul which rises to the forefront—its status as establishing a distinction between humans and material existence based on that which we humans have, which no other organism on earth does. In his address to the Pontifical Academy of Sciences in 1996, former Pope John Paul II quoted Pius XII approvingly that "If the human body take its origin from pre-existent living matter, the spiritual soul is immediately created by God." According to the "wedge strategy," a plan discovered in documentation from the Discovery Institute (1999; the legal defense in the recent Dover trial), they seek to conquer a materialistic outlook on the world fostered by the likes of Charles Darwin which "portrayed humans not as moral and spiritual beings, but as animals or machines who inhabited a universe ruled by purely impersonal forces and whose behavior and very thoughts were dictated by the unbending forces of biology, chemistry, and environment." There is something profoundly disturbing about being equated with animals—it seems to demean, to de-privilege…to disgust.

The relationship of belief in a soul to disgust deserves to be examined more closely. The psychologist Paul Rozin and colleagues (Rozin, Haidt, & McCauley 2000) have identified disgust as the "body and soul" emotion, because according to his research, the things which most often evoke disgust are those which stand as unpleasant reminders of our own animal nature and mortality: corpses, feces, and creatures we associate with the above such as rats and cockroaches; bodily fluids, once they are separated from the body. Body envelope violations, such as injuries and surgery, remind us that we are physical beings, just like the animals, and our lives are also messy. Disgust, interestingly, has the two features of sympathetic magic originally described by George Frazer (1994) in the *The Golden Bough*: contagion and similarity. The law of contagion says that contact makes a particular item suspect—test subjects would refuse to drink a beverage which had been swashed with a sterilized cockroach, and said that they would refuse to wear a sweater which had been worn by an immoral person. The law of similarity says that resemblance should raise suspicion—test subjects interviewed by Rozin and colleagues (2000) refused to eat chocolate fudge which resembles dog feces. The word "disgust" comes from the Latin for "distaste," and Rozin identifies as "core disgust" those things which elicit such visceral reactions as described above. But beyond this, he describes a realm of social disgust in which this same reaction is expanded to include members of certain groups and people who practice certain behaviours. These people are viewed as animalistic, subhuman.

Objects of disgust are alien, foreign, contaminated, and this language can sometimes be used very effectively for persuasion. Leon Kass (1997), former chairman of the U.S. President's Council on Bioethics, has written extensively on what he calls "the wisdom of repugnance." Commenting in an essay by that name on the subject of cloning, he asks "Is cloning a fulfilment of begetting and belonging? Or is cloning, rather, as I contend, their pollution and perversion? To pollution and perversion, the fitting response can only be honour and revulsion; and conversely, generalized horror and revulsion are *prima facie* evidence of foulness and violation. The burden of moral argument must fall entirely on those who want to declare the widespread repugnancies of humankind to be mere timidity or superstition" (Kass 1997, 18). Legislation against bestiality, homosexuality, and obscenity has been argued into existence, and supported, on the strength of sheer moral revulsion. There was quite a lot of outcry and furor when the moral philosopher Peter Singer, seeking to make a case for consistency in our treatment of animals, published an essay in Nerve Magazine in 2001 entitled "Heavy Petting" arguing that sex with animals is not necessarily immoral, especially considering our willingness to put them through great hardship on their way to being killed and eaten. While he sought to make vivid some of our hypocritical attitudes regarding humane treatment toward selected species, the reaction was of incredible disgust that he could speak of such a subject without condemnation (Carnell 2001; Vanderkam 2001). The reaction was certainly not surprising, considering that the essay contained a double-whammy of disgust-invoking subjects: sex *and* animals. If he had thrown in death as well, he might have achieved a trifecta.

The primatologist Frans de Waal (1999) has a term for people who reject out of hand the similarities between humans and other animals: anthropodenial. The opposite of anthropomorphism, it might help to explain why in America, a country where the soul is held in such great esteem, the theory of evolution has encountered such a reaction of enmity and disgust. Joseph Bulbulia makes the suggestion in his work that in order for religious behaviors and professions to function as hard to fake signals of commitment to the group to be fully effective, it might be that they require full commitment to their veracity by individuals themselves, thus predisposing them to be resistant and possibly even offended by explanations which point to ultimate rather than proximate motivations. These ultimate motivations would be unconscious, of course. Dan Dennett and Richard Dawkins have made a similar argument using memetic theory to explain the potency of the meme for faith—it reproduces more effectively by virtue of discouraging questioning, making belief a moral issue rather than one of simply weighing evidence. What if we have evolved to be suspicious of evolution, to find the idea of complex, intelligent, human things to have arisen from simple, unconscious non-human (even non-thinking) things so threatening? What if the thought of evolution, first considered, constitutes such an "animal reminder" that the reaction of disgust for many, especially those trained up in faith and supernatural commitments, is impossible to quell?

I believe this is a question we ought to address if we have any aspirations to reach a wider audience with our research. It's a kind of reformulation of the standard insider/outsider problem well-known to scholars of religion and anthropologists—the interpretation of people's beliefs and behaviours in terms they would not themselves accept: etic versus emic perspectives. We must be careful in applying theories which take as evidence the fact that they will be rejected by "true believers." Edge.org, the web site for scientists and scientifically-inclined intellectuals to converse on issues of meaning in human existence, asks a large number of such people a certain question each year—this year's was "What is your dangerous idea?" A couple of the answers are particularly relevant to this discussion. Jesse Bering's (2006) answer was that "Science will never silence God." Paul Bloom's (2006) was that "There are no souls," though he clearly doesn't expect the world to embrace this idea any time soon. And as he points out, embracing a materialist concept of humanity would affect how many of us think about stem-cell research, abortion, euthanasia, and cloning—not to mention our ideas of personal responsibility and intentionality. In short, getting rid of the soul is the Wedge document's worst nightmare.

When confronting the question of how a non-religious scientist can properly explain what is going on in someone's mind when they experience God or speak with their dead grandmother, Dennett has on occasion suggested (albeit, I'm pretty sure, to some extent jokingly) that the highest authorities of the religion being studied produce a test for the scientist to take to demonstrate sufficient knowledge of the doctrines of the faith they are presuming to examine—provided, of course, that such a test can also be passed by clergy of that faith as well. But I think there may well be some merit in the suggestion that having a past history as an active participant in a religion can allow a greater capacity for empathy. It can help channel some of the gap of understanding between participant and observer. Evolution is apparently not exactly intuitive, and so scientific explanations (which are notoriously counter-intuitive) which rely on it arguably should take some care for the soul. Steven Pinker (2003) has written and spoken extensively on how naturalistic explanations of the mind do not entail or require nihilism, but the very reason why these explanations seem too often to fall on deaf ears deserves an inquiry of its own. Atheism has recently become a hot topic in pretty short order on the pages of magazines such as Time and Wired, leaving the question of whether evolution = atheism on the lips of many. If evolution equals atheism, then how exactly is evolution supposed to explain religion? Doesn't that automatically mean that any consideration of evolution has to prove (or at least claim) that religion is deluded and wrong?

These are not ridiculous questions for a religious person to ask, upon making the choice to pick up a book such as *Why Would Anyone Believe in God?* (Barrett, 2004) or *Religion Explained* (Boyer 2001), both of which I've recommended as good introductions to a cognitive approach to understanding religion. But the question is, how does the necessary reductionism that comes with investigating religion on an ultimate rather than proximate level, and therefore would appear to compromise the soul and all that it stands for, become acceptable to a person? What does it take to bridge that gap? Presumably it is something that has taken place for all of us here, assuming the gap existed in the first place. But the inquiry into what it takes for other people is something we should all be concerned with, because we are all, after all, designing bridges. Hopefully, they will be the kind people are willing to cross.

References

Barrett, J. L. 2004. *Why would anyone believe in God?* Walnut Creek, CA: AltaMira Press.

Bering, J. 2006. Science will never silence God. Retrieved March 1, 2007, from <http://www.edge.org/q2006/q06_12.html#bering>.

Bloom, P. 2006. There are no souls. Retrieved March 1, 2007, from <http://www.edge.org/q2006/q06_12.html#bloom>.

Boyer, P. 2001. *Religion explained: Evolutionary origins of religious thought.* New York, NY: Basic Books.

Carnell, B. 2001. Peter Singer offers moral justification for bestiality. Retrieved March 1, 2007, from <http://www.animalrights.net/archives/year/2001/000040.html>.

Discovery Institute. 1999. The wedge strategy. Cited in P. Handley. Evolution or design debate heats up. *The Times of Oman*, 7 March 2005.

de Waal, F. B. M. 1999. Anthropomorphism and anthropodenial: Consistency in our thinking about humans and other animals. *Philosophical Topics, 27*, 255-280.

Dawkins, R. 2006. *The God delusion*. New York, NY: Houghton Mifflin Company.

Dennett, D. 2003. *Freedom evolves*. New York, NY: Penguin.

Frazer, G. 1994. *The golden bough* Abridged ed. New York, NY: Oxford University Press.

Kass, L. 1997. The wisdom of repugnance. *The New Republic, 2 June,* 17-26.

Meyers, P.Z. 2007. The courtier's reply. *Pharyngula.* Retrieved February 28, 2007, from <http://scienceblogs.com/pharyngula/2006/12/the_courtiers_reply.php>.

Pinker, S. 2003. *The blank slate*. New York, NY: Penguin.

Pope John Paul II. 1996. Address to the Pontifical Academy of Sciences, 22 October. Official translation published in *L'Osservatore Romano,* "Weekly Edition in English," 30 October 1996.

Rozin, P., Haidt, J., & McCauley, C. 2000. Disgust: The body and soul emotion. In M. Lews & J. M. Haviland-Jones, Eds., *Handbook of emotions,* 2nd ed., 637-653. New York, NY: Guilford Press.

Singer, P. 2001. Heavy petting. *Nerve Magazine*. Retrieved March 1, 2007, from <http://www.dailyprincetonian.com/archives/2001/03/08/opinion/2591.shtml>.

Slone, D. 2004. *Theological incorrectness*. New York, NY: Oxford University Press.

Vanderkam, L. 2001. Peter Singer's 'Heavy Petting.' The Daily Princetonian. Retrieved March 1, 2007, from http://www.dailyprincetonian.com/archives/2001/03/08/opinion/2591.shtml>.

Essentialism and Evolution

Benson Saler

Introduction

This paper is divided into three sections. In the first, I describe some of the characterizations of essentialism encountered in a sizeable Western literature extending back to the ancient Greeks. There is variety in that literature, and we may usefully distinguish between stronger and weaker essentialisms in the positions taken by various authors.

In the second section, I consider the possible functional utility of essentialism. In doing so, I offer a conjectural but plausible suggestion: that evolution selected for essentialist dispositions. I also suggest that the strength or intensity of such dispositions may vary somewhat from person to person.

Finally, in the third section I inventory some of the possible costs of essentialism. I also consider briefly certain anti-essentialist advocacies. Assuming (as I do) that essentialist dispositions are grounded in our evolutionary heritage, such advocacies raise the question of whether or not, or to what degree, we may override or transcend natural dispositions in this and perhaps in other cases.

I. Essentialism

In classical Greek philosophy and in medieval Christian theology, essentialism pivots on the idea of essence, the idea that an object is what it is because it has certain unchanging and necessary properties or qualities. Such properties or qualities include developmental potentials that may be actualized in a world of change. Thus, for instance, the essence of the butterfly is in the larva. Essences, in this view, are not always—or even usually—accessible to our perception, but they are held to be determinative both of genuine identity and of true-to-nature behavior. Essence, so characterized, is distinguished from "existence," the state or condition of "being." It is also distinguished from "accidents," contingent features that may be associated with an object at times but are not necessary for the enduring existential identity of that object. Accidental features, though sometimes quite important for initial recognition and for prediction, are nevertheless deemed superficial.

An extreme and peculiar illustration of these ideas is afforded by the Christian doctrine of "transubstantiation," as explicated in High Scholasticism. An ordained celebrant, acting as Christ's agent, participates in a ritual in which bread is transformed into flesh and wine is transformed into blood. The former bread continues to look and taste like bread, and the former wine continues to look and taste like wine. Visual appearance and taste, however, are said to be accidents. The original objects are claimed to have been transformed in essence through the interposition of God's grace. While their new essences are not readily accessible to human perception, communicants must accept it on faith that change has occurred, and that what was once bread is now truly flesh and that what was once wine is now truly blood. This peculiar case inverts the normal course of nature where, in classical and scholastic teachings, change occurs in accidents but continuity in the profoundest metaphysical sense resides in essences. As a claimed example of the inversion of the natural by the supernatural, the doctrine of transubstantiation dramatically illustrates the essentials of strong essentialism.

On a relatively high level of abstraction, and with primary reference to the logic of classes, strong essentialism requires that we postulate or accept the existence of classes—a first condition rejected by uncooperative nominalists (e.g., Goodman 1956, 16)—and that we stipulate or suppose for each class necessary features or conditions that govern class inclusion. More moderate essentialisms sometimes hold that many phenomena have essences, but not all do. Moderate essentialists, moreover, may allow that in some cases family resemblance predicates are sustainable (e.g., Campbell 1965, 243). And moderate essentialists tend to distance themselves in one way or another from strong essentialism's insistence on immutability or fixity.

Scholars generally regard essentialism as an ontological doctrine or set of doctrines. Andrew Sayer (1997), in characterizing it as such, explicitly declares that it is *not* an epistemological doctrine, and he warns us against the "epistemic fallacy of converting ontological issues into epistemological ones" (1997, 466). While I accept Sayer's warning, I think that he is wrong about essentialism. I much prefer what Charles Spinosa and Hubert L. Dreyfus say about it: namely, that essentialism

> makes two general interlocking claims, one about the nature of the world and one about the nature of knowledge. Roughly, the world consists of things that fall into kinds or types. And knowledge consists of recognizing and relating those types and determining which type each thing is an instance of. (Spinosa & Dreyfus 1996, 738)

The epistemological aspects of essentialism deserve more recognition. That is especially the case if we consider essentialism in evolutionary perspective. I see little reason to suppose that our Pleistocene ancestors were sophisticated metaphysicians. But if the Pleistocene were as menacing as Bush's Baghdad, a hesitant or incompetent epistemologist would be decidedly disadvantaged there.

II. Ubiquity, Evolution, and Benefits

Evidence from a diversity of sources indicates that essentialism is widely and deeply distributed among humans. Cross-cultural research on botanical and zoological folk taxonomies, for instance, finds that there are salient structural regularities in classifications among diverse populations (Berlin 1992), and Scott Atran (1990) deems such regularities evidence of underlying—and probably universal—beliefs in essences. Brent Berlin (1992) allows for cultural constructionism in areas such as "social organization, ritual, religious beliefs, [and] notions of beauty," but he holds that "human beings everywhere are constrained in essentially the same ways—by nature's basic plan—in their conceptual recognition of the biological diversity of their natural environment," and that "When human beings function as ethnobiologists...they do not construct order, they discern it" (8). Groups of animals and plants, Berlin writes, "present themselves to the human observer as *a series of discontinuities* whose structure and content are seen by all human beings in essentially the same ways" (9, emphasis added). At the same time, however, Berlin remarks that "if nature's plan is unambiguous, it is not exclusive," and that "it is clear that biological diversity can be organized in several different ways" (9). Most of Berlin's book is given over to identifying and analyzing the principles that usually do apply. His discussion supports the contention that members of various non-Western societies partition nature essentially.

Another source of evidence is research—much of it experimental—on concept formation among children. As Paul Bloom (2004, 46) points out, many contemporary developmental psychologists believe that essentialism is to be found even among young children, and that an essentialist mode of thought is a human universal. Lawrence Hirschfeld (1994) raises the possibility that essentialist dispositions and assumptions among children may apply independently to the biological and social domains, rather than spread by analogy from biological kinds to social kinds (see also Haslam 1998, 308). Based on his research on concept formation, especially as it applies to ideas about race, Hirschfeld writes that

> in virtually every culture anthropologists have studied we find systems of natural taxonomy. We find them, I propose, because *children* are prepared to represent the sociological landscape in a singular manner.

> Their representations are not those of a naïve observer, but a "scientist" equipped with a plausible theory. This is *not* to say that children are prepared to find race. They are prepared to find *some* natural human kinds. The kinds are governed by the culture in which they live. (Hirschfeld 1998, 344)

Thus in South Asia children are likely to develop a proto system of caste, in many sub-Saharan African societies a proto system of age-grades, and in North America and Europe a proto system of race (Hirschfeld 1998, 344).

Experimental and other studies lead the psychologists Douglas Medin and Andrew Ortony (1989, 184) to conclude that "people find it natural to assume, or act as though, concepts have essences." Indeed, scientific inquiry itself, much of which "appears to be focused on trying to get at the 'underlying reality' of phenomena rather than merely describing their observable features," furnishes yet another reason to suppose "that people typically endorse, at least implicitly, some sort of essentialism" (184). But Medin and Ortony add a further wrinkle to our comprehension of essentialism. They direct our attention to what they call "psychological essentialism," which they describe as different from the notion that *things* have essences. It is the view, rather, that people's *representations* of things may reflect a belief that things have essences (183). Cognitive psychology pays attention to such representations, and psychological theorizing about them, Medin and Ortony affirm, must include "descriptions of psychological reality, not metaphysical reality" (183).

Now, the virtually universal proclivities towards essentialism suggested in the above and other sources invite our conjectures as to their possible evolutionary foundations. It is plausible, I think, to hypothesize that essentialism expresses a complex adaptation. Transmitted by polygenic inheritance, it is likely on a person to person basis to manifest quantitative differences in sensitivity to environmental stimuli and in intensity of essentialist discriminations (see Saler and Ziegler 2006, 25-30 for a similar hypothesis respecting distributions of theism and atheism). Essentialism, it can plausibly be argued, affords us and our Pleistocene ancestors several potential benefits that may ultimately (if indirectly) contribute to maximizing fitness:

First, as Medin and Ortony (1989) put it, "organisms have evolved in such a way that their perceptual (and conceptual) systems are sensitive to just those kinds of similarity that lead them toward the deeper and more central properties... Appearances are usually not deceiving. This means that it is quite adaptive for an organism to be tuned to readily accessible surface properties. Such an organism will not be led astray because many of the surface properties are constrained by deeper properties" (186).

Second, essentialism not only facilitates recognition and discrimination on the basis of surface properties, but it often is loaded with inferential power. By assigning a newly encountered object to a familiar kind or type, we can readily make inferences about that object, including predictions as to its behavior. Inferential richness is one of the great attractions of essentialism, even though the inferences may not always be correct.

Third, essentialism tends to enhance the speed of our inferences and predictions. Its facilitation of stereotyping makes for computational rapidity. This might have been especially important in the Pleistocene, where rapid decisions may sometimes have had life or death significance for individuals and small groups.

Fourth and finally, essentialism can be accounted a knowledge acquisition strategy that facilitates learning about some things not only rapidly but also easily (Hirschfeld 1998, 345).

III. Costs and Overrides

While one can envision potential benefits of essentialism, one can also draw up an inventory of potential costs. A major cost, numbers of critics charge, is the deflection of attention away from an appreciation of differences. This may lead to the over-homogenization of classes or types. It need not, since in principle classification could be based on similarities while according recognition to differences. In practice, however, differences are sometimes collapsed or ignored in ways that eventuate in analytical poverty or that lead to distorted representations of reality.

A closely related cost would be incurred if we were to insist on necessary and unchanging core properties as the essences of things. Such insistence would work against the expansion of our understandings of both biological and socio-cultural dynamics. Biological species, for instance, were once deemed essentialist paragons, that is, clearly delineated and immutable groupings. But that is no longer the case in scientific biology. As Ernst Mayr (2001) puts it, "Darwin showed that one simply could not understand evolution as long as one accepted essentialism. Species and populations are not types, they are not essentialistically defined classes, but rather are biopopulations composed of genetically unique individuals" (83).

On more overt ideological grounds, and with specific reference to the human condition, essentialism has been denounced as a support for the *status quo*, as a promoter of prejudice and bias (as in racism and sexism), and as a source of resistance to the idea that people can remake themselves and their societies. Yet the history of ratiocinated anti-essentialism testifies in significant measure to the staying powers of essentialism. Efforts to extirpate essentialism from one aspect of human life sometimes reintroduce it elsewhere. Thus, for instance, Marxists famously proclaimed that humans have no natures, only histories. But personal or idiosyncratic histories, they opine, are constrained and contextually shaped by History with a capital H, that is, an essentialized history.

Reflective or off-line critical thinking about essentialism, nevertheless, does raise questions about whether or not, or to what extent, we may override our proclivities towards essentialism. Assuming (as I do) that essentialist dispositions are grounded in our evolutionary heritage, a heritage that has endowed us with impressive cerebral powers, can we use those powers not only to transcend proclivities towards essentialism but perhaps various other dispositions similarly grounded?

A moment of reflection will lead us to consider a variety of cases of apparent override. Thus, for instance, numbers of people, many with normal or even comparatively strong sexual drives, successfully practice sexual abstinence for long periods of time, often because of religious commitments. And, with greater relevance to this paper, some persons attempt to formulate and use non-essentialist analytical categories, although, as Peter Byrne's (1988) efforts to construct a family resemblance definition of religion illustrate, essentialist recidivism may subvert such efforts (for criticisms of Byrne, see Fitzgerald, 1996 and Saler 1999).

I think that an inquiry into efforts to use our evolutionary endowments to bypass, override, or mitigate certain of our evolutionary leanings is an important enterprise. Such inquiry should draw upon a diversity of sources and fields. One developing field that offers considerable promise for contributing to our understandings of relevant mechanisms is computational neuroscience, as described recently in a stimulating book by Read Montague (2006). My colleague, Charles Ziegler, and I are in the early stages of exploring that and related fields, and I am not prepared at this time to say more about it. Instead, I conclude this paper by briefly considering the moderate anti-essentialism of Charles Spinosa and Hubert Dreyfus. I use their perspective as a springboard for offering an alternative to a claim cultivated within the framework of the cognitive science of religion.

Spinosa and Dreyfus (1996) declare it their ambition to construct an anti-essentialist argument that "does not imply that all stable distinctions obstruct the recognition of difference" (737). In attempting to do so, they suggest that we humans may dwell in multiple or "weakly incommensurate" worlds. We can simultaneously possess the different skills applicable to different worlds, and this allows us to occupy more than one identity at a time. "Since," they assert, "we are able to have multiple identities by dwelling in different worlds, the stable distinctions of any world need not be seen as establishing dangerous exclusionary practices" (737).

The idea of multiple worlds could be profitably utilized by the cognitive science of religion. Some supporters of CSR tell us that in the case of religious beliefs, people often do not really believe what they say that they believe. The evidence for this claim comes largely from experimental data and the close analyses of narratives. Subjects, for example, may affirm that they endorse theological doctrines to the effect that God is omnipresent and outside of time, but when they engage in storytelling about God, the deity goes from place to place, one place at a time. What people really believe, we are told, is usually not theologically correct.

The best case examples are provided by a detectable disparity between "reflective beliefs," beliefs consciously entertained and subject to critical review, and "non reflective" or "intuitive beliefs," which often operate below the level of conscious awareness (although they may sometimes blaze into consciousness as intuitions or when challenged). It is generally supposed that intuitive beliefs have primacy in deciding what a person "really" believes. But how do we make sense of a seeming disparity between reflective beliefs?

Where one of two apparently conflicting reflective beliefs appears to be better supported by intuitive beliefs than the other, we can make a plausible case for claiming that the better supported affirmation has primacy, even if it is counter-intuitive in certain respects. Sometimes, however, we cannot make such a case. Facile talk about what people "really" believe may then smack of backdoor essentialism. If, however, we allow for the existence and importance of multiple worlds and multiple identities, we can also allow that people may genuinely entertain contradictory beliefs without suffering the slings and arrows of an outrageous cognitive dissonance. How they do so needs to be better understood.

References

Atran, S. 1990. *Cognitive foundations of natural history: Towards an anthropology of science.* Cambridge, UK: Cambridge University Press.

Berlin, B. 1992. *Ethnobiological classification: Principles of categorization of plants and animals in traditional societies.* Princeton, NJ: Princeton University Press.

Bloom, P. 2004. *Descartes' baby: How the science of child development explains what makes us human.* New York, NY: Basic Books.

Byrne, P. 1988. Religion and the religions. In S. R. Sutherland et al., Eds., *The world's religions,* 3-28. London, UK: Routledge.

Campbell, K. 1965. Family resemblance predicates. *American Philosophical Quarterly, 2* (3), 238-244.

Fitzgerald, T. 1996. Religion, philosophy, and family resemblance. *Religion, 26,* 215-236.

Goodman, N. 1956. A world of individuals. In *The problem of universals: A symposium* by I.M. Bochenski, A. Church, & N. Goodman, 15-31. Notre Dame, IN: University of Notre Dame Press.

Haslam, N. O. 1998. Natural kinds, human kinds, and essentialism. *Social Research, 65* (2), 291-314.

Hirschfeld, L. A. 1994. Is the acquisition of social categories based on domain specific competence or on knowledge transfer? In L. A. Hirschfeld & S. A. Gelman, Eds., *Mapping the mind: Domain specificity in cognition and culture,* pp. 201-233. New York, NY: Cambridge University Press.

Hirschfeld, L. A. 1998. Natural assumptions: Race, essence, and taxonomies of human kinds. *Social Research, 65* (2), 331-349.

Mayr, E. 2001. *What evolution is.* New York, NY: Basic Books.

Medin, D., & Ortony, A. 1989. Psychological essentialism. In S. Vosniadou & A. Ortony, Eds., *Similarity and analogical reasoning,* 179-195. Cambridge, UK: Cambridge University Press.

Montague, R. 2006. *Why choose this book? How we make decisions.* New York, NY: Dutton.

Saler, B. 1999. Family resemblance and the definition of religion. *Historical Reflections/Réflexions Historiques, 25* (3), 391-404.

Saler, B., & Ziegler, C. A. 2006. Atheism and the Apotheosis of Agency. *Temenos, 42* (2), 7-41.

Sayer, A. 1997. Essentialism, social constructionism, and beyond. *The Sociological Review, 45* (3), 453-487.

Spinosa, C., & Dreyfus, H. L. 1996. Two kinds of antiessentialism and their consequences. *Critical Inquiry, 22* (4), 735-763.

Religion: Accident or Design?

Taner Edis

Creationists often charge evolution with being a product of materialist philosophy rather than genuine science. Materialists, the story goes, need an account of origins, and since they refuse to consider special creation as an option, they have to believe that some kind of evolution took place.

There is some—very little, but some—truth to this charge. After all, materialism has taken its inspiration primarily from physics among the sciences. Modern materialism often goes under the name of physicalism (Melnyk 2003). And before Darwin, extending physical explanations to living things looked very difficult. Functional complexity appeared to call for a designing intelligence beyond mere physics. So if materialism was to become more credible, it needed to account for the kind of complexity exhibited by life. Something like evolution had to be correct. Indeed, skeptical and materialist impulses contributed to the development of evolutionary ideas, and nineteenth century materialists warmly embraced Darwin's theory (e.g., Büchner 1884).

Physicalists today claim that everything that we know exists is physically realized. Alternatively, they say that everything in our world can be captured by explanations combining chance and necessity—rules and randomness, the two ingredients of every physical theory (Edis 2002, 2004; Monod 1971). Darwinian evolution, a perfect example of a theory combining chance and necessity, has become central to modern materialism, not just as a non-magical explanation of the history of life, but as a key to adaptive complexity in general. Biologists, rather than physicists, solved the problem of how to create information from the bottom-up, within a physical world. And today, Darwinian ideas are becoming more central to the modern sciences of the mind, beyond just biology (Dennett 1995).

Physicalists deny spiritual realities over and above the material world. And since the overwhelming majority of humans have religious beliefs, modern materialism attracts plenty of opposition. Darwinian evolution continues to generate public controversy, though alternatives such as "intelligent design" have made few inroads into academic life. Some philosophers attack physicalism concerning minds, though researchers in disciplines such as cognitive neuroscience think that a broadly physicalist approach is most promising. Dualism is not just a part of folk psychology; it has also put down deep intellectual roots. But in the academy, defenses of a spiritual realm more usually rally around religious experience. Especially in the United States, the view from religious studies is often anti-scientific, in some cases holding that religion is sui generis, that religious experiences and traditions can only be understood from within, on their own terms (Wiebe 1999).

So modern materialists face a situation roughly similar to that in the early days of evolutionary thought. The question of why humans have a strong tendency toward spiritual beliefs has always been pressing, particularly for those inclined to think that these beliefs are in error. But today, with academic defenses of the supernatural revolving around postmodern fideism, affirmations of spiritual experience, and similar efforts to protect religion from critical investigation, the search for scientific explanations of religiosity becomes even more important. Materialists think that religion must be accounted for within the natural world, as a combination of historical accidents, social forces, and the way human brains have been shaped by evolution. So the present research program to explain the basis of supernatural convictions within cognitive neuroscience—to construct a sophisticated, well-tested psychology of religion—looks promising. Materialists will be inclined to think that even if the details need a lot of work, something like this has to be right.

A project of explaining religion scientifically need not be intrinsically hostile to supernatural belief (Rue 2005). After all, one likely outcome of such a project is an understanding that religiosity is a deeply ingrained part of human nature. If evolutionary explanations that conceive of religion as an adaptation (e.g., Wilson 2002) prevail, the view that supernatural convictions have vital social functions would be strengthened. If, as is perhaps more likely, religion arose as an evolutionary byproduct, it could still be very difficult to see what else could do the jobs religions have come to perform in human societies (Atran 2002). Even coming to understand spiritual beliefs as an artifact of the way human brains work need not threaten belief. After all, just as religious liberals portray evolution as the divine way of creating, they can assert that God designed human brains so as to make various experiences of spiritual realities available to all. Indeed, such liberal theological interpretations of science will be useful protective coloration for a scientific community that does not like to be associated too strongly with religious nonbelief (Edis 2006).

Nevertheless, the attempt to explain religion within science is, by and large, an impious, materialist project. For most devout people, statements such as "I believe because I respond to the Holy Spirit" account for their conviction; it is only when such a view seems inadequate that outsiders ask for a different explanation. To the extent that explanations that do not grant reality to supernatural agents are successful, they tend to replace religious explanations. Even liberal views that the gods must have designed our brains just so we are religious begin to look more like after-the-fact excuses than statements that do genuine explanatory work.

Now, materialists, and just about anyone interested in extending the natural scientific picture of the world into the realm of culture and experience, have reason to be optimistic about current efforts to explain religion—even beyond their expectation that some such approach should work. Today, we can do more than speculate about how religion might be due to our consciousness of death, or brush off supernatural beliefs as relics of a prescientific mode of explanation, or talk about a spirit realm as a comforting but nontestable idea. Today's ideas are more sophisticated, and they make substantial contact with biology, experimental psychology, and anthropology. Researchers speak of religion as anthropomorphism (Guthrie 1993), relate "theories of mind" to conceptions of supernatural agents, argue that dualism is innate and a part of folk psychology, show how minimally category-violating (counterintuitive) notions tend to be memorable (Boyer 2001), or connect supernatural concepts to innate expectations about predator-prey relationships (Atran 2002). They draw on results from the cognitive science laboratory, and also use interesting theoretical frameworks such as evolutionary psychology and modular conceptions of minds. They extend cognitive science-based explanations of belief in supernatural agents to illuminate sophisticated theological enterprises (Pyysiäinen 2004), and provide a unified framework that can further our understanding of world religions, ancestor cults, and paranormal preoccupations alike.

In other words, current work on explaining religion appears to be making real progress. Hence it attracts attention. Indeed, anyone interested in debates over supernatural realities must take present research into account in order to refine how we understand the very concept of a supernatural agent.

In these conditions of increased interest, it is useful to look at views of religion that contrast with the current scientific direction. Explanations, after all, are also defined by what they exclude, what they deny. A materialist-leaning perspective is best contrasted with a sophisticated supernaturalist point of view. Liberal theological responses, however, will not help here, since many theologians have become too deferential to modern science. Instead of staking out a substantive supernaturalist position, they tend to argue that a suitably reinterpreted religious conviction is not entirely excluded by science. While anti-reductionist perspectives within religious studies tend to support realities transcending nature, they rely too much on philosophical roadblocks in the way of scientific investigation. These are hardly persuasive when a scientific approach is making progress.

In that case, the example of creationist opposition to evolution might be useful once again. Today, especially in the United States, the intelligent design (ID) movement vigorously opposes Darwinian, naturalistic evolution. Much of ID presents a transparently propagandistic misrepresentation of mainstream science. But some of it is worth taking seriously. After all, ID proponents emphasize the question of the origin of *information*, and claim that the information embodied in complex systems cannot be assembled by mindless mechanisms alone. They state that intelligent agency is a third option in scientific explanations, one that is not reducible to chance and necessity. Such themes appear not just in the anti-Darwinian polemics associated with the ID movement, but even in more liberal views that have no quarrel with common descent (Dembski & Ruse 2004). A full reply to ID, then, requires an answer to the question of information. It requires reasons to believe that the physicalist option of relying on chance and necessity alone is sufficient to account for complex information. As it happens, there are excellent reasons to think so. These reasons come not just from biology, but also disciplines such as physics and theoretical computer science (Young & Edis 2004); indeed, it is becoming increasingly clear that intelligence itself can and must be built out of chance and necessity (Edis 2004). The contrast to ID highlights the compelling nature of Darwinian materialist explanations of complexity.

We do not have a scientific explanation of religion that has crystallized to any degree comparable to biological evolution. Furthermore, it is hard to pick out a central theoretical concept such as natural selection in today's scientific thinking about religion; instead, current work proceeds by weaving together insights from multiple disciplines. Therefore we can expect supernaturalist responses to this work to also have many strands. Indeed, many of the favorite arguments of conservative religious thinkers concerned about the influence of scientific materialism are relevant to efforts to provide a naturalistic explanation of religion. The ID movement, for example, resists any extension of Darwinian evolution to help explain minds and culture—a major thrust of current research on religion. ID proponents portray evolutionary psychology as a collection of just-so stories, and insist that phenomena such as morality and religion cannot be captured by naturalistic explanations. They explicitly defend dualist views of minds. As current naturalistic views of religion continue to attract more attention, we can expect that defenders of more conventional views of the supernatural will continue to draw on themes exploited by the ID movement. It will not be a surprise if evolutionary explanations of religion come to take a more visible role in the endless creation-evolution wars taking place in the United States and Muslim countries.

Conservative religious resistance helps us see how present views that anchor religion in evolved human nature—in cognitive and brain science—function in the broader debate over religion. The scientific proposals under debate countenance only chance and necessity, not straying from physicalist views. They rely on Darwinian evolution and on naturalistic conceptions of minds, both which present deep challenges to supernatural realities and therefore attract determined opposition from sources such as the ID movement. For those of us impressed with current scientific views of religion, it becomes hard to avoid the conclusion that religion is ultimately an accident, not a divine design. And so, it seems that evolutionary approaches to religion are in fact linked to materialism, as part of a more ambitious project of constructing a thoroughly naturalistic picture of our world.

References

Atran, S. 2002. *In gods we trust: The evolutionary landscape of religion.* New York, NY: Oxford University Press.

Boyer, P. 2001. *Religion explained: The evolutionary origins of religious thought.* New York, NY: Basic Books.

Büchner, L. 1884. *Force and matter, or, principles of the natural order of the universe. With a system of morality based thereupon,* Translated from the 15th German edition; 4th English edition. London, UK: Asher and Co.

Dembski, W. A., & Ruse, M., Eds.. 2004. *Debating design: From Darwin to DNA.* Cambridge, UK: Cambridge University Press.

Dennett, D. C. 1995. *Darwin's dangerous idea: Evolution and the meanings of life.* New York, NY: Simon & Schuster.

Edis, T. 2002. *The ghost in the universe: God in light of modern science.* Amherst: Prometheus.

Edis, T. 2004. Chance and necessity – And intelligent design? In M. Young & T. Edis, Eds., *Why intelligent design fails: A scientific critique of the new creationism,* 139-152. New Brunswick, NJ: Rutgers University Press.

Edis, T. 2006. *Science and nonbelief.* Westport, CT: Greenwood Press.

Guthrie, S. E. 1993. *Faces in the clouds: A new theory of religion.* New York, NY: Oxford University Press.

Melnyk, A. 2003. *A physicalist manifesto: Thoroughly modern materialism.* New York, NY: Cambridge University Press.

Monod, J. 1971. *Chance and necessity: An essay on the natural philosophy of modern biology.* New York, NY: Knopf.

Pyysiäinen, I. 2004. *Magic, miracles, and religion: A scientist's perspective.* Walnut Creek, CA: AltaMira Press.

Rue, L. 2005. *Religion is not about God: How spiritual traditions nurture our biological nature and what to expect when they fail.* New Brunswick, NJ: Rutgers University Press.
Wiebe, D. 1999. *The politics of religious studies.* New York, NY: St. Martin's Press.
Wilson, D. S. 2002. *Darwin's cathedral: Evolution, religion, and the nature of society.* Chicago, IL: The University of Chicago Press.
Young, M., & Edis, T., Eds. 2004. *Why intelligent design fails: A scientific critique of the new creationism.* New Brunswick, NJ: Rutgers University Press.

Theological Implications of the Cognitive Science of Religion

Justin L. Barrett

For the sake of brevity, I will illustrate the promise for evolutionary and the cognitive science of religion for impacting theology by sketching just three interrelated areas of research with theological implications. First, I will consider the distinction between explicit and implicit religious cognition. Second, I will discuss what might be termed natural versus non-natural religion. I will conclude by sketching what findings might mean for encouraging or discouraging deep commitment to religious beliefs.

Explicit Versus Implicit Religious Thought

The Science

Sometimes people hold different explicit religious concepts and beliefs than their related implicit concepts and beliefs. For instance, Jason Slone (2004) describes in his book *Theological Incorrectness* several cases of discrepancies between explicit and implicit religious thought. While many Theravada Buddhists insist (explicitly) that the Buddha was not divine but only a man, they act and reason (implicitly) that the Buddha is a god. Slone also describes how early Calvinists denied human free will concerning matters of salvation (explicitly) but acted and reasoned (implicitly) as if people could freely choose to accept or reject the Christian faith. Similarly, he contrasts implicit beliefs in luck even in the face of explicit beliefs in divine sovereignty or karma that deny any such thing as luck.

Experimentally, Barrett and colleagues (Barrett 1998, 1999; Barrett & Keil 1996; Barrett & VanOrman 1996) demonstrated that stated beliefs about God's attributes in reflective contexts do not always match implicit beliefs in on-line tasks such as comprehending a narrative. In these studies conducted in the United States and India, participants were asked to *use* their concept of God or Shiva, Vishnu, or Krishna while listening to and answering questions about several stories that included God. Even though control conditions demonstrated that readers did not have to understand God's activity anthropomorphically in the stories (Barrett & Keil 1996, Study 2), participants generally did use an anthropomorphic concept of God—even when it contradicted their own stated theological beliefs. For instance, when explicitly stating that God could attend to many different things at the same time, they assumed one story said that God attended to one prayer and *then* another prayer even though the text entails no such sequential ordering.

These experimental results and Slone's cross-cultural and historical observations suggest that some explicit religious ideas prove cumbersome or difficult to use in many contexts and are consequently temporarily abandoned in favor of simpler beliefs and concepts. Emma Cohen's ethnography of Afro-Brazilian spiritualists illustrates the same set of phenomena (Cohen 2007). Spiritualists explicitly hold that the behaviors of a possessed medium are wholly attributable to the possessing spirit and so the medium is not responsible for inappropriate behaviors. Nevertheless, Cohen observed that people often did attribute negative behaviors to the host and not the spirit. This suggests that the host is implicitly thought to still be active. Cleanly dissociating the host from the host's body's actions proves cognitively difficult.

Similarly, psychologist Nicholas Gibson experimentally demonstrated that two groups of British Christians, claiming similar beliefs about God, showed markedly different salience in their implicit God concepts (Gibson 2006). Evangelical Christians produced faster reaction times in making positively schematic judgments about whether specific trait words applied to God than non-evangelicals who rated the same trait words for God. Gibson interprets these findings as indicating that the evangelicals have a more accessible and affectively developed God concept; they had more intimacy with their theology.

After the attribute-rating task, Gibson's participants were given a surprise recall task for the words they had rated. Research using this experimental paradigm has shown that people remember more words that were processed in relation to an intimately known person (e.g., one's self or mother) than a familiar but not intimately known person (e.g., a celebrity). Consonant with these findings, Gibson discovered that the evangelical Christian group showed facilitated recall for positively schematic material processed in relation to God but the non-evangelical Christian group performed comparably to an atheist group. Even though both Christian groups reported similar explicit God concepts, these results suggest that the evangelicals had a better elaborated, more affective implicit God concept than the non-evangelical Christians.

The Implications

The explicit/implicit distinction may have a lesson for how theological knowledge and commitment are measured. As Gibson (2006) has pointed out, this explicit/implicit distinction may map onto what is sometimes called "head knowledge" versus "heart knowledge". Beliefs that people explicitly claim and those that generate behavior and attitudes in regular moment to moment activities may diverge. For those in the business of helping others acquire theological beliefs and draw out implications for ordinary life, a caution looms here. What people say they believe or think—even quite sincerely—may not do much work for them in practical life. Hence, Barrett and VanOrman (1996) found that though doctrinally rejecting crudely human-like properties of God, Catholic and Protestant college students that encountered more images of God (including Jesus) in worship contexts showed more evidence of implicit human-like God concepts. Implicit (not explicit) measures detected this difference. Indeed, some of these participants may view a crudely anthropomorphic concept of God as heretical and unknowingly implicitly possess such a concept.

Evaluating the success of a sermon or study or course of religious education by checking what people can report explicitly is no guarantee that the transmitted beliefs penetrate enough to change behavior in varied situations. More valuable could be techniques for gauging people's ability to use their theological knowledge rapidly and readily. Similarly, using indirect measures such as Gibson's, one might find that people who report feeling intimately connected to God actually have poorly elaborated God concepts with no broader activation than their concept of Superman.

A second implication of these studies showing explicit/implicit differences in religious thought is that some kinds of theological mistakes or 'theological incorrectness' as Slone (2004) calls them may be more prevalent than others. People do not make arbitrary or random "mistakes" in their implicit theology. Rather, many places where implicit and explicit religious thought contradict appear to be systematically related to non-religious thought patterns. Because we spend so much time thinking about and using concepts of other humans including their physical and mental properties, unsurprisingly this facility may spillover into thinking about God under some conditions. Further, some of these biases toward treating God similar to a human might even be developmentally entrenched. Trying to teach people not to use a human-like God concept or not to think in terms of luck but divine providence instead may be extremely difficult, requiring more than well-meaning correction, but also abundant practice in integrating these less automatic theological positions into day-to-day reasoning and acting.

Natural Religion

The Science

Emerging from evolutionary and cognitive treatments of religion we see another insight related to the explicit/implicit distinction. Religious thoughts and actions may be more or less *natural*. That is, religious thoughts and actions may be more or less well-supported extensions of ordinary, *natural* human mental architecture working in ordinary, *natural* human environments. Generally, the less dependent a religious idea or practice is on special training, instruction, practice, or other culturally-specific support for successful transmission, the more natural it is (in this technical sense).

Anthropologist Pascal Boyer has championed the idea of religion of ordinary laypeople being fairly natural, observing that theological ideas that too greatly deviate from the expected outputs of human minds become difficult to remember, communicate, and use (Boyer 1994, 2001). Religious specialists, using texts, reflection, training, and practice may develop theological ideas that more greatly deviate from natural dispositions, but they will remain minority commitments.

The occasional conflict between explicit and implicit concepts discussed above often is a byproduct of the relative naturalness of theological ideas. If a theology is too unnatural (i.e., under-supported by natural cognition), it may be explicitly embraced but implicitly abandoned. Natural religion also seeps in when explicit theology remains silent or escapes attention. For instance, in American Protestant Christianity, little explicit instruction is given to just which type of divine intervention one should request when praying. If I lose my keys, should I pray that God brings to mind where I left them (a divine action on my psychology) or pray that God places them in my coat pocket (a divine action on the physical-material world)? Strange question, isn't it? And yet, American Protestants were found to have converging intuitions about such scenarios that mapped onto the way they actually pray. Specifically, they tended to ask God to intervene psychologically (as in remembering the location of keys) or socially (as in helping two people communicate effectively) more frequently than biologically (as in healings) or mechanically (as in keys materializing in pockets) (Barrett 2001). This pattern is entirely predictable in terms of ordinary natural cognition: people intuitively know that other intentional beings (persons) are uniquely qualified to bring about psychological and social changes. Seeing God as most likely to operate on the psycho-social level is *natural*. Without any strong reason to think or behave otherwise, the natural religious thought and action takes stage.

The Implications

Recognizing what is more or less natural religion may be important information for theologians. For theologians seeking to describe a natural theology, the cognitive science of religion provides tools for discovering which religious ideas spring most readily from situated human nature. For theologians who regard human nature as fundamentally flawed or "fallen," recognizing natural religion for what it is may be an exercise in identifying the enemy: what it is that people must struggle against. An illustration may help make the point.

As both physical contamination and moral contamination may draw on the same emotional and cognitive subsystems (Boyer 2001, 2003; Boyer & Liénard 2006), we would expect these domains to be conflated in many religious and cultural systems. A doctrine that links physical uncleanness with moral uncleanness may be an example of natural religion. In the Gospel of Mark, Chapter 7, Jesus takes the Pharisees to task for overplaying ritual purity at the expense of moral purity. The exchange begins with the Pharisees and scribes asking Jesus, "Why do Your disciples not walk according to the tradition of the elders, but eat bread with unwashed hands?" (verse 5, New King James [NKJ]). As part of his reply Jesus says, "There is nothing that enters a man from outside which can defile him; but the things which come out of him, those are the things that defile a man" (verse 15, NKJ). One way to understand this disagreement between Jesus and the Pharisees (and perhaps others) is that the Pharisees have developed and codified a relatively natural religion but Jesus is attempting to move them away from these natural moorings. Why did Jesus find the Pharisees (and others) so difficult to move on some matters? Perhaps in part because Jesus' less natural religion found his audiences' more natural religion difficult to dislodge. More natural religion finds greater support in the way human minds ordinarily and reflexively work.

Belief Depth and Multiple Subsystem Activation

The Science

A consensus is emerging among those who study religious belief from cognitive and evolutionary perspectives regarding what factors contribute to the relative success of some religious beliefs. In addition to being natural and consequently likely to be ably used implicitly, successful religious beliefs are those that connect with intuitive reasoning in numerous different domains and contexts (e.g., see Atran 2002; Barrett, 2004; Boyer 2001). Being connected to a wide range of matters intuitively or implicitly means such ideas activate many different cognitive subsystems and, in turn, are reinforced by these subsystems. As Boyer writes, people who have religious beliefs "have them because a lot of inferential work in the basement [implicitly] makes them apparently plausible" (2001, 317). So gods that account for why some hunting expeditions are successful are okay. But god concepts activated when reasoning about fortunes and misfortunes, moral intuitions, social arrangements, ritual experiences, intuitions about natural order, and uncanny feelings around dead bodies are better still. These connections need not be explicitly noticed or reflectively articulated. The key is how many different contexts and subsystems *automatically* use religious commitments.

The Implications

Boyer, then, writes: "So my advice to religious proselytes would be to avoid bombarding people with cogent and coherent arguments for particular metaphysical claims and to provide them instead with many occasions where the claims in question can be used to produce relevant interpretations of particular situations. But religions do not need expert consultants, for they all do that anyway" (2001, 317). Boyer's advice is relevant to anyone trying to improve religious fluency or to solidify belief, their own, their children's, or others'. Instead of *talking* about beliefs, *using* beliefs to generate inferences, attitudes, and feelings in lots of different contexts encourages depth of useful belief.

Compare with language learning. When people learn their native language and acquire fluency, it is not through discussion of grammatical rules. They learn through hearing and using the language, with some occasional correction. They learn about how different words carry different connotations, evoke different emotional responses, and facilitate varieties of social encounters not based upon a set of explicitly taught rules and generalizations, but through exercise and imitation. Likewise, deep and broad religious beliefs, the kind that produce long term commitment, probably come about through a similar process of seeing them used and using them over and over to solve problems, inspire actions, and evoke emotions.

I am not as confident as Boyer that religious people do not require this reminder.

Acknowledgements

The author thanks Emma Cohen and Nicholas Gibson for comments and the John Templeton Foundation for support.

References

Atran, S. 2002. *In gods we trust: The evolutionary landscape of religion*. New York, NY: Oxford University Press.

Barrett, J. L. 1998. Cognitive constraints on Hindu concepts of the divine. *Journal for the Scientific Study of Religion, 37*, 608-619.

Barrett, J. L. 1999. Theological correctness: Cognitive constraint and the study of religion. *Method & Theory in the Study of Religion, 11*, 325-339.

Barrett, J. L. 2001. How ordinary cognition informs petitionary prayer. *Journal of Cognition & Culture, 1* (3), 259-269.

Barrett, J. L. 2004. *Why would anyone believe in God?* Walnut Creek, CA: AltaMira Press.

Barrett, J. L., & Keil, F. C. 1996. Anthropomorphism and God concepts: Conceptualizing a non-natural entity. *Cognitive Psychology, 31*, 219-247.

Barrett, J. L., & VanOrman, B. 1996. The effects of image use in worship on God concepts. *Journal of Psychology & Christianity, 15* (1), 38-45.

Boyer, P. 1994. *The naturalness of religious ideas: A cognitive theory of religion.* Berkeley, CA: University of California Press.

Boyer, P. 2001. *Religion explained: Evolutionary origins of religious thought.* New York, NY: Basic Books.

Boyer, P. 2003. Religious thought and behaviour as by-products of brain function. *Trends in Cognitive Sciences, 7* (3), 119-124.

Boyer, P., & Liénard, P. 2006. Why ritualized behavior? Precaution systems and action-parsing in developmental, pathological and cultural rituals. *Behavioral & Brain Sciences, 29* (6), 595-650.

Cohen, E. 2007. *The mind possessed.* New York, NY: Oxford University Press.

Gibson, N. J. S. 2006. *The experimental investigation of religious cognition.* Unpublished doctoral dissertation, University of Cambridge, England. Retrieved March 1, 2007, from <http://www.divinity.cam.ac.uk/pcp/personnel/nicholas.html#PhD>.

Slone, D. J. 2004. *Theological incorrectness: Why religious people believe what they shouldn't.* New York, NY: Oxford University Press.

Thank God for Evolution!

Michael Dowd

What Are We Pointing to When We Use the Word "God"?

Do you believe in life? This is, of course, an absurd question. What we say *about* life—its nature, its essence, its purposes, its patterns, its meaning—along with the metaphors and analogies we choose to describe it, is wide open for discussion and debate. But the reality of life is indisputable. This is exactly the way that God can be understood, and *is* understood by many who hold the perspective of the Great Story—that is, when human, Earth, and cosmic history are woven into an inspiring, sacred narrative. Such a way of drawing spiritual sustenance from our shared story of deep history offers a refreshingly intimate, scientifically compelling, and theologically inspiring vision of God that can provide common ground for both skeptics and religious believers.

Ever since our ancestors began telling stories to answer life's big questions—Where did we come from? Why are we here? Where are we going? How does one live an honorable life?—analogies/metaphors have been used to describe the nature of reality. Some cultures looked up, out, and around, and (given their experience) proclaimed, "Mother." Other cultures did the same and said, "Father." Both are true. Both are accurate, albeit metaphorical, reflections of the way reality is experienced in different parts of the world, by different peoples. The simple yet rarely appreciated fact is that *every religion makes sense, given the bioregion in which it emerged* and the plants, animals, terrain, climate, and social relations its early believers reflected upon. A religious concept such as "the lamb of God" could only emerge in a culture in which sheep are not only familiar, but represent something of great value.

The diverse ways by which earlier societies referred to reality or spoke about the divine, however, is not central to my thesis. Rather, I suggest that for peoples alive today, any understanding of "God" that does not *at least* mean "Ultimate Reality" or "the Whole of Reality" (measurable and non-measurable) is a trivialized, inadequate notion of the divine. The emergence of the Great Story—a sacred narrative that embraces yet transcends all scientific, religious, and cultural stories—will come to be cherished, I believe, first and foremost for enriching the depth and breadth of our experience of the divine. This is why I say, "Thank God for evolution!"

Day and Night Experience/Language

Human experience is necessarily mediated in symbolic language: words really do create worlds. It is thus vital to remind ourselves from time to time of two complementary sides of the one coin of our reality. On one side there is the realm of what's so: the facts; what is objectively real; what is publicly, measurably true. Let's call this side of reality our "day experience." We communicate about it using "day language," or normal, everyday discourse. The other side of our experiential coin—what I call "night experience," communicated through "night language"—is the realm of symbols, interpretation, and meaning: What does it mean? How shall we interpret the facts? This side of our experience is subjectively real, like a dream, but not objectively real.

Problems arise when we fail to distinguish the factual, *objectively real* side of reality from the meaningful, *subjectively realistic* side—that is, when we mistake our interpretations and meanings for what's so. They are not the same. Facts are delimited; interpretations are manifold.

We cannot solve the problems posed by night-language disagreements by jettisoning that face of reality. We need both day and night expression in order to have a meaningful experience of life. *The important thing is to get the order right.* When we seek clarity on the measurable facts *first* (which is the very mission of science), the night language stories and expressions of meaning that derive from those facts can enrich our lives—and reduce conflict with others who hold different interpretations of the same set of agreed-upon facts.

Private and Public Revelation

We are at a turning point in human history. Catalyzing this transformation is our modern method by which we collectively access increasing knowledge about the nature of reality. New (and revised) truths no longer spring fully formed from the traditional fount of private revelation. Rather, they are hatched and nurtured and challenged in the public arena of science. This is the realm of what I call *public revelation.*

In contrast, by *private revelation,* I'm referring to claims about the nature of reality based only on personal experiences—some of which, of course, can be very compelling. Unfortunately, revelations enshrined in sacred texts occurred to people in the past and cannot be empirically verified today. Such claims cannot be proven or disproved because they are deeply subjective, one-person, one-time occurrences, obscured by the passage of time. Accordingly, private revelations must either be believed or not believed. When private revelations reside at the core of religious understandings, people are left with no choice but to believe or not. Thus, private revelation produces religious believers and unbelievers. Public revelation produces religious knowers.

Thanks to what is generally referred to as the scientific method, assisted by the wonders of modern technologies (themselves a gift of the scientific endeavor), public revelation emerges via a process whereby claims about the nature of reality based on measurable data are proposed, tested, and modified in light of evidence and concerted attempts to disprove such claims. Such a process typically results in a shared understanding that goes beyond belief to broadly shared knowledge that can be considered, for all practical purposes, factual. From this perspective, the history of humanity can be seen as a fascinating story of how Reality has progressively revealed the nature of itself to human beings, which is tied to how we acquire, share, store, and reconsider knowledge. The discovery of facts through science is one very powerful and inspiring way to encounter God directly. Thus, *facts are God's native tongue.*

It is through the now-global community of scientists, working together, challenging one another's findings, assisted by the miracles of technology, and standing on the shoulders of giants (but never blinded by the greatness of past accomplishments)—it is through this wondrous human endeavor that 'God's Word' is still being revealed. It is through this ever-expectant, yet ever-ready-to-be-humbled, stance of inquiry that God's Word is discerned as bigger, as more wondrous, as more this-world relevant than could have possibly been comprehended in any time past.

Nested "Holons" Within the Holy One

One of the most significant scientific discoveries/revelations of the last few hundred years, and something that could not have been known/revealed prior to telescopes, microscopes, and computers, is that reality as a whole is creative in a nested emergent sense. Subatomic particles reside within atoms, which comprise molecules, cells, organisms, and societies, like nesting dolls of expanding size and complexity. Outward, we find planets within star systems, within galaxies, within superclusters of galaxies. Each of these is a whole/part or "holon"—it is both a whole in its own right *and* a part of some larger whole.

At every level, each of these holons expresses its own unique forms of divine creativity, powers that bring emergent novelty into existence. Protons and other subatomic particles churning in the cores of stars fuse into most of the atoms in the periodic table of elements. In turn, atoms of hydrogen and oxygen, when bonded in environments less explosive than that of stars, give birth to a molecule (water) with properties that transcend those of mere atoms. Together, Sun and Earth bring forth fishes and forests, dragonflies and dancers. Out of human cultures emerge art, music, religious theologies, and scientific theories. Thus, reality understood as "nestedly creative" is *not* a belief. It is an empirical fact accepted by virtually everyone—religious conservatives and atheists alike.

"God," from this perspective, can be understood as a legitimate proper name for the largest "nesting doll": the One and Only Creative Reality that is not a subset of some larger, more comprehensive creative reality—that which sources and infuses everything, yet is also co-emergent with and indistinguishable from anything and everything. There are, of course, innumerable other ways one can speak about Ultimate Reality and/or theologize about God. But *if "God" is not a rightful proper name for "the One and Only Reality which transcends and includes all other realities," what is?*

Unnatural, otherworldly images and concepts of the divine notwithstanding, when "God" is understood foundationally as a sacred, proper name for "Ultimate Reality" or "the Whole of Reality, measurable and non-measurable," everything shifts. Theists, atheists, agnostics, religious non-theists, pantheists, and panentheists can stand on common ground and move beyond the quagmire of old disputes. When "God" is understood as *no less* than a sacred name for the Whole of Reality, new possibilities open for ways of thinking about creativity, intelligence, "the Universe," and our role in the evolutionary process. Although the metaphor of a clock-like Universe helped birth the scientific revolution and served ably through the early days of the industrial revolution, scientists working today and in virtually all disciplines are moving beyond the constraints of a mechanistic worldview. Creative evolution, self-organization, autopoiesis, cosmogenesis, chaos and complexity sciences, evo-devo: these terms exemplify the shift from a mechanistic to a nestedly emergent worldview. In the words of 20th century biologist Theodosius Dobzhansky, "Evolution is neither random nor determined, but creative." Like water is to hydrogen and oxygen, creativity is to the interplay of chance and necessity.

Scientists regard "the Universe" (a *day language* name that many people in the West use for "reality as a whole") as evolving in accordance with the dictates of natural law, the happenstance of initial conditions, the unpredictability of chaotic components, and the striking dependability of evolutionary emergence. Theologians (using *night language*) speak of Creation and all living creatures as coming into being as a result of God's will and God's grace. Only now can we appreciate that these are different ways of speaking about the same fecund processes. To argue over whether it was God, evolution, or the self-organizing dynamics of emergent complexity that brought everything into existence is like debating whether it was me, my fingers moving on the keyboard, or the electrical synapses of my nervous system that produced this sentence.

Prayer, from this perspective, is truly an intimate process, and one that even an atheist might embrace, because prayer is no longer an act of petitioning a far-off Supernatural Being to miraculously intervene in the world according to one's wishes. With an understanding of "God" as no less than a proper name for the Wholeness of Reality, prayer can be understood analogously as a cell in the body communicating (or in deep communion) with the larger body of which it is part.

Creatheism

Occasionally, someone who has heard me speak only briefly inquires, often with an edge of frustration, "Well, what *are* you, anyway? A theist? Atheist? Pantheist? I can't tell what you are." My standard response goes something like this: "I'm all of those and none of those. Actually, my wife and I had to coin our own term. I'm a creatheist (cree-uh-THEIST), and my wife, well, she's a creatheist (cree-AYTHEIST). We spell it the same way. We mean the same thing. We just pronounce it differently." This response almost always evokes smiles or laughter.

Here is why this new word can bridge the theist-atheist divide: *One need not believe in anything in order to be a creatheist.* It's not a belief system. It is based on what we know, not what we believe. I call creatheism a "meta-religious scientific worldview" and posit the following three points as core to its understanding:

1. The Whole of reality is creative in a nested, emergent sense.
2. Humanity is an integral and increasingly conscious part of this process.
3. Because we're a subset of the Whole (and thus cannot get outside the Whole to examine it), there is no one right way—and many legitimate ways—to interpret, think, and speak about Ultimate Reality.

A creatheistic view of the Universe—whichever way one chooses to pronounce it—celebrates the nested, emergent nature of divine creativity. This perspective embraces and includes, yet transcends, previous attempts to articulate the relationship of God to the world. The array of "isms" already on the religious menu (including theism, pantheism, deism, atheism, religious non-theism, and panentheism) have all played roles in helping us get to this point, and all offer interesting perspectives on creatheism. Each of these perspectives has a piece of the truth, yet none can deliver the whole truth (nor, of course, can creatheism).

The Role of Humanity in an Evolving Universe

When considering the role of the human in the evolutionary process, it is essential to remember that, from an evolutionary perspective, we are not so much separate creatures *on* Earth, living *in* a Universe, as we are a mode of being *of* Earth, an expression *of* the Universe. We didn't come into the world; we grew out from it, like a peach grows out of a peach tree. When the Bible (Genesis 2:7) tells of God forming us from the dust of the ground and breathing into us the breath of life, we can now appreciate this as a true, albeit metaphorical (mythic or *night language*), description of the same basic process, with "God" presented in terms poetically and personally up to the task of moving us into felt relationship with the Creative Reality that made it all happen.

Concerning our evolutionary role in the big picture, it is crucial to comprehend that human destiny and the destiny of Earth are inextricably linked. If we can know in our bones that everything that we are has emerged through billions of years of evolution and that no species can live in isolation from others, then we will finally grasp that the future of *our* species depends upon the future of this planet—no less than a child in the womb depends upon the mother. This is one of the great lessons of the evolutionary worldview.

The entire enterprise is integral: soil, air, water, and life. There is only one grand purpose for humanity: to further evolution in ways lifegiving for the whole (in night language; to know, love, *and* serve God). As Thomas Berry (personal communication) has said, "The human community and the community of life will go into the future as a single, sacred community, or we will both perish in the desert." The time is at hand *now* to become positive and conscious agents of the next stages of evolution, thereby fostering a future in which the vast diversity of life shall flourish. All other issues rest within that over-arching context, within that comprehensive understanding.

Author's Note

This paper was excerpted from my 2007 book "Thank God for Evolution!: How the Marriage of Science and Religion Will Transform Your Life and Our World" (Tusla: Council Oak Books).